MW00608396

GREAT RIVERS

GREAT RIVERS

AN ILLUSTRATED HISTORY OF THE WATERWAYS
THAT SHAPED CIVILIZATIONS

GEORDIE TORR

ARCTURUS

ARCTURUS

This edition published in 2023 by Arcturus Publishing Limited
26/27 Bickels Yard, 151–153 Bermondsey Street,
London SE1 3HA

Copyright © Arcturus Holdings Limited

All rights reserved. No part of this publication may be reproduced, stored in
a retrieval system, or transmitted, in any form or by any means, electronic,
mechanical, photocopying, recording or otherwise, without prior written
permission in accordance with the provisions of the Copyright Act 1956 (as
amended). Any person or persons who do any unauthorised act in relation to this
publication may be liable to criminal prosecution and civil claims for damages.

ISBN: 978-1-83940-871-7
AD008140UK

Printed in Malaysia

Contents

Introduction

As they make their way from source to sea, rivers shape the world around us, carving out deep canyons and broad valleys, and building fertile floodplains and deltas. Dynamic landscape engineers, they bring both destruction and renewal, causing devastating floods that leave behind the nutrient-rich sediment that nurtured the development of agriculture.

Throughout history, rivers have provided us with drinking water and food, sustained crops and industry, acted as vital conduits for trade and transport, and inspired great works of art. They host some of the world's oldest and largest cities, form international boundaries and are increasingly acting as sources of conflict between nations. They sustain livelihoods and underpin economies, and provide sites for recreation. They are home to some of the world's most productive fisheries – at

least 12 million tonnes of river fish are caught each year, providing cheap protein to low-income communities. Given their centrality to the lives of so many people, it's unsurprising that in some parts of the world, they are even worshipped as gods.

Since prehistoric times, people have used rivers as routes for migration and sites for settlement, drawn by the availability of the fresh water and food they provide. In Africa and Asia, rivers such as the Tigris, Euphrates, Nile, Indus, Yellow and Yangtze acted as cradles of civilization, as the people who lived along their banks learned to exploit the nutrient-rich soils in the river's deltas and floodplains.

Rivers facilitated trade and exploration, bringing prosperity. However, they also brought ruin when they broke their banks, and over time, people began to look for ways to tame them and to harness their

power. From the building, first, of simple levees, engineers graduated to the construction of enormous dams, replete with turbines that generated the electricity needed to power industrial development. Complex irrigation networks used river water to support the expansion of agriculture; toady, about a quarter of all food production depends on irrigation from rivers. In recent years, the economic importance of rivers has been starkly revealed as falling water levels due to drought have disrupted global trade and the production of hydroelectric power.

Rivers represent one of the Earth's most valued and important ecosystems, containing a wealth of biodiversity within their waters and helping to sustain the surrounding biological communities. However, riverine ecosystems are also extremely vulnerable and sadly, today, the health of many rivers has been compromised by a toxic mixture of pollution, over-extraction of water for irrigation, the erection of dams along their length and the increasingly damaging effects of anthropogenic climate change. Many are considered to be biologically dead, while others no longer reach the sea for part or all of the year. Despite these problems, rivers continue to exert a powerful pull on our collective imagination, enthralling us with their majesty, mystery and beauty.

The chapters that follow explore the physical characteristics of rivers, their ecology and the complex ways in which they have become intertwined with human societies, as well as profiling 38 of the world's greatest rivers, highlighting the remarkable diversity and fascinating histories of these liquid ribbons of life.

A view of the Danube River as it passes through Vienna. To the left can be seen the New Danube, a side channel created in 1972–88 to provide flood relief. It's separated from the main river by the Donauinsel (Danube Island), which was built from the removed material.

The Physical Geography of Rivers

There are rivers on every continent except Antarctica; together, rivers and streams cover about 0.1 per cent of earth's surface. Rivers come in all shapes and sizes, but while no two are exactly alike, all rivers share certain features and follow a similar pattern as they age.

Put simply, rivers flow downhill under the influence of gravity from their source (or, more often, several sources), which is usually on high ground, across the land in a channel flanked by raised banks, and eventually empty into another body of water – the ocean, a lake or another river – through their mouth.

Rivers are powerful, dynamic landscape features, constantly undergoing change as they erode their channel and alter their path. Most rivers can be classified as either alluvial, bedrock or a combination of the two. Alluvial rivers flow through channels that they have cut into deposited sediment, or alluvium; bedrock rivers are confined within

The Amazon River flows through its delta and empties into the Atlantic Ocean.

Meltwater runs down the slope of a toe of the Athabasca Glacier in Jasper National Park, Alberta, Canada. The water will eventually feed the Athabasca River.

channels that they have cut into the underlying rock. Also sometimes known as entrenched rivers, bedrock rivers rarely alter their course.

The moving water in a river is known as the current. The current is usually strongest near the river's source and at the centre of the river's channel. The volume of water flowing in a river is known as its discharge. The river with the largest average discharge is the 6,650-km (4,132-mile) Amazon River, which releases roughly 209,000 cubic metres per second (7,380,765 cubic ft per second) of water into the Atlantic Ocean. The Amazon also has the largest drainage basin – the total area over which falling precipitation feeds into a river, either directly or through its tributaries – of any of the world's rivers, covering an area of some 7 million sq km (2,702,715 sq miles). These two facts are linked – typically, the larger a river's drainage basin, the larger its discharge because it can catch more rain.

The total volume of water that a river transports downstream is typically a mixture of the surface water flow with which we're familiar and a substantial additional flow that passes through underlying sub-surface rocks and gravels, known as the hyporheic zone. For rivers that flow through large valleys, the amount of water that passes through the hyporheic zone may be much greater than the visible flow.

A river's journey begins at its source, also known as its headwaters. The romantic image of a river's source is of a clear stream issuing from a muddy ice cave at the base of a vast mountain glacier and tumbling over the rounded pebbles of a glacial moraine, but it could just as easily be a spring bubbling up from the ground in a flower-dotted meadow in rolling countryside, or simply the outflow from a lake. Falling rain and melting snow are also common sources.

The nature of the source will often determine whether a river is perennial, flowing all year round, or intermittent. The latter, which are known generally as ephemeral rivers, can be either periodic, or episodic. Periodic rivers flow seasonally, when regular seasonal weather leads to periods of increased rainfall or snowfall. The Ugab River in Namibia, for example, only flows for a few days or weeks each year when there's enough rain for the water table to rise above the riverbed. Episodic rivers similarly require increased volumes of rainwater or snow in order to flow, but those increases are less predictable and may not happen for years. Water hasn't flowed through the Nossob River, which runs through Namibia, South Africa and Botswana, since 1989.

Ephemeral rivers are typically found in arid and semi-arid regions, where rainfall tends to be rare and evaporation is high. Once the rain has stopped, turning off the river's 'tap', the remaining water may evaporate or simply be absorbed by the ground and become groundwater. Due to their short-lived nature, many ephemeral rivers don't carve out a defined river bed, but if their seasonal flow is powerful enough, or the underlying geology weak enough, they may create steep channels.

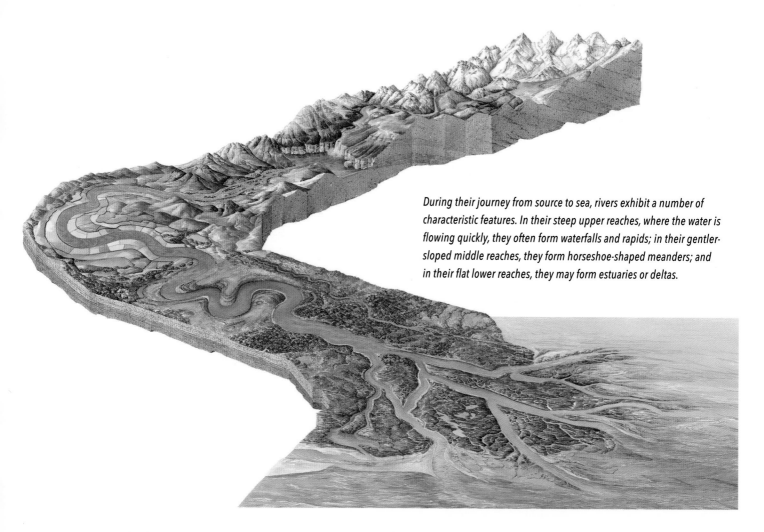

During their journey from source to sea, rivers exhibit a number of characteristic features. In their steep upper reaches, where the water is flowing quickly, they often form waterfalls and rapids; in their gentler-sloped middle reaches, they form horseshoe-shaped meanders; and in their flat lower reaches, they may form estuaries or deltas.

A river's path is known as its course and can be divided into three distinct sections – upper, middle and lower – known as reaches. In their upper reaches, rivers typically flow in narrow channels through steep-sided, V-shaped valleys and gorges. The water flow is often turbulent, forming tumultuous rapids as it tumbles over shallow sections and waterfalls as it drops over precipices. The steep gradient makes the water flow quickly, causing it to cut deep into the underlying rock and soil. If the underlying rock is particularly tough, the river will often change direction, creating what are known as interlocking spurs – a series of ridges that project out on alternate sides of a valley like the teeth of a zip and cause the river to take a zig-zagging course.

When a river flows over rocks of different strength, it can result in the formation of a waterfall. Waterfalls tend to be most common in the upper and middle reaches of rivers, where the gradient is steeper. They typically form as water flows from soft to hard rock. As the softer rock erodes away, only a hard ledge remains and it's over this that the water falls. As a river approaches a waterfall, it speeds up, increasing the rate at which erosion takes place. The falling water and sediment then erode the plunge pool (the basin at the base of a waterfall into which water flows) below.

Waterfalls are dynamic, the constant erosion by moving water and the sediment it contains causing them to 'recede' or retreat. As the rock behind the waterfall is worn away, it creates a cave-like structure known as a rock shelter. The rocky ledge above, known as an outcropping, eventually collapses, causing the waterfall to move upstream and the

process begins again. The rate of retreat can be as high as 1.5 m (5 ft) per year and will often lead to the creation of a steep-sided gorge on the downstream side. Niagara Falls has retreated 11 km (9 miles) from its original position. The waterfall with the largest flow is Khone Falls on the Mekong River in Laos, over which an estimated 11,600 cubic m (409,650 cubic ft) of water flows each second.

When rivers flow through karst regions, in which the underlying rock, usually limestone, is water soluble, the formation of caves and other spaces can lead to a river flowing partly or completely underground. These so-called subterranean rivers often disappear into a sinkhole and then flow along the top of the water table in an underground cave system before resurfacing either as a continuation of the river or as a karst spring. The world's longest subterranean river is found on the Yucatan Peninsula in Mexico. The Sistema Sac Actun is more than 150 km (93 miles) in length.

In Germany, a subterranean connection between the Danube and Rhine rivers is leading to what's known as stream capture. A proportion of the flow of the headwaters of the Danube seeps down into underground channels at two locations before resurfacing 12 km (7.45 miles) to the south and flowing into the Rhine at Lake Constance. It's believed that this section of the Danube's upper course will eventually be completely captured by the Rhine.

During its journey from source to mouth, a river's flow is bolstered by so-called tributaries or affluents – smaller rivers and streams that flow into a large river rather than flowing directly into the ocean. The Amazon

The American Falls, the second-largest of the three waterfalls that are together known as Niagara Falls on the Niagara River along the Canada–USA border.

River receives water from more than 1,000 tributaries. Together, a river and its tributaries make up what's known as a river system.

As a river enters its middle reaches, its gradient will tend to flatten out and the river will cut less deeply into its bed. It will usually flow through a valley that is wider and shallower, and its channel will begin to widen and deepen.

Water never flows in a straight line. Even within what appears to be a straight channel, the water will be moving this way and that as it bumps into obstacles such as rocks and logs, and flows over dips and rises in the riverbank and riverbed, creating areas of faster and slower water. Due to these variations in flow, along with differences in the strength of the riverbank and riverbed, a river will gradually begin to take a more winding course.

Where a river makes a bend, its water will erode and undercut the river bank on the outside of the bend, where the water is flowing fastest, while simultaneously depositing sediment on the inside of the bend, where its flow is slower. This often results in the formation of a horseshoe-like loop called a meander. When a river creates a new channel that isolates one of these looping meanders, it leads to the formation of an oxbow lake. The river's meandering will often widen the river valley.

Rivers follow the path of least resistance. If they come up against a barrier of some sort, such as a ridge or a hill or even a large rock, they will find a way to flow around it. When a river meets an obstacle, it can also lead to a process known as bifurcation, in which the channel splits in two. If the new channel rejoins the main river, the river may be braided. If, however, the new channel remains separate, it's known as a distributary – the opposite of a tributary.

Braided rivers are formed of multiple small interweaved channels that flow around exposed bars of sediment, creating a characteristic braided pattern. Braided channels are found in a variety of environments, including gravelly mountain streams, sand-bed rivers, on river deltas and across floodplains. However, braided channels tend to form in fast-flowing rivers with a steep profile, a regularly fluctuating discharge and readily erodible bank material. They will also typically carry a significant amount of relatively coarse sediment. Braided channels are typically extremely dynamic, as the mid-channel bars are continuously formed, consumed and re-formed, thanks to the rivers' highly variable discharge rates.

Towards the end of their journey, as they enter their lower reaches, rivers will typically be flowing through a wide, flat-bottomed valley and across a floodplain – the area next to a river that is inundated when the river floods. Their channels are generally wide and deep.

While the water in a river's middle and lower course is less obviously turbulent than in the upper course, it's actually moving with greater velocity. This is because the water's velocity is affected by how

The heavily braided Tasman River on New Zealand's South Island with Mount Cook in the background.

The tidal bore on the Qiantang River near Haining City, China, known locally as the Silver Dragon, is the world's largest.

Tidal bore

Tidal bores are natural phenomena that occur in the estuaries of some rivers in which the leading edge of the incoming tide forms a wave (or waves) of water that travels upriver. They typically occur in areas that experience a large tidal range (usually more than 6 m/20 ft between high and low water) and where the incoming tide is funnelled into a shallow, narrowing river. They are highly turbulent and produce a rumbling noise. Of the 100 or so rivers around the world that are known to produce bores, around a fifth are found in the UK. The world's largest tidal river bore is on the Qiantang River in southeast China. Some 3 km (1.9 miles) wide, it can reach a height in excess of 4 m (13 ft) and travel at more than 24 km/h (15 mph). Its roar can be heard for more than an hour before it arrives.

much of it is in contact with the bed and banks. In the upper course, the narrow channel means that there is more friction, which slows the water down. By the time it gets to the lower course, a lower proportion of the water is in contact with the bed and banks, so there is less friction and thus the velocity is higher.

Just before a river reaches the sea it will often flow through a section known as an estuary, where fresh water from the land mixes with the salt water of the ocean. Subject to inflow and outflow from the rising and falling tides, and changing levels of input from the river, the salinity in an estuary varies widely over time and distance. Because salt water is denser than fresh water, estuaries are often stratified, with a distinct layer of fresh water floating at the surface. Most of the world's estuaries formed about 10,000–12,000 years ago as the earth entered an interglacial period and the sea level began to rise due to the melting of the vast ice sheets and glaciers in the higher latitudes. The Gulf of St Lawrence at the end of the St Lawrence River in Canada is considered to be the world's largest estuary, with an area of about 250,000 sq km (96,526 sq miles).

Estuaries are among the world's most productive ecosystems, supporting a diverse assemblage of species, acting as breeding sites and nurseries for many fish species and stopovers for migratory birds; about three-quarters of commercial fish use estuaries as nurseries. Thanks to the mixing of fresh and salt water, as well as the influx of sediment, the water in an estuary will be high in nutrients, which stimulate the growth of plants that provide food for fish and other animal life.

Coastal estuaries are generally protected from the full force of ocean waves and storms by geographical features such as reefs, barrier islands and sand spits. However, in many areas, rising sea levels are causing sea water to intrude further and further into estuaries – even up into the rivers themselves – which can negatively affect the creatures that live there.

A river's journey ends at its mouth, where most rivers empty into another body of water – the ocean, a lake, or a larger river (the exceptions are rivers that flow in so-called endorheic basins, which never reach the ocean; the Okavango and Volga rivers both flow within endorheic basins). The land around a river's mouth tends to be relatively flat and the river's banks far apart.

Rivers have been described as 'the gutters down which run the ruins of continents'. As they flow, friction between the water and the river's bed and banks leads to erosion, as tiny pieces of rock and soil, known as silt or sediment, are worn away and picked up by the current and carried away, often turning the clear water opaque. A river's flow also causes broken pieces of rock to tumble over each other, breaking off sharp edges of the riverbed and the rocks themselves, processes known as abrasion and attrition. The three divisions of a river's course outlined above are pertinent when it comes to sediment: in a river's upper reaches, sediment is mobilized; in the middle reaches, sediment is transported, deposited and remobilized; and in the lower reaches, sediment accumulates.

The nature of the underlying geology, both of the river itself and of its tributaries, which are often major sources of sediment, also determines how much suspended material a river carries. Old, hard, crystalline rocks such as granite and basalt, for example, yield little in the way of sediment, whereas the loose, windblown soil of the Loess plateau of central Asia is extremely easily eroded, loading China's Yellow River with millions of tonnes of sediment. Glaciers, which are essentially

slow-moving rivers of ice, similarly wear away at the underlying rock, and this material often ends up being swept up into streams and rivers.

More than 70 per cent of the sediment that enters the world's ocean comes from rivers that drain Southeast Asia and the relatively small rivers of the so-called maritime continent – the islands of the Indonesian archipelago and the Philippines. The combined suspended sediment load of the Ganges-Brahmaputra river system amounts to some 1.87 billion tonnes (1.84 billion tons) a year – the world's highest.

While a river's current is swift, it carries the sediment along in suspension, but if it slows down, some of the sediment will settle on the river bed. When a river's sediment load is particularly large, the rate

The Gulf of St Lawrence, the world's largest estuary.

at which the newly settled sediment accumulates can be such that it blocks the river's channel, causing the water to back up and, in extreme cases, break its banks, causing the river to flood. However, floods are more often caused by the flow rate of a river exceeding the capacity of its channel, which usually happens when there has been a significant amount of rainfall or snowmelt upstream. Extreme flood events are often the result of the coincidence of factors, such as when warm, heavy rain falls on and melts a thick snowpack.

Floods can also occur when the river's channel is blocked by debris, perhaps from a landslide, causing water to back up and flow over the

The Yellow River in Liujiaxia, China, on the Loess Plateau. The river's name is a reference to the yellow-coloured windblown loess sediment that the river picks up as it crosses the plateau.

river's banks. During spring, as frozen rivers in the high latitudes and at high elevation begin to thaw, large chunks of ice may be swept down in the current. If the river takes a sharp turn, the ice can get stuck, causing other chunks of ice to build up behind it. These so-called ice jams can quickly lead to flooding as they block the flow of water. In 2009, the water level in Eagle, a village on the Yukon River near the Canada–USA border, rose more than 9 m (29.5 ft) in 48 hours as a result of an ice jam 16 km (10 miles) downstream. The ice itself can also create dangerous situations, as the current shoves large sheets up onto riverbanks and islands. Bank erosion can also be accelerated to an extreme level.

When a river is in flood, it can prevent water entering from its tributaries, causing the water to back up, which can cause flooding on the tributary far upstream of the confluence with the mainstem river.

Floods are the most common and widespread weather-related natural disasters, potentially causing devastating damage and terrible loss of life. The deadliest flood in recorded history took place in 1931, when a flood of China's Yangtze River killed an estimated 2.5–3.7 million people.

Many rivers experience regular or periodic flooding, as annual phenomena, such as heavy monsoon rains or significant snowmelt in their headwaters, cause their levels to rise significantly, triggering downstream

Salty seas

River water is what makes the sea salty. The presence of dissolved carbon dioxide and sulphur dioxide in rainwater makes it slightly acidic. When rain falls on rocks, this acid breaks them down, releasing mineral salts that are then washed into rivers and, eventually, the oceans. Over billions of years, these salts have built up, making seawater salty. Each year, an estimated 4 billion tonnes (3.9 billion tons) of dissolved salts deposit into the ocean by the world's rivers. It's believed that a similar amount of salt is deposited on the ocean floor each year, so the ocean's salinity remains roughly constant.

floods. These floods are ecologically important because they deposit fresh fertile alluvium, replenishing soils that help to maintain the plant communities and associated wildlife on a river's floodplain. This is one of the primary reasons why the floodplains of the Nile, Tigris, Euphrates, Indus and Brahmaputra acted as cradles of early human civilizations.

Sometimes, sudden, intense rainfall can trigger a flash flood, particularly when it falls in steep, rocky mountainous areas or in deserts – areas where there is little vegetation and water tends to infiltrate poorly, producing rapid run-off. Flash floods can occur far from the storm that initially spawned them. The speed at which a river is transformed can be

astounding, a placid, clear waterway morphing into a churning, raging, rapidly rising, coffee-coloured torrent in just tens of minutes. Most flooding-related deaths occur as a result of flash floods, when the sudden, unanticipated rise in the river's level catches people unprepared.

The blocking of a river's channel through the build-up of sediment can lead to a process known as avulsion, where the river changes course and creates a new channel. Because water always flows downhill, when the existing channel becomes blocked, the river will eventually find a steeper, more direct route to the ocean. Sometimes this is a gradual process, perhaps caused by the erosion of the river banks or the formation of a large

Flooding in Hankou, China, 1931, after the Yangtze River burst its banks. The flood eventually killed as many as 3.7 million people, the deadliest such disaster in recorded history.

sandbar in the middle of the river's channel; but it may also be sudden and catastrophic, perhaps taking place as the result of an earthquake. In 2008, the Kosi River in India shifted its course by more than 100 km (62 miles) in a matter of days, displacing more than three million people.

By the time the river is nearing the end of its journey and is approaching its mouth, it will typically have slowed down to the point where a significant amount of sediment begins to drop out of suspension and settle on the river bed. The heavier, coarser material settles first, followed by the finer material. Over time, the sediment accumulates to create new land. This is how rivers form what are known as deltas.

When a river empties into the ocean, deltas form when they deposit sediment more rapidly than the sea removes it. The area in which sediment is building up is known as a deltaic lobe. Deltas tend to be dynamic landscapes. The constant deposition and accumulation of sediment in a lobe eventually causes the river channel to silt up, forcing the river to change its course or even split into more than one channel, which tends to slow it down even further. As the existing channels undergo avulsion, the delta grows laterally, producing the characteristic triangular shape (they are named after the triangle-shaped upper-case Greek letter delta). As the river enters its delta, it often branches repeatedly.

Deltas are often less than 1 m (3.3 ft) above sea level. They can be divided into three main types, based on their shape: arcuate (arc-like) deltas are triangular or fan-shaped (for example, the Nile River delta); cuspate deltas, where the land around the river mouth juts out into the sea like an arrow, are formed when waves are strong at the river mouth (for example, the Tiber River delta); and bird's foot deltas, where a river has split and each new channel has a delta of its own that juts out into the sea (for example, the Mississippi River delta). The delta formed by the Ganges and Brahmaputra rivers (among others) as they flow into the Bay of Bengal is the world's largest, covering an area of more than 105,000 sq km (40,541 sq miles).

Not all rivers form deltas. If the continental shelf adjacent to the river's mouth is very narrow or if the ocean currents and/or tides are too strong, sediment can't accumulate and a delta won't form. Among the major world rivers that don't have true deltas are the Amazon, the Congo, the Orinoco, the St Lawrence and the Narmada.

Where rivers enter the ocean, they sometimes cut deep, steep-sided canyons into the sea floor of the adjacent continental shelf. These so-called submarine canyons can be of a similar scale to the USA's Grand Canyon. The Hudson Canyon extends 750 km (466 miles) into

The Ganges–Brahmaputra Delta, the world's largest. The Ganges can be seen entering from the left, the Brahmaputra from the right. The snow-covered Himalaya can be seen at the top of the image.

the Atlantic Ocean from the mouth of the Hudson River in the US states of New York and New Jersey, while the Congo Canyon, located at the mouth of the Congo River, is 800 km (497 miles) long and 1,200 m (3,937 ft) deep. The heads of these canyons were cut by rivers at a time when the global sea level was much lower than today, probably during the Pleistocene Epoch (between 2.6 million and 11,700 years ago).

River Ecology

Numerous species across the animal and plant kingdoms depend on rivers for their food, water and habitats. Although they occupy less than 1 per cent of the earth's surface, river ecosystems support an outsized proportion of the planet's biodiversity, while also acting as significant corridors for the movement of plants, animals and nutrients.

A kayaker battles the Kinsuka Rapids on the lower Congo River near Kinshasa in the Democratic Republic of the Congo.

Rivers are lotic ecosystems; lotic refers to flowing water, from the Latin word *lotus*, meaning 'washed'. (Relatively still terrestrial waters such as lakes and ponds are known as lentic ecosystems.) As such, they have a number of defining characteristics, including unidirectional flow, continuous physical change, including variability in flow rates and regular catastrophic change in the form of floods, and a large diversity of microhabitats. All of these factors have an effect on which animals and plants are found where and also on the organisms themselves, which are often specially adapted to the flow conditions in which they live.

A river's physical characteristics, including flow velocity and level of turbulence, depth, light penetration and the nature of the substrate (the surface on which the river organisms live; it may be inorganic, consisting of material such as boulders, pebbles, gravel, sand, silt or bedrock, or it may be organic, such as leaves, wood and plants; it is generally not permanent, subject to significant changes during flooding events), vary both across its channel and along its length, creating a diverse range of potential niches for aquatic organisms, which in turn can lead to high levels of biodiversity. Water velocity tends to be highest in the middle of the channel. Tree limbs that fall into rivers increase the habitat heterogeneity and often remain in place for long periods – usually at least 20 years. This debris can help to stabilize the riverbed, modify erosion and deposition, and create essential fish habitat.

A river's biodiversity can be enhanced by the presence of rapids and waterfalls, which can act as barriers to movement up- and down-river, isolating populations that can then diverge into different species. The impressive, extensive rapids of the lower Congo River present just such a barrier and have contributed to the high levels of endemism among the river's fish. The Congo is the world's second most biodiverse river; only the Amazon has a higher diversity.

For animals that live in rivers, simply resisting the current and staying in one place can be energetically costly. However, staying within the current provides access to a conveyer-belt-like food-delivery system, as organic matter zips past. Most fish tend to remain close to the bottom, the banks or behind obstacles, only swimming in the current to feed or change location; some species never enter the current. Some fish have particular adaptations that help them to resist the flow. For example, loach catfish, which are abundant throughout tropical Africa, have thick lips that feature several soft lumps, tentacles around their mouths and minute spines on their fin rays, all of which enable the fish to cling to rocks in fast-moving streams. Other species have a flattened body shape and large, horizontally oriented fins that help to push the fish down against the substrate.

In a river's upper reaches, there is often an interlocking, overhead tree canopy that helps to keep the river cool and supplied with a food base of fallen leaves, which are broken down into fine particles of organic matter by biological communities in the streams. Organic matter in suspension is by far the largest food base in large rivers. River water contains large quantities of bacteria, which play a significant role in decomposing this organic material into inorganic compounds that can be used by plants and by other microbes.

Further downstream, the canopy will open up, so more light can reach the river, increasing the in-stream primary productivity as aquatic plant life can photosynthesize; however, riparian plant communities still provide shade and leaf-litter input.

Invertebrates found in rivers include crayfish, snails, limpets, clams and mussels, but insects are generally by far the most diverse and abundant group; in some river systems 90 per cent of the invertebrates are insects. River invertebrates can be divided into shredders that eat leaves, collectors that consume fine particulates, grazers that scrape periphyton (a complex mixture of algae, cyanobacteria, microbes and detritus) from substrates, and predators.

The groups of insects most commonly found in river ecosystems include mayflies, caddisflies, stoneflies, true flies, beetles, dragonflies and damselflies, and true bugs. They can be found in almost every available habitat, from the water surface to beneath the rocks and sediment on the riverbed. Some avoid strong currents by sheltering on the downstream side of rocks. They mostly rely on the current to bring them food and oxygen.

A large proportion of the insects found in rivers are only aquatic during their larval stages. Larval aquatic insects can spend weeks – or more typically a year or longer – in streams before the adults emerge. They often do so synchronously, emerging in large numbers at the same time to 'swamp' predators and improve the ease of finding a mate. In the process, they provide vital nutrition for fish (terrestrial insects

In their upper reaches, rivers are often shaded by the trees along their banks.

that fall into streams form an important part of the diets of stream fish, in some cases making up as much as half of their diet), terrestrial invertebrates, amphibians, birds and mammals.

The high flow rates during periods of flood can be devastating for organisms within a river, particularly the invertebrates; in some cases, they can reduce the abundance of large invertebrates by half. Some insects, such as the giant water bug, avoid floods by leaving the river when they sense rainfall. Others time their life events based on when floods typically take place. Some mayflies, for example, synchronize their emergence as flying adults with snowmelt floods.

A wide variety of plants can be found growing within a river system, some free-floating, such as duckweed and water hyacinth, others rooted in areas where the current is weaker and there is sediment on the riverbed. Rooted plants are typically flexible, with elongated leaves that offer minimal resistance to the current. The constant flow of water around them provides them with a steady supply of oxygen and nutrients, and they in turn can help to protect animals from the current and predators, and provide a food source. In most rivers, algae are the most significant source of primary food. Most are free-floating so can only build up significantly in slow-moving rivers or backwaters.

The world's rivers provide habitats for more than 14,000 fish species. They range in size from tiny gobies less than 1 cm (0.4 in) in length to the giant freshwater stingray, which can weigh as much as 300 kg (661 lb) – about the same as a grizzly bear – and reach a length of

Above: *Lacking gills, the Japanese giant salamander lives in cold, fast-flowing streams, where dissolved oxygen is abundant.*

Main image: *Migrating salmon attempt to jump over Brooks Falls in Katmai National Park, Alaska.*

Top right: *The giant freshwater stingray grows to a length of up to 2.2 m (7.2 ft) across and can reach up to 300 kg (660 lb) in weight.*

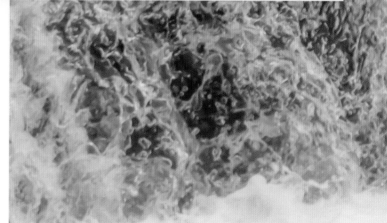

almost 4 m (13 ft), and the beluga sturgeon, which can reach a length of more than 7 m (23 ft) and a weight of more than 1 tonne (0.98 ton). Because larger rivers can accommodate larger fish as well as small fish, the range of sizes of fish within a river tends to increase as rivers become deeper.

Many fish species have life cycles that require periods in both fresh and salt water. Salmon, for example, are anadromous species – they hatch in freshwater but spend most of their adult life in the ocean, returning to freshwater only to spawn. Eels, on the other hand are catadromous species, living in freshwater as adults but migrating to the ocean to spawn. The upstream migrations of anadromous fish can bring an input of marine-derived nutrients to a river's upper reaches.

Some fish also migrate within a river system, often in response to flooding. This is particularly true in the Amazon, where many species move from the main channel into seasonally flooded forests to feed or to breed, the input of nutrients in the floodwater triggering a burst of productivity that can be exploited by both adults and baby fish.

With the exception of a few species, most of the other vertebrate groups that inhabit river systems are not tied to water in the way that fish are, often spending part of their time in terrestrial habitats.

The presence of predatory fish in rivers means that amphibians tend to avoid breeding in them and there are relatively few river specialists. Those that do breed in rivers often do so in the turbulent upper reaches, where fish are typically smaller and less abundant, or among the reeds and other vegetation close to the river banks, where refuges are more common. Some, such as the goliath frog in Africa, even go so far as to construct nests in the sand at the river's edge within which they spawn, the walls of the nest protecting the eggs and tadpoles from fish.

Cold, fast-moving, turbulent water typically contains greater concentrations of dissolved oxygen. Hence, the upper reaches of rivers that rise at high elevations are sometimes home to fully aquatic amphibians, such as the giant salamanders of Japan and China, which can breathe through their skin thanks to the high oxygen concentration. There's even an aquatic frog that lives at high elevations on the island of Borneo that lacks lungs. The tadpoles of species that live in high-flow environments often have broad fins that enable them to swim strongly in the current and strong, sucker-like mouths that enable them to hang on to rocks.

When it comes to reptiles, the crocodilians (caiman, alligators, gharial and true crocodiles) are generally the most conspicuous river inhabitants. Being ectothermic (cold-blooded), these ancient creatures spend a significant amount of time hauled out on riverbanks basking in the sun. They tend to be found in the middle and lower reaches of rivers, where the current is slower.

Turtles, too, are often seen basking beside slower-moving sections of rivers. River turtles typically have webbed feet and spend much of their time submerged in the water. Some exhibit what's known as bimodal respiration. When their heads are above the water, they take in oxygen through their lungs, but when submerged – as they may be for days at a time – they can absorb oxygen through their cloaca, the posterior opening through which their bodily waste is expelled.

Lizards are less likely to be found primarily around rivers; however, there are numerous exceptions. For example, there are a number of monitor lizards that are strongly associated with river habitats, including the Nile monitor of Africa, the Asian water monitor, which is found in South and Southeast Asia, and Mertens' water monitor, a species endemic to northern Australia. All of these species have long, strongly laterally compressed tails, which help them to move quickly through the water. Mertens' water monitors can also close their nostrils while they're underwater.

The basilisk lizards of Central and South America are known colloquially as Jesus Christ lizards, a reference to their ability to walk (or, more accurately, run) on water. Often found alongside rivers, the lizards

The Mary River turtle, native to the Mary River in the hinterland behind Brisbane, Australia, can breathe through its cloaca, enabling to stay underwater for days at a time.

escape predators by taking to the water and skipping along the surface, an ability enhanced by the presence of fringes on their toes.

North America is home to several species of snake that are often found in and around rivers. Among them are the nine species of water snake (genus *Nerodia*), which feed mainly on aquatic and semi-aquatic organisms such as fish, amphibians, crayfish and other invertebrates, and baby reptiles, including small turtles. They can often be found basking on tree branches that overhang slow-moving rivers, taking to the water if disturbed and sometimes diving down and remaining submerged for up to 90 minutes to avoid predators. Piscivorous snakes like these often have special adaptations such as extra-rough scales and specialized teeth, both of which improve their ability to hold on to slippery fish.

Birds are often the most conspicuous animal inhabitants of rivers. Long-legged herons stalk the shallows, waiting to spear an unlucky fish or frog with their long, sharp beaks; colourful kingfishers perch on overhanging branches, ready to drop on unsuspecting prey; flotillas of ducks, swans and moorhens float on the water's surface, periodically diving down to the river bed to harvest aquatic vegetation.

Among the more unusual avian river specialists is the dipper, a small, rounded, short-tailed bird that is only found along the edges of fast-moving rivers and streams with cold, clear water. Dippers feed on aquatic invertebrates and small fish such as minnows, catching and consuming them underwater as they walk and 'fly' in the turbulent water, holding their position and moving around using their wings. They also have nictitating eyelids, which act like a pair of goggles when the birds are underwater, sharp claws that help them to hold on to rocks on the river bed, nasal flaps to stop water entering their nostrils, and the ability to store a large amount of oxygen in their blood, enabling them to remain underwater for up to 30 seconds.

Thanks to their high levels of productivity and hence availability of food, as well as the presence of fresh water, estuaries and river deltas make ideal staging posts for migrating birds, which often gather in their tens and even hundreds of thousands at particular times of year to refuel. This behaviour isn't limited to water birds. Research has revealed that about 17 million migrating land birds, including more than a quarter of the North American continent's tree swallow population, stop off in the Colorado River Delta each year in autumn and 14 million use the delta in the spring. The forests along the Mississippi River are also vital for migrating land birds.

Many kingfisher species live alongside rivers.

Many small-bodied shorebirds making these migratory stopovers feed on what's known as biofilm, a thin layer comprised of tiny photosynthetic organisms such as diatoms and cyanobacteria, invertebrates and sediment bound in a polysaccharide matrix rich in carbohydrates and essential fatty acids that sits on the surface of intertidal estuarine mudflats.

Several mammal species are closely associated with rivers – among the best known are hippos, otters and beavers. Hippos have extremely sensitive skin, which can easily burn or dry out in the brutal African sun, so spend a significant amount of time in the water. Their bodies are so dense that they sink in the water, rather than floating, and they often move from place to place by walking along the riverbed. They can hold their breath for five minutes and, while submerged, their ears and nostrils shut tight to keep water out.

No mammal species has a greater impact on rivers than beavers. Often described as 'ecosystem engineers', beavers coppice trees along the riverbank and use the wood to create lodges and dams, in the process creating diverse and dynamic wetlands, increasing water retention, removing excess nutrients, pesticides and herbicides from the water and reducing flooding and siltation.

Several bat species are also closely associated with rivers. In the UK, Daubenton's bat feeds on insects that have just emerged from fresh water or fallen into it, flying a few centimetres above the surface and

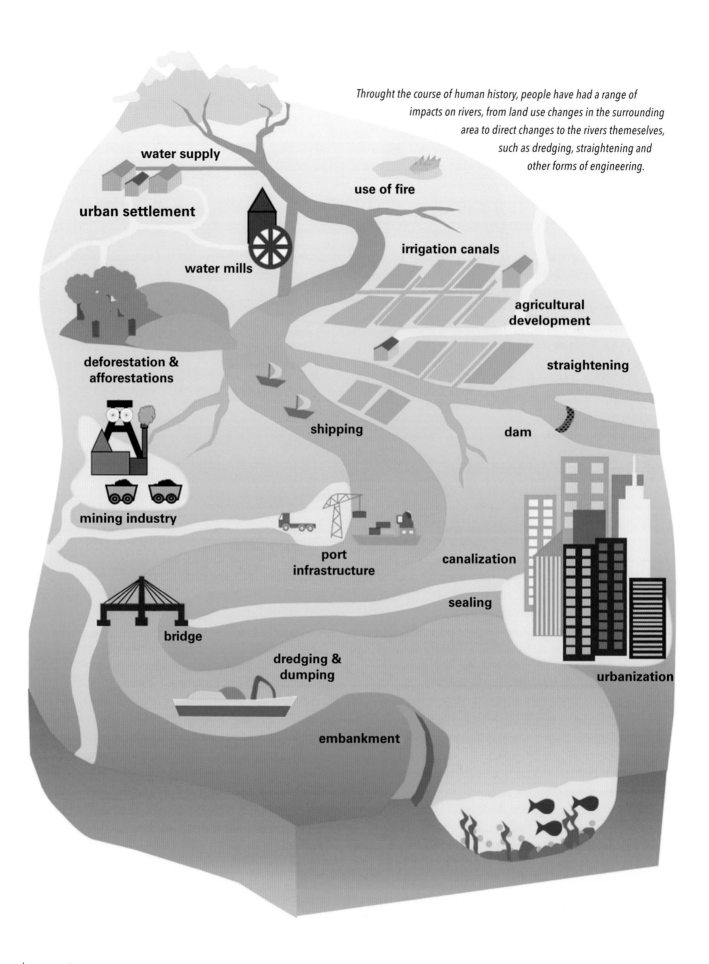

Throught the course of human history, people have had a range of impacts on rivers, from land use changes in the surrounding area to direct changes to the rivers themeselves, such as dredging, straightening and other forms of engineering.

water supply

use of fire

urban settlement

irrigation canals

water mills

agricultural development

deforestation & afforestations

straightening

shipping

dam

mining industry

port infrastructure

canalization

sealing

bridge

dredging & dumping

urbanization

embankment

Above: *Beavers can help to reduce downstream flooding.* **Inset:** *the water hyacinth forms dense, impenetrable mats that clog waterways.*

snatching its prey from the water with its feet. The greater bulldog bat, a species found in Latin America, hunts fish in rivers using echolocation, homing in on ripples on the surface and then grabbing the fish swimming beneath.

While they're most commonly associated with oceans, dolphins and porpoises are present in several of the world's great rivers. There are six extant species of river dolphin spread over Asia and South America; the Yangtze River dolphin of baiji hasn't been seen in 40 years and is likely extinct. Having evolved in warm, shallow water and strong river currents, river dolphins are smaller than marine dolphins, with little blubber. Because the water in which they live is often high in sediment, they rely mostly on echolocation for hunting and navigating, so their hearing is particularly well developed, adapted for both air and water (the Indus River dolphin is functionally blind). All of the species have declined dramatically in numbers and range, especially in Asia.

All over the world, river ecosystems have been significantly damaged by human activities. Many are heavily polluted, suffering the effects of industrial waste and chemical spills, sewage, plastic and other solid waste, pharmaceuticals and personal care products, salt from roads and irrigation return flows, pesticides and excess nutrients from agricultural runoff (which can lead to eutrophication, the progressive enrichment of a river with nutrients and minerals), even heat from thermal pollutants such as power station cooling water. Water is transferred among river basins and diverted for irrigation and drinking water, starving downstream areas; in some cases, over-abstraction is so extreme that once-mighty rivers no longer reach the sea. Dams starve deltas of sediment – causing them to become less fertile and to slowly erode – change water temperatures, create barriers to fish migration up- and down-river, and change flow regimes to

which organisms were previously adapted. In other areas, increased erosion due to land clearing leads to damaging levels of sediment entering rivers. Urbanization and channel modification destroy riparian zones and cut rivers off from their floodplains. Overfishing causes populations to crash. Climate change affects water temperatures and flow regimes.

Another significant threat to river ecosystems comes from invasive species, both animal and vegetable, that have been introduced to river systems around the globe through a mixture of both deliberate acts and unintentional events. These interlopers can negatively affect native species in numerous ways, including competition for prey or habitat, predation, habitat alteration, hybridization or the introduction of harmful diseases and parasites. Once established, they can be extremely difficult to control or eradicate.

Many have been devastating to rivers. In Australia, for example, the root mats of willow trees choke watercourses; carp, which now account for more than 90 per cent of fish biomass in the Murray-Darling Basin, reduce water quality by stirring up sediment, and uproot and eat aquatic vegetation; tilapia are invading river systems in far north Queensland, pushing out native species. Elsewhere, the coypu, a large semi-aquatic South American rodent, which has established invasive populations in Africa, Asia, Europe and North America, contributes to the erosion of river banks by burrowing into them.

The world's worst introduced aquatic plant is the water hyacinth, a South American species that floats on the water surface. It has been widely introduced in North America, Europe, Asia, Africa and Oceania. Spreading quickly, it chokes rivers, blocking off the oxygen supply to native plants and fish in the water below, a problem exacerbated when the plant dies, sinks and begins to decay.

People and Rivers

The fundamental requirement for a source of clean freshwater has ensured that rivers have played a central role in human history and development for tens of thousands, if not hundreds of thousands, of years. From the early hunter gatherers who congregated on their banks, exploiting the rich food resources that rivers offered, to the early civilizations that learnt to cultivate the fertile soils in deltas and floodplains, humans have long recognized the myriad benefits that rivers bring. They facilitated transport and trade, and even offered a convenient way to dispose of waste.

Main image: *Built in around 2,500 BCE on the banks of the Indus River in what is now Sindh, Pakistan, Mohenjo-daro was the largest settlement of the ancient Indus Valley Civilisation and one of the world's earliest major cities.*

The birth of civilization

Six fertile river valleys acted as the cradles of the world's earliest civilizations: the Tigris and Euphrates in Mesopotamia, the Nile in Egypt, the Indus in South Asia, and the Yangtze and Yellow in China. A key factor in the rise of these civilizations was the development of irrigation. Indeed, it could be argued that without irrigation, civilization would not have been possible, or at the very least its progress would have been severely delayed.

Irrigation first developed in areas that lacked sufficient natural rainfall to support crops for rainfed agriculture. The earliest archaeological evidence of irrigation in farming dates back to about 6000 BCE in the Jordan Valley; it's widely believed that irrigation was being practised in Egypt at about the same time.

From around 4500 BCE, the Indus Valley Civilization began to develop sophisticated irrigation and water-storage systems that enabled its people to exploit the fertile soils on the alluvial plains adjacent to the Indus River. And by at least the 3rd millennium BCE, farmers were using irrigation water from the Tigris and Euphrates rivers to cultivate the Mesopotamian plain.

Early farming along rivers often simply involved planting seeds in the rich, damp soil left behind when the annual floodwaters receded. The Ancient Egyptians went on to develop basin irrigation, creating plots of land surrounded by dykes to hold the floodwaters and the fertile sediment that it contained. Although effective, basin irrigation had limitations; only a single crop could be grown each year and farmers were at the mercy of annual fluctuations in the size of the flood. It was eventually replaced by perennial irrigation, first used in Mesopotamia, in which ditches and canals were dug to bring river water to planted fields, enabling crops to be grown year-round.

In South America, the Inca, Maya and Aztecs made wide use of irrigation, while in North America, there is archaeological evidence of an agricultural irrigation canal system that dates to between 1200 BCE and 800 BCE; however, the use of irrigation by North American indigenous groups was limited. Between the 7th and 14th centuries, the Hohokam culture used more than 1,000 km (621 miles) of irrigation canals connected to weirs on the Salt and Gila rivers to water their crops – which included cotton, tobacco, maize, beans and squash. By 1300 CE, their sophisticated irrigation systems supported the largest population in the American southwest. Today, some of these ancient canals are used to supply water to residents of the city of Phoenix, Arizona.

Great Britain's colonization of South Asia during the 19th century led to a significant expansion of irrigation as it looked to increase yields of crops such as cotton and rice. In the Indus, Irrawaddy and Ganges valleys and deltas, British engineers replaced temporary earthworks with permanent canals and extended networks set up by earlier indigenous empires. At around the same time, large-scale irrigation was being rolled out in the USA and Australia. Russia followed suit at the beginning of the 20th century – and particularly following the end of World War II – largely in response to fears that the USA would monopolize cotton production.

Intensive irrigation has one major problem – salinization. As water passes along irrigation canals and moves through the soil, it dissolves minerals, which make the water increasingly salty. These salts rise to the surface through evaporation and can eventually accumulate to the point where the soil becomes infertile. Return flows pick up some of the salt, causing the river water to become more saline and compounding the problem downstream.

Rivers and religion

Thanks to their role as providers – of water, food and soil fertility – and destroyers, all over the world, rivers have taken on sacred meaning among the peoples who live along their banks. Each of the world's major religions revere one or more rivers. In Hinduism, the Ganges, personified as a goddess, the embodiment of all holy waters in Hindu mythology, is one of seven rivers considered to be sacred; many of the founding stories of Islam, Judaism and Christianity are set along the banks of the Jordan River, in whose waters Jesus is said to have been baptized; within the Abrahamic religions, four rivers – among them the Euphrates and Nile – flow from the site in the Middle East commonly identified as the Garden of Eden/Paradise.

Ancient Egyptians worshipped numerous gods related to the Nile, including Hapi, Anuket, Satet, Khnum and Sobek, many of whom

A scene from the tomb of Sennedjem, a workman in the Valley of the Kings, painted in around 1295–13 BCE, shows irrigation canals from the Nile in the afterlife running through lush agricultural land.

A view of the Lower Ganges Canal, which forms part of the larger Ganges Canal irrigation system, in mid-construction in around 1872.

represented the personification of the annual, life-bringing floods. To the Inca, the Urubamba River, which flows through Peru's verdant Sacred Valley, was a direct reflection of the Milky Way, itself considered to be a celestial river known as Mayu. The river was believed to act as a collection point of the earth's water, which would then flow into the sky.

For thousands of years, the native peoples of the Pacific northwest in the USA and Canada revered the Columbia River as *Nch'i-Wána* ('the great river'), provider of salmon and steelhead trout; the acts of catching, collecting, consuming and respecting the foods found in and around the river have been inextricably linked with the tribes' religious practice. The Maori people who live along New Zealand's Whanganui River view it as a living, breathing ancestor; in 2012, it became the first river to be granted the same legal rights as a human being. And in the Yoruba religion, practised by the Yoruba people in present-day southwestern Nigeria, rivers hold important natural, cultural and spiritual values, playing a key role in different forms of divine worship and ceremonies. Female spirits, or *orishas*, such as Oya, goddess of the River Niger, act as custodians of river landscapes.

Rivers as borders

Rivers often prevent significant barriers to movement – treacherous and difficult to cross – so it's hardly surprising that they have come to act as territorial borders in many parts of the world. Historically, river borders were also often relatively easily defensible. Around the turn of the first millennium CE, the Romans built a series of defensive positions along the Danube and Rhine rivers, and maintained naval fleets on them, with these rivers often forming the eastern limit of the Roman Empire. Even today, many river borders – such as the section of the Rio Grande that separates the USA from Mexico, the section of the Limpopo River that separates South Africa and Zimbabwe, and the section of the Amur River that separates Russia and China – are heavily fortified as countries attempt to deter crossings by those seeking a new life in a more prosperous neighbouring nation.

According to a recent analysis, rivers currently make up 23 per cent of the world's international borders, separating almost 220 pairs of countries; almost half of South America's international borders are defined by rivers. The geographical distribution of the various river borders isn't random; the continents that have more borders defined by

Granite statue of the Egyptian Nile god Hapi.

borders require a certain level of stability, but many rivers are inherently itinerant, shifting position regularly and thus potentially transferring territory from one owner to another. When the Rio Grande, which serves as part of the border between Mexico and the USA, did exactly this during the mid-19th century, it eventually triggered a diplomatic incident that almost led to the assassination of the presidents of both countries.

There is also the tricky question of where the border actually lies – is it along one or other (or even both) of the river's banks, or along some part of the channel? This question is generally answered using the so-called thalweg doctrine, the legal principle that states that if a waterway marks the boundary between two political entities (be they countries or states within a country) but there's no further description of that boundary, it will follow the thalweg – the deepest part of the channel – or 'the mid-line of the main navigation channel' of that watercourse. This ensures that both countries have an equal share of the navigable channel.

The growth of cities

Many of the world's oldest, largest and most important cities were established on the banks of rivers, including numerous national capitals – London, Paris, Moscow, Amsterdam, Budapest, Vienna and Baghdad to name just a few – and several of today's megacities, including Jakarta, Tokyo, Shanghai and Kolkata.

As mentioned, many early settlements sprang up close to rivers thanks to the easy access to drinking water and food resources. Several of the great cities of antiquity, such as Babylon and Ur on the Euphrates, and Harappa on the Indus, grew as the young civilizations that built them exploited the opportunities for agriculture offered by the fertile river alluvium brought down in the annual floods.

As cities grew, rivers also helped with sanitation. In tandem with the development of irrigation, many early civilizations, including the Indus Valley Civilization and the Babylonians, used drains to carry human effluent away from dwellings and into the adjacent river, where the current conveniently swept it downstream.

rivers tend to be those on which European powers established colonies and exerted great influence, primarily because European explorers, cartographers, politicians and diplomats found rivers to be a convenient way to divide up territories. Consequently, Asia has fewer river borders than the other continents because of the limited influence and colonialism of the European powers there. South Asia, is the exception to this rule thanks to the colonial exploits of Great Britain and France in the region.

While notionally convenient, rivers typically make for troublesome borders. Cartographic and legal/political conceptions and depictions of

US Border Patrol agents on the Amistad Reservoir on the Rio Grande in Texas.

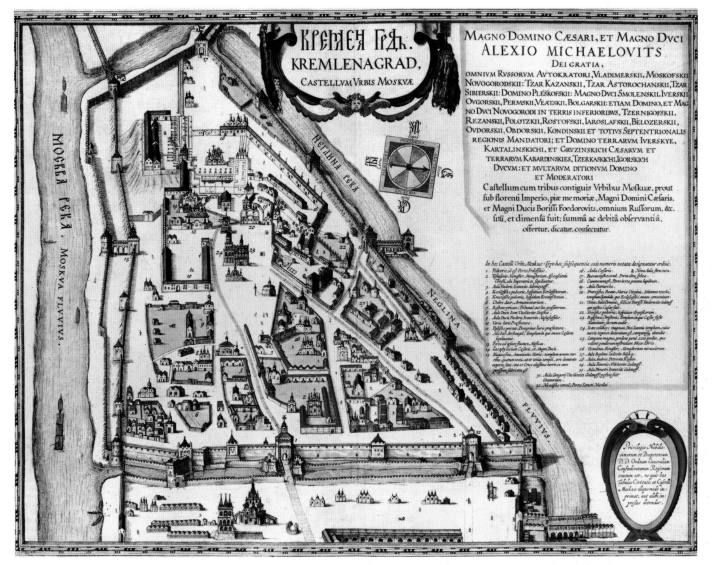

The first detailed map of the Kremlin in Moscow, from 1663, shows the two rivers – the Moskva and Neglinnaya – that framed the citadel. The latter is now underground.

Defence was often another factor. Rivers formed natural barriers against invaders, while also providing a route for the movement of troops and supplies. Moscow was founded near the confluence of the Neglinnaya and Moskva rivers, providing the nascent city with protection on two sides.

However, it was trade and transport that drove the development of most river-based cities. Rivers were effectively liquid highways, providing a ready-made network that connected population centres and thus facilitating both trade and communication. Key to this was the fact that the buoyancy afforded by water made it possible to carry much larger loads by river than by road – particularly true in the past, when roads were poorly made. This meant that the cost per unit of volume was significantly reduced. Road travel was slow, expensive and presented hazards such as attacks by bandits.

River settlements were often convenient transhipment points. Various resources, from furs, gold, timber and ivory to agricultural products such as wool and grain, were transported overland to river ports such as Manaus in Brazil, St Louis in the USA and Kolkata in India, where they were loaded onto boats and barges to be carried downstream to even larger ports built in river deltas and estuaries, such as Hamburg, Rotterdam and Shanghai, where they were transferred to ocean-going vessels for export.

Vibrant trade brought prosperity, and prosperity led to growth. The convenience of river transport for heavy loads also facilitated the growth of cities by providing a convenient way to bring in the building materials needed for the cities' expansion.

Rivers have also been key to industrial development in many parts of the world. From the 18th century on, many water-intensive industries, such as textiles, paper and the chemicals industry, were established along rivers, along with others that depended on the cheap transport of raw materials. This led to enormous changes to many rivers around the world, as dams were constructed to create reservoirs and to produce hydroelectricity, channels were engineered to improve navigability and, inevitably, pollution was dumped.

While riverside cities are able to reap these myriad benefits, they are also at the mercy of their rivers. Many have to contend with regular, sometimes catastrophic flooding, while others have been left high and dry after avulsions – rapid changes in a river's flow from one channel to

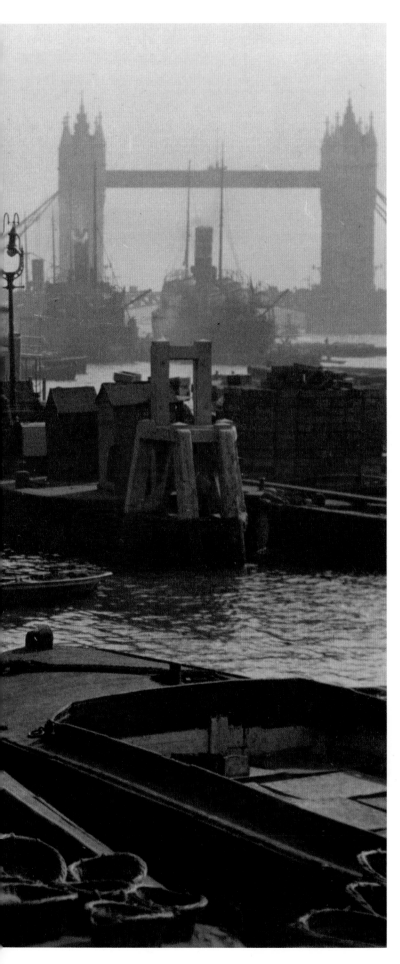

a new one – shifted the river channel to a location outside the city limits. The ancient city of Uruk, for example, is thought to have gone into decline when the Euphrates River changed course.

Engineering a 'better' river

Humans have had a greater influence on rivers than practically any other ecosystem on earth. From the time that they first began to settle along rivers, people have been altering them. The birth of agriculture led to siltation of secondary channels; the development of irrigation changed flows and water chemistry; levees built to reduce flooding cut rivers off from their floodplains.

As long as 5,000 years ago, people were building dams and diversion projects in the watersheds of the Tigris, Euphrates and Nile rivers – even before the states that came to depend on them had developed. The Sadd-el-Karafara Dam, a masonry embankment on the Nile just south of Cairo, was built in about 2500 BCE. One of the world's oldest examples of large-scale and formalized water management was recently uncovered in the Yangtze Delta. About 5,100 years ago, engineers from the Liangzhu culture built an extensive network of dams, levee ditches and other landscape-transforming features over an area of about 300 ha (741 acres) to support the ancient city of Liangzhu.

By the turn of the 1st millennium CE, the Romans were undertaking remarkably sophisticated river-engineering projects, building dams for water supplies and for smelting and smithing metal, and then constructing aqueducts to transport the water to where it was needed. They built 72 dams in Spain alone for both consumption and irrigation. Large-scale watercourse transformation in China began to accelerate at around the same time, primarily on the Yellow and Yangtze rivers.

Other examples of early hydraulic engineering involved river straightening, dam and weir construction, and the creation of mill canals and ponds. During the Middle Ages, water mills were an important energy source and they began to proliferate significantly along waterways. By the time England's Domesday Book was compiled in 1086, there were no fewer than 5,562 mill weirs in England and Wales.

The invention of the steam engine in 1712 led to the creation of the pumps and hydraulic earthmovers that enabled river engineers to carry out larger projects, but large-scale river engineering really accelerated with the start of the Industrial Revolution. The first hydroelectric power station was developed at Cragside in Northumberland, England, during the 1870s and in the following decades, the number of hydropower dams grew quickly as new technologies, such as the development of electrical wires, enabled the transfer of power from rivers to urban centres. Power-intensive industries such as steel production created an insatiable demand for hydroelectricity, which meant more dams; increased trade and the development of steamboats, which could travel faster than sailboats and horse-drawn barges but needed to travel in a straight line, called for improvements to navigation, including the removal of obstacles and the widening, deepening and straightening of channels, the construction of locks and the digging of canals to connect river systems; and the increasing agricultural development and

Left: *Barges on the River Thames near Tower Bridge in the early 20th century.*

Painted in 1896, Morning, An Overcast Day, Rouen, *by Camille Pissarro depicts the Boieldieu Bridge over the Seine.*

urbanization of lowland areas, especially on floodplains, demanded measures to reduce flooding. In cities, increasing levels of pollution saw many rivers paved over or redirected into sewers.

However, rivers have proven to be extremely difficult to tame. Hydraulic engineering often has unintended or predictable but unfortunate consequences. The channelization of the Alpine Rhone, Isar and Danube rivers during the mid- to late-19th century caused braided structures and large gravel bars to form. River straightening and the building of levees are often accompanied by an increase in the stream velocity, which can lead to increased bank erosion and an increase in peak flows in downstream areas. Indeed, the overall effect of many artificial structures is simply to either delay flooding, shifting it farther downstream, or to make the effects of floods that occur when they are breached or channels shift that are much more dramatic and destructive than they otherwise would have been. For example, levees can exacerbate the impact of floods by preventing floodwaters from draining back into the river bed as they normally would.

The reservoirs that develop upstream from dams often submerge important cultural sites, farmland and whole communities. The building of the Three Gorges dam on China's Yangtze River forced the relocation of about 1.3 million people, while several dams in the Middle East have flooded important archaeological sites. Dams obviously have a significant effect on the flow rates, but they also remove large quantities of sediment from the river as the water slows upon reaching the dam's reservoir. This can lead to the dam silting up, but it also starves downstream areas of sediment, threatening the river's delta, causing it to shrink and become less fertile, and can cause the river to erode its downstream banks rather than building them up, leading to an increase in flooding.

Today, few rivers remain unaltered by human hands. Only 59 of the world's 177 largest rivers are wholly free flowing. According to a recent study, Europe is the most obstructed river landscape in the world, with at least 1.2 million barriers blocking the continent's rivers, with a mean density of 0.74 barriers per kilometre. These barriers range from large dams to structures less than 2 m (6.6 ft) in height such as culverts, fords, sluices, ramps and weirs. An earlier report documented 21,387 hydropower plants on European rivers with another 8,785 additional plants either planned or under construction.

In recent years, there has been a growing recognition of the damage caused by river engineering and governments in some countries have

The excavation of a 5,000-year-old dyke near the remains of the ancient city of Liangzhuin in China's Zhejiang province.

been actively working to roll back some of the installed infrastructure. In the USA, small dams are being removed from rivers to restore natural flows and revive fish migrations. The US Department of the Interior has also been experimenting with flow modification at the large Colorado River dams, releasing substantial flows from the dams during spring that mimic the spring floods that once naturally occurred on the river, helping to redistribute sediment, modify the channel bed and sandbars, and flush unwanted detritus and contaminants from the river. Engineers are also increasingly looking to natural solutions to flooding, restoring water-soaking habitats in upland areas, removing levees to reopen connections to floodplains and even reintroducing beavers.

Polluted rivers

Humans have been using rivers as convenient waste-disposal receptacles for millennia. It's easy to see the appeal of dumping waste into a river: the constant flow quickly sweeps it downstream, replacing it with new, fresh water; out of sight, out of mind.

The Romans were notorious for dumping untreated human waste into the Tiber River through the *Cloaca Maxima*, one of the world's earliest sewage systems. However, it was the dawning of the Industrial Revolution that brought the polluting of the world's rivers to a new level. Cities began to grow as more and more people moved from rural to urban areas, leading to increased levels of sewage being dumped into rivers. The new factories that sprang up became sources of entirely new forms of toxic waste that also found its way into rivers. From the 19th century onwards, power stations became another significant source of pollution. Such was the level of contamination in many of the world's great rivers – and the levels of associated waterborne diseases – that it eventually led to a revolution in wastewater treatment.

An image from a Medieval manuscript from 1420–75 shows a woman carrying a sack of wheat to a water mill.

Mratinje Dam, located in the canyon of the Piva River in Montenegro, is one of Europe's tallest dams.

Today, the main sources of river pollution are agricultural run-off, sewage and urban run-off, and industry. From abandoned cars to plastic drinking straws, solid waste is also a significant river pollutant, whether dumped deliberately or simply blown in on the wind; estimates suggest that about 2 million tonnes (1.97 tons) of plastic waste currently enters the ocean every year from rivers. Rain and snow can even be sources of pollution, containing dissolved pollutants picked up from the atmosphere.

The growth of industrial agriculture since the end of World War I has led to significant pollution of the world's rivers. Globally, agriculture is the leading cause of water degradation. Chemicals used in farming, such as fertilizers, pesticides and herbicides, along with animal waste that may contain pathogens and pharmaceutical by-products, are washed into rivers by rain or irrigation water. Return flows from irrigation are also a significant cause of river salinization. The influx of fertilizers and sewage can lead to eutrophication, the excess nutrients causing algae to bloom and then decay, removing dissolved oxygen from the water and eventually leading to the creation of so-called dead zones in which fish and other aquatic life can no longer thrive.

Estimates suggest that, globally, some 80 per cent of domestic wastewater and sewage is dumped back into the water supply untreated. Sewage pollution is particularly harmful to human health because it can potentially contain a variety of contaminants, including pathogenic bacteria, viruses, parasites and other microorganisms, toxic household chemicals and pharmaceutical residues, as well as nutrients from garden fertilizers. According to the World Health Organization, at least two billion people drink water from sources that are contaminated by faecal matter.

Urban run-off, also known as stormwater because it is mostly generated by heavy rainfall, contains pollutants such as oil, petrol, household and industrial chemicals, and road salt, and large quantities of solid waste such as discarded plastic and other debris.

Despite increasing regulation, many industries continue to release chemicals and other pollutants directly into rivers as part of their operations. According to the UN, in developing countries as much as 70 per cent of industrial waste is dumped untreated into rivers and streams. Leaking underground storage tanks are also a source of chemicals, as is the cooling water from power plants. The Cuyahoga River in Cleveland, Ohio, which flows into Lake Erie, became so polluted with industrial waste that between 1868 and 1969 it caught fire at least ten times.

In some regions, particularly Siberia, radioactive waste is also a potential problem. Uranium mining, nuclear power plants and waste-storage facilities, the production and testing of nuclear weapons, and universities and hospitals that use radioactive materials for research and medicine are all potential sources.

Since the 1980s, many governments around the world have begun to recognize the need to improve the condition of their rivers and are increasingly enacting regulations that restrict sewerage companies, industry and agricultural operations from allowing pollutants to enter rivers, although enforcement continues to be patchy. Many countries are also carrying out extensive clean-up operations that are starting to show positive results. In 1957, the Thames was declared 'biologically dead' by the Natural History Museum; today, it is considered one of the world's cleanest rivers to flow through a city.

Rivers in a changing climate

Climate change is already having a significant impact on many of the world's rivers. In particular, changing patterns of precipitation – both rainfall and snowfall – are wreaking havoc on flow patterns. Drought conditions have caused water levels to drop in rivers the world over, affecting both shipping and electricity production. In several cases this has caused once great rivers to dry up completely in places. Extreme precipitation events have also led to devastating floods in many regions.

Above: *Firemen spray water on the tug Arizona from a bridge over the Cuyahoga River in Cleveland, as a fire, started in an oil slick sweeps the docks of the Great Lakes Towing Company on 1 November, 1952*

Left: *The heavily polluted Yamuna River in New Delhi, India. About 800 million litres of largely untreated sewage and 44 million litres of industrial effluent enter the river each day.*

In the longer term, there are fears for the future of snow- and glacier-fed rivers such as the Indus, Ganges, Brahmaputra, Rhône and Rhine, and the people who depend on them; more than a billion people worldwide live in river basins fed by glaciermelt and/or snowmelt, depending heavily upon them for water for drinking and irrigation, and on the hydropower they generate. Already, the lower contribution of melting snow and glaciers is causing the flow of some of the large European rivers, including the Rhône, Rhine, Danube and Po to decrease considerably over the summer.

Melting glaciers are also having more dramatic short-term effects on some rivers. In spring 2016, a period of intense melting of the Kaskawulsh glacier, Canada's largest, permanently redirected water from the Slims River, or *Ä̈äy Chù*, which had previously carried the meltwater northwards into the Kluane River and then into the Yukon River towards the Bering Sea, and sent it eastwards down a steeper gradient via the Kaskawulsh River into the Gulf of Alaska, thousands of kilometres from its original destination.

Another climate-change-related problem for many of the world's rivers comes from rising sea levels. With temperatures rising, many glaciers and ice sheets are melting and the water in the oceans is expanding, causing the sea level to rise. This rise is pushing saltwater further and further upstream. When combined with reduced flows due to drought, over-abstraction and/or dam building, the effects can be devastating for those living in a river's lower reaches. Saltwater intrusion is already killing crops and fish and crustaceans in aquaculture farms in

In 2016, intense melting of the Kaskawulsh glacier, Canada's largest, permanently redirected water from the Slims River.

the Mekong Delta, and there are fears that it will soon begin to threaten drinking water supplies for tens of millions of people living in coastal cities.

Sea-level rise may also make avulsion events more common. As sea level rises, rivers respond by depositing more of their sediment into their channel, raising the riverbed relative to the adjacent land and making the rivers unstable. Eventually, they will break their banks and find a shorter, steeper path to the sea, giving birth to a new channel.

Taking too much

Along with pollution and climate change, one of the most significant modern threats to many of the world's great rivers is over-abstraction – the removal of more water from a river system than can be replenished naturally. Rivers face competing demands from agriculture, which accounts for 70 per cent of freshwater use, industrial uses such as power generation and the thirsty populations of ever-growing cities.

Over-abstraction leads to lower flows, which can have significant impacts on river ecosystems as pollutants become more concentrated, sediment build-up muddies the water and clogs up channels, there is shelter and food availability and water temperatures increase and oxygen levels decrease. In endorheic basins – those that don't have an outlet to the ocean – it can lead to the shrinking of lakes that rely on river flow to maintain their water levels; since 1960, the Aral Sea in Central Asia, once the world's fourth-largest lake, has shrunk by some 90 per cent due to the diversion for irrigation of water of the Syr Darya and Amu Darya rivers. On transboundary rivers, over-abstraction can also be a source of human conflict as upstream nations leave their downstream neighbours high and dry.

Today, due to a combination of over-abstraction, over-engineering and climate change, numerous once mighty rivers no longer reach their mouths for part or all of the year, including the Colorado, Teesta, Murray, Yellow, Rio Grande and Indus rivers. In China alone, some 24,000 rivers are said to be drying up. In response, many of the world's cities have been forced to either ration water or import it from elsewhere.

Water wars

As transboundary landscape features, rivers have long been flashpoints for regional conflict. Upstream nations can effectively hold downstream nations to ransom by exerting control over the flow of water that they need for drinking, agriculture and power production. The building of a dam in one nation can be – and frequently has been – seen as a direct threat to a nation located downstream; suddenly, water security becomes a national security issue. Climate change is stoking these tensions, as the increased frequency of drought and the melting of the glaciers that feed many great rivers reduces the amount of water available.

Shortly before his death in 2010, US diplomat Richard Holbrooke expressed the belief that falling water levels in the Indus River 'could very well precipitate World War III'. There are fears that China will use its ability to control the Mekong River's flow to put pressure on downstream countries, in effect 'weaponizing' water. The construction of the Grand Ethiopian Renaissance Dam by Ethiopia on the Nile is straining the nation's relations with Egypt. Other regional flashpoints include the Jordan, Euphrates and Tigris rivers, and the area around the Aral Sea.

Tensions over water sharing can also arise within countries. Across India's northern plains, conflict between communities has long been provoked by competition for water. And in Pakistan, the government's diversion of water to supportive upstream communities is inflaming sectarian loyalties and stoking unrest in the downstream Sindh region.

One of the primary drivers of water-sharing disputes is the fact that large engineering projects are often carried out without consultation or co-ordination with the affected parties, and without acknowledgment of cross-border water rights. Hence, the solution has been for the countries involved to set up regional commissions to discuss the issues and draw up international water-sharing agreements. For example, the Permanent Indus Commission was created to implement and manage the goals and objectives of the Indus Waters Treaty, signed by India and Pakistan in 1960. The treaty allocated the waters of the Jhelum, Chenab and Indus rivers to Pakistan and those of the Ravi, the Beas and Sutlej rivers to India.

The Grand Ethiopian Renaissance Dam on the Blue Nile in Ethiopia. Under construction since 2011, the dam's primary purpose is to produce electricity to relieve Ethiopia's acute energy shortage.

Rivers of the World

The world's great rivers are each fed by a vast array of smaller streams and rivers that together constitute what's known as a river basin, drainage basin, watershed or catchment area.

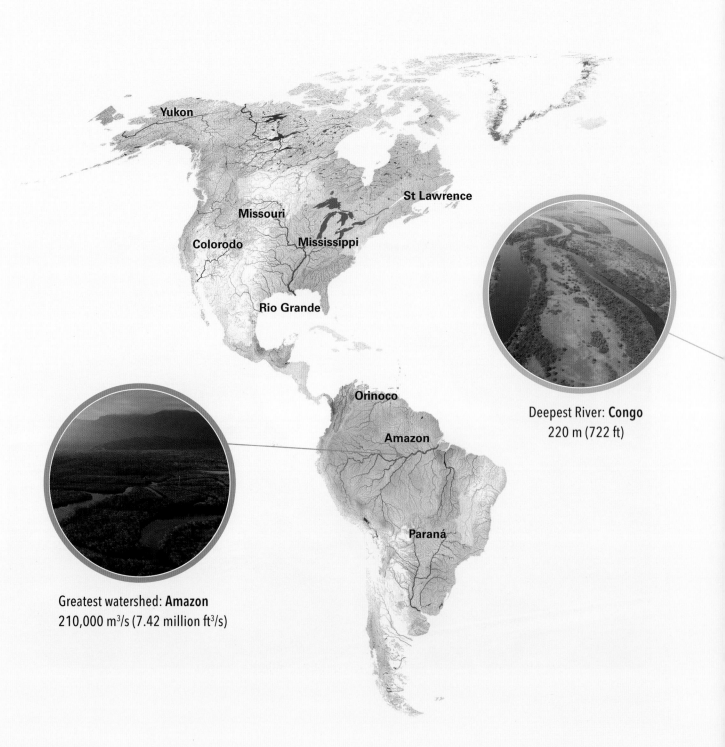

Yukon

Missouri

Colorodo

Mississippi

St Lawrence

Rio Grande

Orinoco

Amazon

Paraná

Deepest River: **Congo**
220 m (722 ft)

Greatest watershed: **Amazon**
210,000 m³/s (7.42 million ft³/s)

This map by Adam Symington depicts the world's major river basins, highlighting the vastness of the Amazon and Congo basins and the basins of the great Siberian rivers, as well as interesting anomalies such as the lack of drainage in the Sahara Desert, which leads to the northern half of the Nile River appearing as a stark, squiggly blue line.

Longest River: **Nile**
6,650 km (4,132 miles)

CHAPTER ONE

Rivers of
Africa

A continent characterized by extreme variability of rainfall and large areas of extreme aridity – roughly half of its territory is occupied by deserts and semi-deserts – and a largely agrarian society, Africa's rivers have been extremely important in shaping its history. Millennia ago, the great rivers of Africa acted as routes for human migration and went on to nurture and sustain some of the world's earliest and most important civilizations. More recently, they were central to the 'opening up' of Africa by European explorers and the subsequent colonization of huge swathes of the continent.

Among Africa's great rivers are the world's longest, the Nile, and its deepest and second-largest by discharge volume, the Congo, which also supports the planet's second-largest tropical rainforest. The continent is home to more than 50 transboundary rivers, which consequently play an outsized role in its international relations, a situation that is likely to be exacerbated as population growth and climate change put further pressure on Africa's water resources.

Victoria Falls on the Zambezi River.

The Congo River

Formerly also known as the Zaire River, the Congo is Africa's second-longest river and the world's second-largest river by discharge volume.

The Congo River has a dark and storied history. Blessed with an abundance of natural riches, the Congo Basin has become a byword for colonial brutality and the poster child for the so-called resource curse.

From its headwaters in the highlands and mountains of the East African Rift, the Congo flows in a long, wide counter-clockwise arc – northwest, west and southwest – before draining into the Atlantic Ocean at Banana in the Democratic Republic of the Congo (DRC). From source to mouth, the river passes through three contrasting sections: the upper Congo is characterized by confluences, lakes and rapids; the middle Congo is mostly a steady stream; and the lower Congo features potentially dangerous gorges and waterfalls.

The Chambeshi River, which rises in the highlands of northeastern Zambia between Lakes Tanganyika and Nyasa, is the river's most remote source; however, the 1,800-km-long (1,118-mile) Lualaba, which rises near Musofi on the Katanga Plateau in southeastern DRC, carries the greatest volume of water and thus may be considered to form the Congo's original main stream.

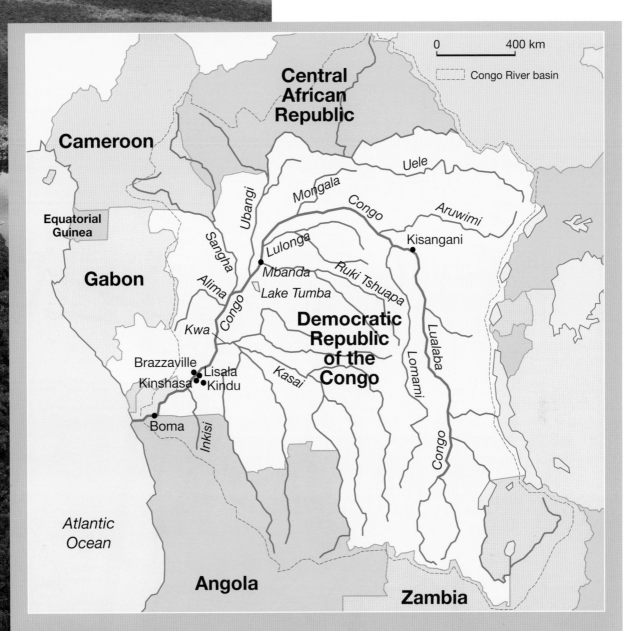

At a glance

Length: 4,700 km (2,920 miles)

Watershed: 4 million sq km (1.54 million sq miles)

Vertical drop: 1,590 m (5,216 ft)

Main tributaries: Ubangi, Kwa-Kassai, Lualaba, Lomami and Aruwimi rivers

Annual mean discharge: 40,000 cubic metres per second (1.4 million cubic ft per second)

Countries: Republic of the Congo, Democratic Republic of the Congo, Zambia, Angola

Cities: Kinshasa, Brazzaville, Kisangani

The river officially becomes known as the Congo below Boyoma Falls, formerly known as Stanley Falls, a series of seven cataracts spread over a section of the river 97 km (60 miles) long. Downstream, the river becomes statelier, flowing more slowly for about 1,600 km (994 miles). At first, the Congo is narrow, but it widens and islands begin to appear midstream as it enters its alluvial plain, dividing the river into several arms. Natural levees, formed by silt deposits, line the river's banks, which are more than 12 km (7.4 miles) apart in places.

Fishing traps

Virtually all of the indigenous peoples who live along the Congo engage in fishing. For centuries, the Wagenya people have used a unique method to catch fish in the lower reaches of Boyoma Falls (the seventh and final cataract is named the Wagenia Falls). They first build a system of wooden tripods, their feet anchored in natural depressions in the river's rocky bed. To these they attach large conical wicker baskets, which they lower into the maelstrom below. Fish caught up in the tumbling water are effectively 'sieved' out by the baskets. Gaps in the walls of the basket ensure that only large fish are captured. The traps are checked twice a day and any fish caught are divided among family members. Fishing sites are passed down through the generations, although in recent years, dwindling fish numbers have seen many of the fishermen turn to tourism for their livelihoods.

Henry Morton Stanley observed the fishermen at work during his famous voyage down the river in 1877. 'There are probably sixty or seventy baskets laid in the river on each side, every day; and though some may be brought up empty, in general they seem to be tolerably successful, for out of half-a-dozen baskets ... twenty-eight large fish were collected,' he later wrote.

Wagenya fishermen use traditional conical baskets to catch fish in Boyoma Falls on the Lualaba River near Kisangani in the Democratic Republic of the Congo.

The Congo's middle reaches end as it enters a narrow section called the Chenal ('Channel') or Couloir ('Corridor'), where the river is not much more than 1 km (0.62 mile) wide and the current becomes rapid. Here it flows through a valley that the river has cut several hundred metres down into the soft sandstone bedrock of the Batéké Plateau, swelling considerably as it receives several tributaries.

As it leaves the Chenal, the Congo divides into two branches, forming Malebo Pool (formerly known as Stanley Pool), where the river slows to a virtual stand-still for some 32 km (20 miles). Here, the capital of the Republic of the Congo, Brazzaville, faces off against the capital of the DRC, Kinshasa, the former on the pool's northern bank, the latter on the southern. The pool comes to an abrupt end as the river begins to tumble over some of the most spectacular rapids on earth. Known colloquially as the Gates of Hell, Livingstone Falls (misnamed as David Livingstone never reached the Congo) is a series of 32 tumultuous cascades and rapids, confined within deep canyons, over which the river falls 270 m (886 ft) in 354 km (220 miles) until it's only a few metres above sea level. Here the river's speed surges as the enormous quantity of water it's carrying – almost three times more than the Mississippi River – is forced through a gorge less than 250 m (820 ft) wide in places.

The Congo's 134-km (83-mile) estuary begins at Matadi, downstream from the rapids, and forms the border between Angola and the DRC. At first, the estuary is narrow, at most 2.4 km (1.5 miles) in width, but downstream from Boma it widens. Several islands obstruct the river, dividing it into several arms. In places, the depth can be only 6 m (20 ft) or so, making dredging necessary to allow ocean-going vessels to reach Matadi.

Each year, the Congo transports 86 million tonnes (84.6 million tons) of suspended sediment to the Atlantic Ocean, but the river lacks a delta; beyond the mouth of the estuary, which sits near the small town of Muanda, the river's course continues offshore as a deep underwater canyon that extends out about 200 km (124 miles), so the sediment that it carries doesn't accumulate.

Bordered by the Sahara Desert to the north, the Atlantic Ocean to the south and west, and the East African lakes region to the east, the Congo Basin is the world's second-largest river basin, spanning nine countries in west-central Africa and occupying 13 per cent of the African continent – an area the size of Europe. The basin straddles the equator and the river itself crosses the equator twice, the only major river to do so. It's said that water from the source takes more than six months to reach the Atlantic Ocean.

Because its drainage basin is draped over the equator, the river's flow remains relatively stable throughout the year, as some part of the river or its tributaries will always be experiencing a rainy season. At Malebo Pool, the river's flow typically peaks in December and then again in May. Low flows occur in July and March–April.

Thanks to its equatorial climate, characterized by high rainfall and high, stable temperatures, the Congo Basin supports the world's second-largest rainforest, extending continuously from about 4°N to about 5°S and bordered on either side by belts of savannah. An estimated 10,000 species of vascular plants are found in this vast jungle, about 30 per cent of which are endemic. The Congo basin has Africa's most valuable timber resources; however, exploitation has been limited by the region's inaccessibility, which makes the cost of transporting timber to the coast extremely high.

The river itself contains more species than any other African river system and is second only to the Amazon in terms of diversity. About 400 species are known to live in the Congo, more than 60 per cent of which are found nowhere else. Among the more unusual species is the elephant nose fish, which has a long snout and electricity-producing organs in its tail, which are used for navigation and communication. One of the reasons for the river's high fish species diversity is the

Paddling a traditional pirogue – a long, narrow canoe made from a single tree trunk – on the Congo River.

The elephant nose fish uses electrical signals, which enable it to 'see' an 'electrical image' of its surroundings, to hunt and navigate in the murky the waters of the Congo River.

abundant regions of whitewater, which have acted as barriers to fish movement for tens of thousands of years, allowing species on either side of the rapids to diverge.

The Congo is the world's deepest recorded river; in places there are canyons more than 220 m (722 ft) deep – too deep for light to reach the riverbed. Immense vortices of water plunge over the canyon walls like underwater waterfalls and currents flow both downstream and upstream. The canyons are so deep that there are fish living in them that are blind and unpigmented, just like fish that live in caves. Occasionally, strong currents shoot the fish up to the surface, where they die of the bends as the reduction in pressure causes bubbles of nitrogen gas to form in their bloodstream and tissues.

Humans have been living in the Congo Basin for about 50,000 years. Today, the basin is home to about 75 million people from 150 distinct ethnic groups.

In 1482, Portuguese explorer Diogo Cão discovered the Congo estuary after noticing a muddy brown plume spreading out into a bay while searching for water for his thirsty crew. After marking it with a stone pillar, fragments of which still exist, he sailed up the river for a short distance, establishing contact with the Kingdom of Congo. Cão was followed by other Portuguese explorers, some of whom established trading outposts along the river. Portuguese and Arab traders quickly entered into the slave trade – which by that time had already existed in Africa for centuries – sending enslaved persons to plantations that other Portuguese traders had established on islands off the African coast, including Madeira and the Canary Islands.

In 1871, David Livingstone became the first European to reach the village of Nyangwe, which is situated on the banks of the Lualaba River. He hoped to prove that the river was connected to the Nile, but after witnessing Arab slavers massacre 400 locals, he was too horrified to continue his mission and turned back to Lake Tanganyika. Henry Morton Stanley, who was also looking for the source of the Nile, reached Nyangwe in 1876. He continued on, travelling first down the Lualaba and then down the Congo. He passed Boyoma Falls, Malebo Pool and Livingstone Falls, before eventually reaching Boma, not far from the Congo's mouth, some nine months later, by which point he had come to realize that the river wasn't connected to the Nile.

In 1879, Stanley returned to Africa under the employ of King Leopold II of Belgium, who was keen to acquire a colony in order to increase his nation's prestige and wealth. Travelling as the representative of the Belgian branch of the International African Association, Stanley was charged with exploring the country and establishing a series of settlements.

In addition to guiding efforts to establish four steamers on the Congo (upon one of which the writer Joseph Conrad travelled in 1890), Stanley founded some 22 small towns along the river, including a trading post near Malebo Pool that he named Léopoldville in the king's honour. Although it was the first navigable port on the Congo above Livingstone Falls, all goods travelling to or from the sea had to be carried by porters between Léopoldville and Matadi, the port below the rapids, located 150 km (93 miles) from the coast. The settlement

'Going up that river was like travelling back to the earliest beginnings of the world, when vegetation rioted on the earth and the big trees were kings. An empty stream, a great silence, an impenetrable forest. The air was warm, thick, heavy, sluggish. There was no joy in the brilliance of sunshine. The long stretches of the waterway ran on, deserted, into the gloom of overshadowed distances.'

– Joseph Conrad, *Heart of Darkness*

A 19th-century male 'power figure', made to house mystical forces that enable it to heal illness, settle disputes or punish wrongdoers, from the Kingdom of Congo.

Opposite: *Rubber tappers collect latex in the rainforest near Lusambo in Congo Free State during the 19th century.*

Right: *A pirogue loaded with cane furniture on the Congo River.*

grew rapidly following the completion of the Matadi-Kinshasa portage railway in 1898, which bypassed the rapids. The city became the capital of the Belgian Congo in 1923 and was renamed Kinshasa in 1966.

In 1885, Leopold claimed the Congo Basin for himself as Congo Free State, triggering 23 years of brutality. The king enlisted a force of violent mercenaries to use torture and murder to force the native population to extract and export the region's ivory, rubber, copper and other natural resources. Estimates suggest that over the period of Leopold's reign in Africa, some ten million people in the region died at the hands of the Belgian colonists. Following the king's death, the region was annexed by the government of Belgium, which ruled until 1960.

Today, the Congo River is the key to economic development in west-central Africa. As it passes through a land with few roads or railways, the river still represents an important conduit for trade and communication. With its many tributaries, the Congo forms Africa's largest network of navigable waterways; within the DRC alone, there are some 14,000 km (8,699 miles) of navigable waterway. Malebo Pool represents the point of departure for inland navigation along the river and it was here that the capitals of the former states of the French Congo and the Belgian Congo were founded. Below the pool, Livingstone Falls create a barrier for craft moving upriver from the ocean, but beyond the falls, most of the river is readily navigable in sections, especially between Kinshasa and Kisangani. The volume of material, mostly agricultural produce, wood, minerals and fuel, that is transported on the river is relatively small compared to that on European rivers (commercial traffic

from Kinshasa does not reach 1 million tonnes/980,000 tons), but transport along the river – typically in pirogues, simple boats carved out of a single tree trunk and manoeuvred by one or two paddlers, and infrequent barges – remains essential for communication and small-scale trade. Large river steamers plied the river's waters until relatively recently. The three major falls are now bypassed by railways. Few bridges cross the Congo, primarily due to its width and the general lack of funds for infrastructure in the region. Instead, ferries are typically used to cross the river.

As well as fishing, people living along the river cultivate cassava (manioc) sweet potatoes, bananas and yams, building dykes, often of monumental size, and growing crops on the fertile land thus sheltered from the river.

Africa's most powerful river, the Congo has enormous potential for the generation of hydropower; estimates suggest that 13 per cent of global hydropower potential resides within the Congo Basin – enough to power the whole of sub-Saharan Africa. The basin currently hosts about 40 hydropower plants. The largest are the two Inga dams, located on the Congo about 200 km (124 miles) southwest of Kinshasa, which together generate 1,776 MW. They form part of the ambitious 'Grand Inga' scheme, which called for the construction of five dams with a total generating capacity of 34,500 MW.

There are more than 4,000 islands within the river, more than 50 of which are some 15 km (9 miles) long. In places, it is in danger of being overgrown by aquatic vegetation, particularly the introduced water hyacinth.

The Limpopo River

The second-largest river in Africa to drain into the Indian Ocean after the Zambezi, the Limpopo is a lazy, sluggish river that is struggling to survive due to over-abstraction.

'The great grey-green, greasy Limpopo River, all set about with fever-trees': Rudyard Kipling's *Just So* story 'The Elephant's Child' accurately evokes the sediment-heavy Limpopo's sluggish, meandering nature. Rising at an elevation of just 872 m (2,861 ft), the river makes a mostly leisurely descent to the coast, past banks lined with sweeping yellow-sand beaches and scrub. It is only really when it's falling from southern Africa's inland escarpment, where it quickly drops some 250 m (820 ft), that it truly wakes up, frothing its way through some 43 km (27 miles) of rapids.

Rising in the Witwatersrand in South Africa as the Krokodil (Crocodile) River, the Limpopo flows in a wide, generally eastward arc, forming a 400-km (249 mile) section of the border that separates South Africa to the southeast from Botswana to the northwest, and then a 240-km-long (149 mile) stretch that separates South Africa to the south and Zimbabwe to the north, before flowing through Mozambique and emptying into the Indian Ocean near the port town of Xai-Xai.

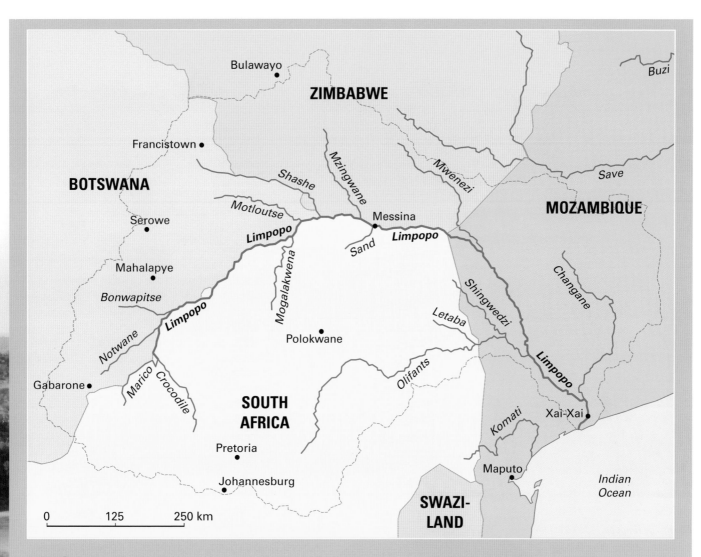

At a glance

Length: 1,750 km (1,087 miles)

Watershed: 410,000 sq km (158,302 sq miles)

Vertical drop: 872 m (2,861 ft)

Mean annual discharge: 170 cubic metres per second (6,003 cubic ft per second)

Countries: Botswana, Mozambique, South Africa and Zimbabwe

Main tributaries: Notwane, Olifants (Elephant), Shashe, Mzingwane, Crocodile, Mwenezi and Luvuvhu rivers

Cities: N/A

As on the Zambezi, large numbers of crocodiles laze in serried ranks on the low banks of the lazy river (it's no coincidence that one of its main tributaries is named the Crocodile River). The bloated brown bodies of hippos, too, are a common sight, particularly between the confluences with the Mokolo and Mogalakwena rivers.

Humans and their ancestors have lived in the sweeping savannah through which the Limpopo flows since time immemorial; *Australopithecus* fossils that date back some 3.5 million years have been found at sites in the Makapans Valley near Mokopane. About 2,000 years ago, the San people, hunter-gatherers also known as the Bushmen, became the first modern humans to occupy the Limpopo River basin.

Above: *The Limpopo, reduced to little more than a trickle, flows through Mapungubwe National Park, South Africa*

Below: *The earliest-known human-made artistic object – a pebble resembling a human face – from Makapansgat, South Africa, that dates from around 3 million years ago.*

The first European to set eyes on the river was the Portuguese explorer Vasco da Gama, who anchored in its mouth in January 1498 in order to stock up on freshwater. Seeing the local Bantu chiefs and their wives bedecked in copper ornaments, he named the waterway the Rio Cobre (Copper River).

Today, the Limpopo basin is home to about 15 million people, evenly divided between rural and urban areas. Most are poor and starvation and malnutrition are not uncommon during droughts or following crop failures. The fertile lowlands are more heavily populated.

The section of the river that forms the South Africa–Zimbabwe frontier, in common with the stretch of the Rio Grande that separates the USA and Mexico, is heavily guarded and fortified, with several electrified barbed-wire fences on the South African side erected to deter Zimbabweans willing to brave the crocodile-infested waters in the hope of crossing over. There is also a 1.8-m-high (6 ft) barbed wire fence that runs along the length of the South African bank of the river, established to halt the spread of foot and mouth disease from Zimbabwe and Botswana.

The Limpopo basin's climate ranges from the harsh aridity of the Kalahari Desert through tropical dry savannah to the rainy coastal plain

of Mozambique. The basin is prone to both flooding and drought. Situated in the transition between major climatic zones, its climate is highly variable, tossed and turned by the unpredictable interactions of different air masses. Rainfall, in particular, is highly variable, both seasonally and spatially. About 95 per cent falls between October and April, typically concentrated in bursts that last a few days and in isolated locations, which makes crop cultivation difficult. During dry years, the river's upper reaches may only flow for 40 or fewer days.

Indeed, water scarcity is a problem across the river basin, with demand frequently exceeding supply. This fact is reflected in the basin's infrastructure; while there is only one dam on the Limpopo's main stream, there are more than 47 large dams with a storage capacity of more than 12 million cubic metres (423 million cubic ft) in the basin, all of which are used for water storage for domestic, agricultural and industrial (mining) use, rather than for hydroelectricity generation. The construction of numerous weirs along the river's main channel, also for water storage, has been beneficial for its crocodile and hippo populations, which now tend to congregate in the deep pools they have created.

During winter, the river's lower and middle courses dry out, forming little more than a series of isolated pools. But then, come the summer rainy season, it frequently reaches flood proportions, occasionally breaking its banks in its lower reaches. In February 2000, a period of heavy rainfall, exacerbated when Cyclone Eline made landfall, caused catastrophic flooding across much of Mozambique.

The size of the river's basin has shrunk since the Late Pliocene or Pleistocene. At that time, the upper course of the Zambezi River drained into the Limpopo, but tectonic activity uplifted the land north of the present-day Limpopo, diverting the Zambezi into its current course.

Pesticides and nutrients from agricultural runoff, as well as releases from municipal wastewater-treatment plants, are polluting the Limpopo, but one of the main sources of pollution is the intensive mining activity that takes place within the river basin. As Vasco da Gama's experience attests, the Limpopo basin is rich in mineral resources; it hosts about 1,900 operating mines and a further 1,700 or so abandoned mines. It was the rush to exploit these resources from the mid-19th century that led to the creation of Africa's great railways. Today, mining activity accounts for about 10 per cent of water use in the basin. Coal mining, for example, consumes a significant quantity of the river's water during processing – roughly 250 litres (55 gallons) per tonne/ton – using it to reduce the risk of fire and explosions, and to manage dust. Sand mining along the river, particularly in South Africa and Botswana, is also a problem, frequently damaging its banks and increasing the amount of sediment in the water.

The Limpopo is navigable from its mouth to the confluence with the Olifants River, a distance of about 209 km (130 miles), but due to the presence of a sandbar that partially blocks the river's mouth, large ships must wait until high tide before they can enter the river.

The Niger River

The principal river of West Africa and the continent's third longest, the Niger is the main water source for people living in the harsh Sahara Desert.

The Niger begins life as the Tembi River, flowing out of a deep ravine and heading due north before describing an enormous arc that takes it through Mali, Niger, along the border between Niger and Benin, and then through Nigeria, before eventually emptying into the Atlantic Ocean via the Gulf of Guinea.

At Lokoja, the arrival of the Niger's largest tributary, the Benue, effectively doubles its volume and the two rivers form a lake-like stretch of water dotted with islands and sandbanks. The river then enters a narrow valley, flanked by low hills and, in places, sandstone cliffs up to 45 m (148 ft) high. At Aboh, the river emerges from the valley and begins to splay out into Africa's largest delta, a complex,

shifting network of thousands of channels, many named as separate rivers, whose mouths are typically obstructed by sandbars. Covering an area of some 70,000 sq km (27,027 sq miles), or 7.5 per cent of Nigeria's landmass, the densely populated delta region was once known as the Oil Rivers, because it was a major producer of palm oil. Today, it's a centre of crude oil extraction, producing some two million barrels per day.

It wasn't until the late 18th century that the true course of the Niger was revealed; for many years, it was thought that the river was connected to the Nile. The mystery of the river's source, and of the location of Timbuktu, provided the impetus for the formation of the

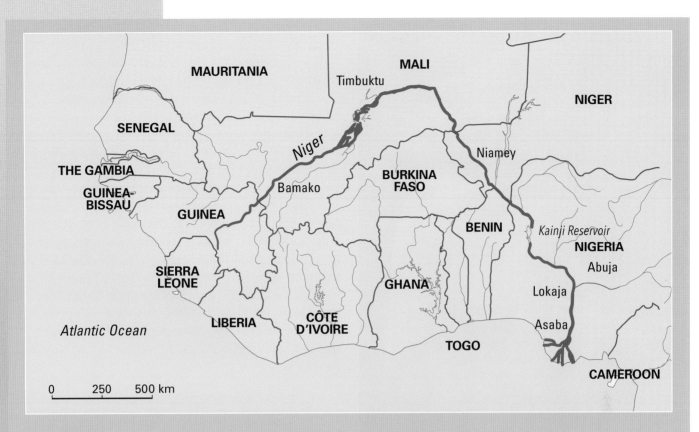

At a glance

Length: 4,180 km (2,597 mikes)

Watershed: 2.1 million sq km (819,815 sq miles)

Vertical drop: 850 m (2,789 ft)

Main tributaries: Benue, Shemankar, Faro, Donga, Bani and Katsina Ala rivers

Mean annual discharge: 6,100 cubic m per second (215,419 cubic ft per second)

Countries: Mali, Niger, Nigeria, Benin, Guinea

Cities: Bamako, Timbuktu, Niamey, Onitsha

African Association in England in 1788. Among the explorers recruited by the association was the Scotsman Mungo Park, who, travelling overland from the Gambia region, reached the Niger near Ségou in 1796 – becoming possibly the first European to lay eyes on the river's middle reaches – and established that it flowed eastward. In his account of his expeditions, *Travels in the Interior of Africa*, Park proposed that the Niger and Congo were the same river, a theory that became dominant in Europe. In 1805, while attempting to prove the Niger–Congo connection, Park sailed more than 2,400 km

Transporting passengers and firewood across the Niger River in Djenné, Mali.

(1,491 miles) down the river, but he and his party were drowned in the rapids at Bussa (now covered by Lake Kainji). It wasn't until 1830 that the mystery was solved, when brothers Richard and John Lander became the first Europeans to follow the river's course to the ocean.

The modern Niger River was formed when two ancient rivers joined. For millions of years, the river's upper reaches – from its source on the eastern side of the Guinea Highlands near the border with Sierra Leone to the great sweeping bend that it makes near what is now Timbuktu in Mali – ended in a series of large lakes in a green, humid savanna-like environment in the Djouf depression, while the lower Niger rose some way to the south in the mountainous Adrar des Ifoghas massif and flowed south into the Gulf of Guinea. Then, about 18,000 years ago, at the peak of the last ice age, the Sahara region began to dry out and turn into desert. Near Timbuktu, the trade winds blew desert sand into high dunes, forming a natural dam that blocked the flow of the upper Niger, creating a vast lake. About 10,000 years ago, climatic fluctuations brought heavy rainfall to the region, causing the lake to overflow. Because the dune barrier was still in place, the water flowed to the southeast – where the lower Niger had its source – and the two rivers became one.

'I saw with infinite pleasure the great object of my mission, glittering in the morning sun, flowing slowly to the east... the long sought for, majestic Niger.'

– Mungo Park

Above: *A 13th-to-15th-century terracotta statue of a woman from near Djenné, Mali.*

Main image: *Fishermen cast their nets into the Niger river near Niamey in Niger.*

The savanna plains through which the river flowed began to dry out once again about 5,500 years ago, eventually transforming into today's Sahara Desert. As sand replaced vegetation, the local inhabitants migrated to the great bend region near Timbuktu. Seen from space today, this vast crescent appears as a green arc cutting through the brown of the Sahel and the surrounding savanna. To the left is a verdant mass – the Inner Niger Delta, a labyrinth of braided streams, backwaters, marshes and large lakes on the southern edge of the Sahara in central Mali where the river abruptly flattens out and widens. In this fertile region, the migrants found abundant fish and good grazing for animals. The seasonal floods that inundate the Inner Niger Delta bring fresh inputs of sediment and nutrients, making it extremely productive for agriculture and, as in the Fertile Crescent of the Middle East, people living there began to domesticate food crops, including yams, African rice and pearl millet, and settlements such as Djenné-Djenno arose.

Eventually, the Niger bend became a key hub for trans-Saharan trade – a great source of wealth for a succession of powerful empires; between the 13th and 16th centuries, the Niger valley represented the heartland of the Mali and Songhai empires. A number of the towns that dot the river's banks today, including Timbuktu and Gao – once the seat of the Songhai Dynasty – were first established during this period. The Songhai amassed a powerful navy and used the river to extend its reach until it became one of the largest states in African history.

From May to September, heavy rain in the highlands of Guinea creates a flood surge that reaches the inland delta in October, turning the vast floodplain into a 30,000-sq-km (11,583 sq mile) network of channels, pools and levees that can host as many as a million birds,

including up to 500,000 garganey and 200,000 northern pintail; during the dry season, the wetland contracts to cover about 3,900 sq km (1,506 sq miles). The region provides an estimated 30 per cent of Mali's rice, 80 per cent of its fish production and dry-season grazing for up to 60 per cent of its cattle.

The Niger flows through almost all of western Africa's vegetational zones, from desert, savanna grassland and thorny shrublands to dense woodlands, rainforest and the mangrove swamps of the delta. The river rises among ancient rocks that provide little in the way of sediment, so its waters are relatively clear, containing about a tenth of the silt found in the Nile. The extensive swamps and vegetation in the inner delta filter out what little silt is in the river and the water that leaves the delta is remarkably clear.

The middle Niger experiences two floods. The first, known as the white flood because of the light sediment content of the water, takes place between July and October, soon after the rainy season. The second, known as the black flood because of the heavier sediment load, starts in December. The difference between high and low water can be as much as 11 m (36 ft), a range rivalled only by the Amazon.

In general, the Niger valley is sparsely settled, with most of the population concentrated in the Inner Niger Delta region and near the confluence of the Niger and Benue rivers. All along the river system, fishing is one of the more important economic activities, particularly during the dry season, when ocean catches typically drop off. Indeed, river fishing is a specialized occupation for a number of local Indigenous peoples. Unfortunately, however, the pollution generated by the discovery and exploitation of petroleum in the Niger delta region has seriously disrupted fishing there.

The Nile River

The longest river in Africa, and arguably the world, the Nile was critical to the development of the great civilization of ancient Egypt

Thanks to the miracle of the black mud that it carried down from the Ethiopian highlands to the edge of the Mediterranean Sea each year, the Nile River nurtured one of the greatest civilizations of the ancient world. Surrounded by the harsh Sahara Desert, the Nile acted as a lifeline for the settlements that formed along its banks and within its fertile delta, and ultimately developed into the world's first nation state.

Rising south of the Equator in Uganda, the Nile flows northwards across northeastern Africa, before draining into the Mediterranean Sea. The Nile River system has two principal tributaries: the White Nile

(named for the whitish clay suspended in its waters), which flows from Lake Victoria and is traditionally considered to be the headwater stream, and the larger Blue Nile, which flows from Lake Tana in the Ethiopian highlands (although its ultimate source is believed to be three small springs located near the town of Gish Abay, considered holy by the Ethiopian Orthodox Church, which give rise to a small stream, the Abay, that flows into the lake). The two rivers join at the Sudanese capital of Khartoum. The Blue Nile provides about 80 per cent of the Nile's water and silt, even though its basin accounts for only 10 per cent of the Nile's total catchment.

At a glance

Length: 6,650 km
(4,132 miles)
Watershed: 3.3 million sq
km (1.27 sq miles)
Vertical drop: 1,135 m
(3,724 ft)
Main tributaries: White Nile,
Blue Nile, Atbara (Red Nile)
Mean annual discharge: 1,500
cubic metres per second (52,972
cubic ft per second)
Countries: Egypt, Sudan, South
Sudan and Uganda
Cities: Khartoum, Cairo, Luzor,
Aswan

The White Nile used to exit Lake Victoria at Ripon Falls near Jinja, Uganda, as the Victoria Nile, but the falls were submerged in 1954 following the completion of the Owen Falls Dam (now the Nalubaale Dam). After flowing over Karuma Falls and Murchison Falls, it enters Lake Albert on the border of the Democratic Republic of the Congo, where it forms a significant internal delta. Upon leaving the lake, the river, now known as the Albert Nile, continues north through Uganda and into South Sudan, where it takes on the name Mountain Nile and flows through the extensive swamps of the Sudd region, losing more than half of its water to evaporation and transpiration. The marshes occupy a level clay plain on which the river regularly overflows its banks, feeding the great mass of aquatic vegetation that give the region its name: sudd literally means 'barrier'.

After the White and Blue Niles join at Khartoum, the river officially becomes the Nile (although it is sometimes called the United Nile). Just north of the Sudanese capital, the river flows over the first of six groups of cataracts – outcropping of granite and other crystalline rocks that cross the river's course and render it incompletely navigable. The last is located just north of the Aswan High Dam in Egypt. Between these sections of broken water, the river flows gently, populated by a plethora of river steamers, motorboats, ferries and sailing vessels, including the traditional wooden sailing boats known as feluccas.

Just before it crosses the border into Egypt, the Nile flows into Lake Nasser, the second-largest man-made lake in the world, created by the flooding of the Nile Valley by water backed up by the Aswan High Dam. (Strictly speaking, only the part of the 480-km-long/298-mile-long lake in Egyptian territory is called Lake Nasser; in Sudan it's known as Lake Nubia.)

After passing through the dam, the river flows over the last of the cataracts and then, north of Cairo, it enters its triangular delta, a monotonous plain said to boast Africa's most fertile soil that slopes gently to the sea. Where the delta now resides was once a gulf of the prehistoric Mediterranean Sea, filled in with silt as much as 25 m (82 ft) deep. The river eventually empties into the Mediterranean at Alexandria.

From source to sea, the river passes through tropical rainforest, mixed woodland and grassy and thorny savanna, and swampy areas thick with papyrus and tall bamboo-like grasses, before the rainfall decreases and the vegetation thins out into true desert. As it flows across Egypt, virtually all of the vegetation along its banks is the result of irrigation and cultivation. From space, the river appears as a lush green line drawn across the barren brown Sahara Desert.

Recent research suggests that the Nile drainage has been stable for about 30 million years, thanks to a downhill gradient along the river's path that has apparently held steady for such a long time because of currents that circulate in the liquid rock beneath the earth's crust. A plume within the mantle that mirrors the river's northward flow is believed to have shaped the topography on the surface, inducing uplift in the region around Ethiopia and Yemen, and subsidence in the eastern Mediterranean and northern Egypt. The cataracts along the river are also the result of this uplift, as is an area of land known as the Nubian Swell, which has diverted the Nile's course so that it flows

Lake Nasser, formed due to the construction of the Aswan High Dam on the Nile in Egypt, straddles the Sudan–Egypt border

Traditional sailing boats known as feluccas ply the waters of the Nile near Aswan, Egypt.

southwest before resuming its northward journey towards the first cataract at Aswan, forming an S-shaped section of river known as the Great Bend of the Nile.

Later, from about six million years ago, during what's known as the Messinian Salinity Crisis, the Mediterranean was closed off and virtually disappeared due to evaporation. Consequently, the Nile cut its bed down several hundred metres below the global sea level at Aswan and 2,400 m (7,874 ft) below at Cairo, creating a long, deep canyon that was eventually filled with sediment when the Mediterranean refilled.

Early humans (in this case *Homo erectus*, rather than *H. sapiens*) are believed to have first moved into the Nile Valley more than 500,000 years ago. During the beginning of the Upper Palaeolithic, in around 30,000 BCE, the Sahara region began to dry out and many people in the region migrated closer to the Nile River valley. By about 6000 BCE, Nile peoples had begun to build permanent settlements and were exploiting domesticated plants and animals, possibly thanks to the arrival of migrants from the Fertile Crescent, who brought agriculture to the region, and by about 5000 BCE, they had settled within the Nile Delta.

The river provided water for both people and livestock, as well as a convenient, efficient way of transporting people and goods (recent research suggests that the builders of the Great Pyramids used a now-defunct arm of the Nile to transport the massive limestone blocks to the construction site). Delivering a year-round water source in the desert, the Nile enabled Egyptians to live in an otherwise harsh and inhospitable region, making it possible to cultivate the rich soils of the

delta. Consequently, the Nile played a crucial role in the development of Egyptian civilization, its annual floods bringing fertile silt and water that enabled the Ancient Egyptians to cultivate and trade wheat, barley, beans, flax, papyrus and other crops. The development of irrigation enabled them to increase the amount of land under cultivation to support a growing population.

Irrigation using the Nile's water is thought to have begun in about 3800 BCE. By 3100 BCE, large irrigation works were being constructed, involving dams and canals up to 20 km (12 miles) in length. Irrigation along the Nile was feasible because the land slopes very gently from south to north and slightly more away from the riverbanks to the desert on either side. At first, seeds were simply sown into the damp mud left behind after the water from the annual flood had seeped away. Over time, this practice was replaced by a method known as basin irrigation, whereby earth banks were used to divide fields on the flat floodplain into large basins, some as large as 20,000 ha (49,421 acres). The basins were filled during the annual flood and the water was allowed to remain for up to six weeks before being permitted to drain away as the river's level fell. Seeds were then planted into the soil, which had been rejuvenated by a thin deposit of rich silt.

Although the land in the Nile delta was intensively cultivated, its fertility was maintained by the regular deposition of large quantities of silt washed down from the rich highlands of Ethiopia. The ancient Egyptians are said to have called the river Ar or Aur, meaning 'black', a reference to the rich, dark sediment left behind after the floodwaters receded each year in late summer.

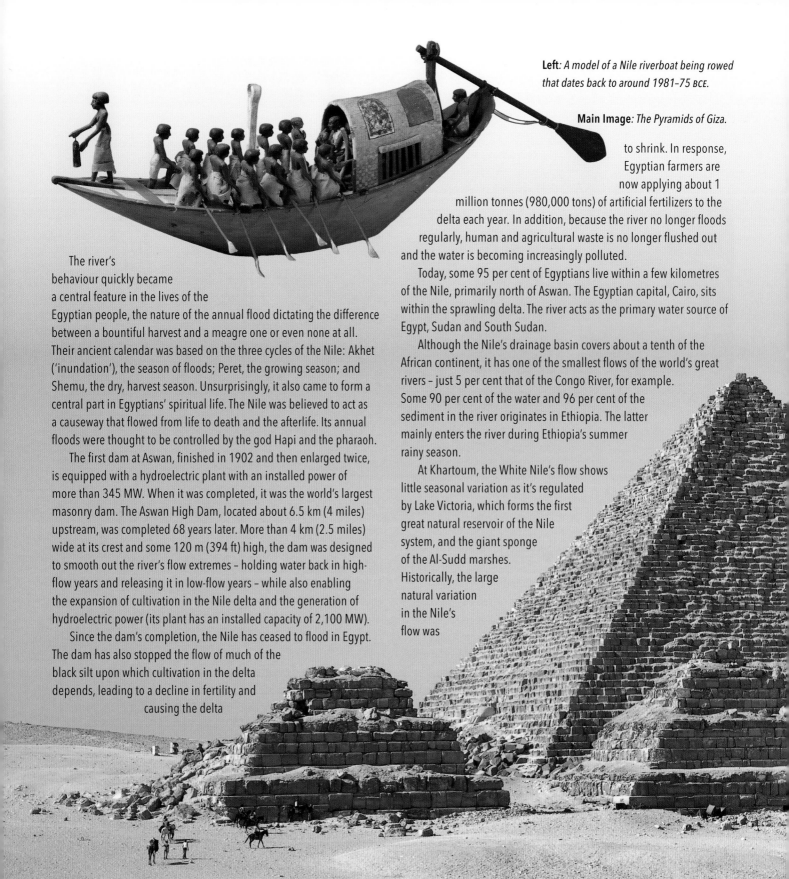

Left: *A model of a Nile riverboat being rowed that dates back to around 1981–75 BCE.*

Main Image: *The Pyramids of Giza.*

The river's behaviour quickly became a central feature in the lives of the Egyptian people, the nature of the annual flood dictating the difference between a bountiful harvest and a meagre one or even none at all. Their ancient calendar was based on the three cycles of the Nile: Akhet ('inundation'), the season of floods; Peret, the growing season; and Shemu, the dry, harvest season. Unsurprisingly, it also came to form a central part in Egyptians' spiritual life. The Nile was believed to act as a causeway that flowed from life to death and the afterlife. Its annual floods were thought to be controlled by the god Hapi and the pharaoh.

The first dam at Aswan, finished in 1902 and then enlarged twice, is equipped with a hydroelectric plant with an installed power of more than 345 MW. When it was completed, it was the world's largest masonry dam. The Aswan High Dam, located about 6.5 km (4 miles) upstream, was completed 68 years later. More than 4 km (2.5 miles) wide at its crest and some 120 m (394 ft) high, the dam was designed to smooth out the river's flow extremes – holding water back in high-flow years and releasing it in low-flow years – while also enabling the expansion of cultivation in the Nile delta and the generation of hydroelectric power (its plant has an installed capacity of 2,100 MW).

Since the dam's completion, the Nile has ceased to flood in Egypt. The dam has also stopped the flow of much of the black silt upon which cultivation in the delta depends, leading to a decline in fertility and causing the delta

to shrink. In response, Egyptian farmers are now applying about 1 million tonnes (980,000 tons) of artificial fertilizers to the delta each year. In addition, because the river no longer floods regularly, human and agricultural waste is no longer flushed out and the water is becoming increasingly polluted.

Today, some 95 per cent of Egyptians live within a few kilometres of the Nile, primarily north of Aswan. The Egyptian capital, Cairo, sits within the sprawling delta. The river acts as the primary water source of Egypt, Sudan and South Sudan.

Although the Nile's drainage basin covers about a tenth of the African continent, it has one of the smallest flows of the world's great rivers – just 5 per cent that of the Congo River, for example. Some 90 per cent of the water and 96 per cent of the sediment in the river originates in Ethiopia. The latter mainly enters the river during Ethiopia's summer rainy season.

At Khartoum, the White Nile's flow shows little seasonal variation as it's regulated by Lake Victoria, which forms the first great natural reservoir of the Nile system, and the giant sponge of the Al-Sudd marshes. Historically, the large natural variation in the Nile's flow was mostly caused by the considerable annual fluctuation in the volume of the Blue Nile – which in some cases could amount to a factor of 50. At Khartoum, the river's change in height between low and high water averages more than 6 m (20 ft). Rapid runoff from summer monsoon rain falling on the Ethiopian Plateau swells the Blue Nile and its tributaries, causing a pronounced flood season that typically runs from late July to October. At this time, the prodigious flow of the Blue Nile can actually hold back the White Nile, turning its lower reaches near the confluence into a large lake.

As with other transnational rivers, the Nile's water has long been a bone of contention for countries in the region, with several nations unhappy about Egypt's dominance. The most recent dispute, between Ethiopia and Sudan and Egypt, was triggered by start of construction of the Grand Ethiopian Renaissance Dam on the Blue Nile in 2011. Egypt fears that the dam could reduce the amount of water flowing into Lake Nasser, which would in turn have a detrimental effect on the production of electricity by the hydroelectric station attached to the Aswan High Dam.

As far as we know, the ancient Egyptians made little attempt to explore the Nile, limiting their travels to the region around the

Aswan High Dam, one of the world's largest embankment dams, was built across the Nile between 1960 and 1970.

An aerial view of Luxor and the Nile.

coast. The Greeks made a number of efforts to travel upriver with mixed success. In 457 BCE, the Greek historian Herodotus travelled as far as the first cataract near what is now Aswan, as did the Greek geographer Strabo and a Roman governor of Egypt, Aelius Gallus, in 25 BCE.

Around 62 CE, the Roman emperor Nero sent one, possibly two, expeditions to search for the source of the Nile. Travelling overland first, to bypass the unnavigable sections closer to the coast, the Romans reached the confluence of the White and Blue Niles, and continued up the former. It's believed that they were eventually thwarted, like so many who came after them, by the Al-Sudd marshes, but there are some who think that they may have reached as far as Murchison Falls, where the White Nile plunges into Lake Albert – very close, indeed to the source that they sought.

In 1618, a Spanish Jesuit priest named Pedro Páez located the source of the Blue Nile, but the river's ultimate source remained elusive. European missionaries and traders ascended as far as the border of Uganda, but beyond there the river's course was unknown. During the mid-18th century, Scottish traveller James Bruce spent five years travelling in Sudan and Ethiopia searching for the source of the Nile, although he focused on the Blue Nile, whose source he did indeed reach in 1770. He also became the first European to trace the Blue Nile to its confluence with the White Nile. The publication in 1790 of his five-volume *Travels to discover the source of the Nile in the years 1768–73* helped to stimulate interest in Africa in general and the source of the Nile in particular.

By the 19th century, the Nile's source had taken on an almost mythical quality. Eventually, the Royal Geographical Society decided that it was time to settle the matter and it supported an expedition headed by British explorers Richard Francis Burton and John Hanning Speke. In 1858, Speke became the first European to reach Lake Victoria. At the time, Burton was resting farther south on the shores of Lake Tanganyika while he recovered from an illness, and he was later outraged when Speke claimed to have proved that his discovery was the Nile's true source. A bitter and very public quarrel ensued, sparking intense debate within the geographical community and interest by other European explorers.

In 1860, Speke and James A. Grant, also travelling under the auspices of the Royal Geographical Society, returned to the region, travelling farther around the lake and reaching Ripon Falls in 1862, at which point Speke wrote, 'I saw that old Father Nile without any doubt rises in Victoria Nyanza [Lake Victoria].' Speke and Grant then headed north, travelling partly along the White Nile, until they reached Gondokoro, a trading-station on the river's eastern bank. General Charles George Gordon finally settled the question of the Nile's source when he and his officers travelled up the White Nile from Khartoum to Lake Victoria between 1874 and 1877, mapping a significant length of the river. Speke's discovery was also confirmed by Henry Morton Stanley, who circumnavigated Lake Victoria in 1875 and described the great outflow at Ripon Falls on the lake's northern shore.

Known locally as Tis Abay ('Great Smoke'), Blue Nile Falls on the Blue Nile River at Tis Issat, Ethiopia, are the most dramatic falls on the Nile river system.

At Murchison Falls, the White Nile is forced through a 7m (23ft) gap in the surrounding rocks and drops 43 m (141 ft), before flowing into Lake Albert.

The Okavango River

Nourishing one of Africa's most diverse and important concentrations of wildlife, the Okavango River remains one of the largest virtually pristine river systems on the African continent.

It begins each year in late December or early January. Storm clouds, dark and bruised, gather ominously over the Angola highlands. Lightning arcs brilliantly across the sky and thunder rumbles as heavy afternoon thunderstorms inundate the grasslands and patches of montane forest. Tumbling down from the mountains, torrents of rainwater eventually converge to swell the Okavango River, creating a wave of floodwater that flows down through Namibia and into Botswana. A month after the first few fat drops fell in Angola that wave reaches the Okavango Delta, triggering one of the world's most extraordinary wildlife spectacles.

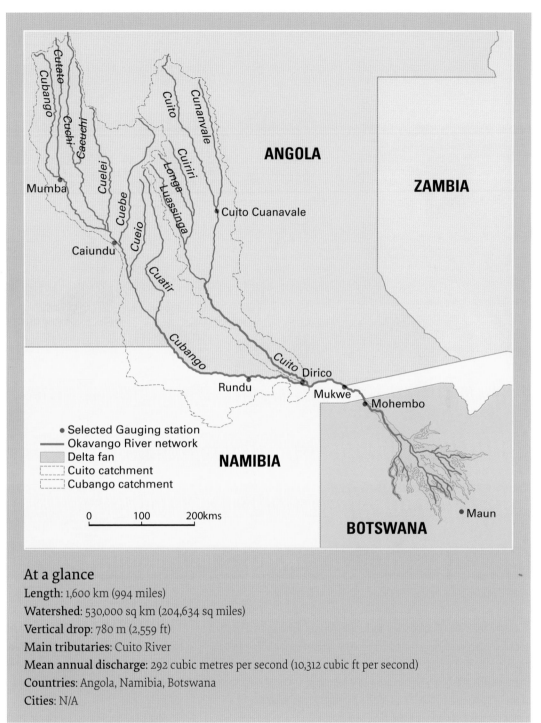

At a glance

Length: 1,600 km (994 miles)

Watershed: 530,000 sq km (204,634 sq miles)

Vertical drop: 780 m (2,559 ft)

Main tributaries: Cuito River

Mean annual discharge: 292 cubic metres per second (10,312 cubic ft per second)

Countries: Angola, Namibia, Botswana

Cities: N/A

The Okavango River's basin is endorheic – that is, it doesn't drain into the sea. Instead, the river ends in a triangular inland delta in the Kalahari Desert that covers an area of about 16,800 sq km (6,487 sq miles). Less than half of the delta is swamp year-round, but each year, about 11 cubic km (2.6 cubic miles) of water spreads out across the delta, causing it to swell to about three times its permanent size, transforming vast areas of desert and savannah into a sprawling wetland. During a big flood year, the swamp can stretch as far as 150 km (93 miles) from east to west.

This lush oasis, the only perennial water body for hundreds of kilometres, draws in wildlife from far and wide; when flooded, the delta plays host to some 125 mammal species, including all of Africa's 'big five': lions, leopards, buffalo, elephants and rhinoceroses (both black and white). The most populous large mammal is the lechwe, a marsh-loving antelope with elongated hooves and a water-repellent substance on its legs, which together enable rapid movement through knee-deep water; estimates suggest that some 88,000 individuals occupy the delta.

A heard of elephants crosses the Okavango River in Botswana.

More than 440 bird species, including African fish eagles, Egyptian geese, marabou storks, crested cranes and African spoonbills, can be found in the delta. It also supports 71 fish species, including the African sharp-tooth catfish, which can grow to a length of 1.4 m (4.6 ft); many of these species are also found in the Zambezi River, evidence of a historical link between the two river systems.

The Okavango's water is startlingly clear, containing very little silt. Instead, the river's sediment load consists almost entirely of sand, which is captured by plant roots, taking on the role of 'glue' that silt would normally play and helping to create islands on which more plants can take root. The river and its floodplain channels are dominated by dense clumps of papyrus reeds and other aquatic plants, while the slightly higher ground hosts patches of woodland and savanna. Because the delta is extremely flat, varying by less than 2 m (6.6 ft) in height across its entire area, even small amounts of sand deposition can lead to significant changes to the river's course. The dense growth of papyrus reeds also continually blocks the river's channels, further altering the pattern of flow. Hence, the delta and the river's course are ever-changing.

Many of the islands scattered across the delta have a central barren white patch, caused by the accumulation of salt. About 70 per cent of these islands began life as termite mounds; if a tree starts to grow in these insect condominiums, its roots stabilize it and an island forms.

The river begins its journey in the sandy highlands of central Angola, just south of Vila Nova on the Bié Plateau, where it's known by its Portuguese name, Rio Cubango (some consider the Cubango to be a separate river; the river officially takes the name Okavango at the confluence of the Cubango and Cuito rivers). It then flows generally southeastwards, first forming part of the border between Angola and Namibia, and then making its way towards Botswana, dropping 4 m (13 ft) as it passes through a series of rapids known as Popa Falls and then beginning to spread out as it enters the flat, arid Kalahari Desert just over the border. In its upper reaches, the river flows through woodland, but as it meanders southwards, the trees become increasingly sparse as the country is transformed into dry savanna grassland dotted with spiny acacia trees and then into desert.

Linear islands

Many of the more than 150,000 islands within the delta are long, thin and curved, resembling a gently meandering river. This resemblance isn't coincidental – the islands are actually the banks of old river channels that have become clogged by vegetation and sediment, causing the river to change course.

During the summer wet season (January–February), Angola receives three times more rainfall than Botswana, but it takes a month for the surge of water to reach the delta and a further four months to filter through the plants and numerous channels of the delta's final 250 km (155 miles). Hence the delta's area peaks during Botswana's winter (June–August).

Virtually all of the water that reaches the delta eventually either evaporates or is transpired through the vegetation; only about 5 per cent flows into regional groundwater. Only in years with heavy flooding do significant amounts of water flow out of the delta at Maun, filling the dry beds of rivers such as the Boteti and Thaoge, which, in especially large floods, then flows on into Lake Ngami. As the water recedes, it leaves behind a series of canals, waterholes and lagoons, which attract increasing numbers of animals, concentrating the wildlife.

The delta and its wildlife act as a powerful tourist draw, welcoming some 200,000 visitors annually and bringing in £65 million in annual revenue. The area was made a game reserve in 1962 in response to the depletion of the wildlife due to poaching and encroachment by cattle.

The first European known to have seen the Okavango, the famed Scottish missionary and explorer David Livingstone, reached the delta in 1849. He didn't venture far into the swamp for fear of the particularly deadly local malaria. Indeed, mosquitoes and tsetse flies have long protected the swamp from human exploitation. The devastating trypanosomiasis, or sleeping sickness, a disease caused by microscopic parasites transmitted by the tsetse fly, was and still is rife in the drier areas.

The river, which takes its name from the Okavango (Kavango) people of northern Namibia, has been under the political control of the Batawana people since the late 18th century. The Batawana have traditionally lived on the delta's margins, wary of the dangers that the tsetse fly poses to their cattle; however, from 1896 through to the late 1930s, the tsetse fly retreated and most Batawana lived in the swamps.

The Okavango Delta is a maze of channels that are often fringed by tall reeds.

The Zambezi River

Flowing from the highlands of Zambia to the Indian Ocean, the Zambezi is Africa's fourth-longest river and the largest of the continent's rivers to drain into the Indian Ocean.

The mighty Zambezi River played a pivotal role in the 'opening up' of Africa. The celebrated Scottish missionary and explorer David Livingstone hoped to use the Zambezi as a 'highway' to bring 'Christianity, commerce and civilization' to the African continent. If the river could be used as a conduit for trade, he argued, it would hasten the end of the horrors of slavery.

In November 1853, Livingstone set out from Linyanti, in what is now Namibia, and headed north up the Zambezi, which was then called the Zanbere, with a small group of the local Makololo people. He hoped to find a route to the Atlantic coast, stating, 'I shall open up a path into the interior, or perish.'

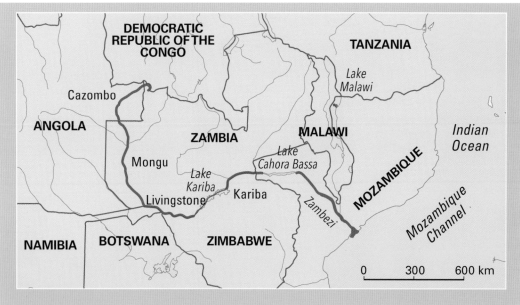

At a glance

Length: 2,574 km (1,599 miles)

Watershed area: 1.39 million sq km (536,682 sq miles)

Vertical drop: 1,524 m (5,000)

Main tributaries: Shire, Luangwa and Kafue rivers

Mean annual discharge: 3,400 cubic metres per second (120,070 cubic ft per second)

Countries: Zambia, Angola, Mozambique, Namibia, Botswana and Zimbabwe

Cities: Livingstone

After an arduous journey, during which Livingstone almost died from fever, in May 1854 the small party reached the coast at Luanda, in Angola, a Portuguese port city heavily involved in the slave trade. However, Livingstone realized the route would be too difficult for future traders, so he retraced the journey back to Linyanti. He then headed east down the Zambezi in a fleet of canoes, accompanied by more than 100 Makololo. About two weeks into the journey, Livingstone spied columns of spray rising to the sky some 10 km (6 miles) in the distance, accompanied by a deep, thundering roar. The source of these peculiar phenomena was soon revealed as an immense waterfall, which his companions called Mosioatunya: 'The smoke that thunders.'

Upon reaching the falls, Livingstone's men paddled his canoe to one of the small islands perched on the lip, where he lay on his stomach and peered over the edge, marvelling at the sight of rainbows in the spray, which drenched him to the skin. Twice the size of Niagara, the falls are located at a point where the Zambezi is 1,700 m (5,577 ft) wide on what is now the border between Zimbabwe and Zambia. Some 935 cubic metres (33,019 cubic ft) of water tumble over a sheer, 108-m (354-ft) precipice each second.

Livingstone described the falls, which he renamed Victoria Falls in honour of his Queen, 'the most wonderful sight I had seen in Africa'.

Eventually, Livingstone reached Quelimane in Mozambique, not far from the Zambezi's mouth, having mapped most of the river's course and becoming the first European to cross south-central Africa. His maps remained the most accurate available until the 20th century, when further surveys finally traced the Zambezi to its source.

About a year and a half later, Livingstone returned to the Zambezi for a much better organized expedition, featuring a paddle steamer and impressive stores. However, it ended in failure when it became clear that it would never be possible for boats to pass the Cahora Bassa rapids, a series of cataracts and torrents that Livingstone had failed to explore during his earlier travels. Two attempts to find a route along the Ruvuma River also ended in failure, and in July 1863 the British government recalled the expedition.

Today, the Zambezi passes through three countries – Zambia, Angola, Mozambique – and forms the borders between Zambia and three of its neighbours: Namibia, Botswana and Zimbabwe.

Its long journey to the Indian Ocean begins on

the Central African Plateau in a patch of marshy black wetland, known as a dambo, in the centre of the iconic undulating Miombo Woodlands in the Mwinilunga District in north-western Zambia at about 1,524 m (5,000 ft) above sea level.

Along its upper and middle course, the river mostly flows through savanna, populated by an array of 'classic' African mammals, including lions, buffalo, zebras, giraffes, baboons and elephants. The river itself is often fringed by forest that contains valuable hardwood trees including Rhodesian teak and ebony. In slower sections, the river often teems with hippos, floating, yawning and flicking their ears, and ranks of Nile crocodiles basking on the muddy banks. In the river's lower course, the savanna gives way to dense bushland and evergreen forest, dotted with mangrove swamps.

Although the Zambezi River valley is home to an estimated 32 million people, there are surprisingly few large towns and cities, or crossings, along its length. One of the few significant crossings is located atop the 579-m-long (1,900-ft-long) wall of the Kariba Dam, which bears a busy road that carries traffic moving between Zambia and Zimbabwe. Located 483 km (300 miles) below Victoria Falls at Kariba in Zimbabwe, the dam provides most of Zimbabwe and Zambia's electricity.

Lake Kariba, which formed when the dam was completed in 1959, covers an area of about 5,180 sq km (2,000 sq miles), making it one of the world's largest man-made lakes. Nyami-Nyami, the Zambezi snake spirit, is said to live in the lake. Locals blamed the spirit for the floods that took place during the 1950s, killing workers and slowing the dam's construction. In recent times, when drought took hold in the region local leaders planned a series of rituals in order to placate Nyami-Nyami.

Left: At Victoria Falls on the Zambia–Zimbabwe border, the full width of the Zambezi River plunges over a single vertical drop into a 1,708 m (5,604 ft) wide, transverse chasm carved by the river along a fracture zone in the underlying basalt plateau, forming the world's largest sheet of falling water.

Below: The completion of Kariba Dam, in the Kariba Gorge between Zambia and Zimbabwe, created Lake Kariba, the world's largest man-made lake.

Geological history

Until roughly two million years ago, during the Late Pliocene or Pleistocene, the Upper Zambezi flowed south across what is now the Makgadikgadi Pan in Botswana, before emptying into the Limpopo River. Tectonic uplift between the two rivers then caused a vast lake to form and the Upper Zambezi shifted eastwards.

Around the same, 1,000 km (621 miles) to the east, a western tributary of the Shire River eroded a deep valley on its western escarpment and began to move further westwards at the rate of a few centimetres per year. This river, which eventually became the Middle Zambezi, captured a number of south-flowing rivers, including the Luangwa and Kafue.

When the Middle Zambezi reached the large lake trapped at Makgadikgadi, the lake waters began to empty eastwards and the Upper Zambezi was also captured. The upper river flowed across a basalt plateau that was about 300 m (984 ft) higher than the Middle Zambezi, so a waterfall formed in the Batoka Gorge, near where Lake Kariba is now located – the first Victoria Falls.

CHAPTER TWO

Rivers of the Americas

From the frigid and often frozen rivers of northern Canada and Alaska to the steamy-jungle-fringed waterways of the equatorial regions, the Americas are blessed with some of the world's greatest rivers. And none, perhaps, is greater than the mighty Amazon, the world's largest river by discharge volume, whose vast basin supports the planet's largest rainforest the so-called lungs of the planet. In North America, economic prosperity has been underpinned by rivers such as the Mississippi, St Lawrence and Colorado, while in South America, the Amazon, Orinoco and Parana sustain remarkably diverse ecosystems. Over the past century, many of these rivers have been transformed, dammed and straightened, dredged and leveed, their water captured for drinking and irrigation, their tributaries starved by climate-change-induced drought, but recent restoration efforts are slowly bringing them back to life.

The Amazon River.

The Amazon River

The world's largest river by discharge volume and the (disputed) longest river in the world, the Amazon flows through the world's most biodiverse terrestrial ecosystem.

The Amazon is a river of superlatives. Its average discharge – about 209,000 cubic metres per second (7,380,765 cubic ft per second) or 6,591 cubic km per year (1,579 cubic miles per year) – is larger than that of the next seven largest independent rivers combined. The Amazon's drainage basin is the world's largest, covering an area of more than 7 million sq km (2,702,715 sq miles) – about 40 per cent of South America. More than 1,100 tributaries flow into the Amazon along its length (the most of any river), 17 of which are more than 1,500 km (932 miles) long. Among its tributaries are two of the world's top ten rivers by discharge. When the Amazon enters Brazil, it contains only a fifth of the flow that will eventually discharge into the Atlantic, but that is still more water than is discharged by any other river.

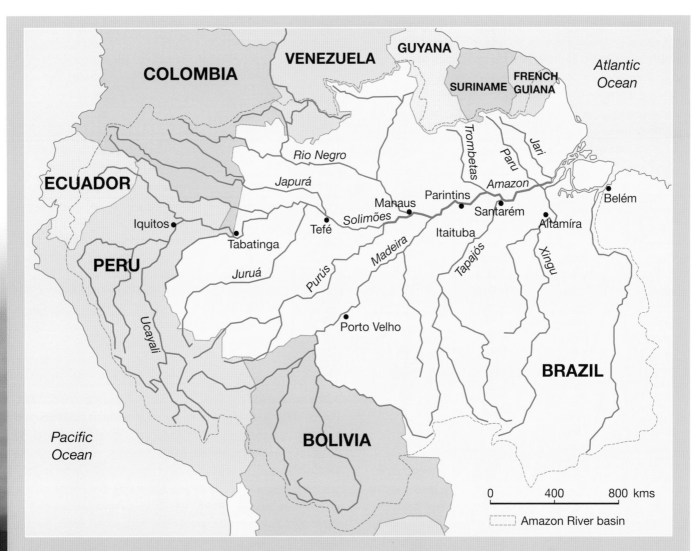

At a glance

Length: 6,650 km (4,132 miles)

Watershed: 6.7 million sq km (2.59 million sq miles)

Vertical drop: 5,220 m (17,126 ft)

Main tributaries: Madeira, Rio Negro, Purús, Japura and Tocantins rivers

Mean annual discharge: 210,000 cubic metres per second (7.42 million cubic ft per second)

Countries: Peru, Colombia, Brazil

Cities: Belem, Iquitos, Manaus, Santarem

Estimates suggest that about a fifth of all the water that runs off the earth's surface eventually flows into the Amazon. The immense volume of fresh water that flows from the river into the ocean forms a plume that is about 400 km (249 miles) long and up to 200 km (124.5 miles) wide; it reduces the salinity and alters the colour of the ocean surface over an area up to about 2.5 million sq km (965,255 sq miles).

For almost a century, the headwaters of the Apurímac River on Nevado Mismi, a 5,597-m (18,363 ft) Andean mountain in Peru, were considered to be the Amazon's most distant source, but according to a 2014 study, the headwaters of the Mantaro River on the Cordillera Rumi Cruz, also in Peru, represent a more distant source, adding 80 km (50 miles) to the river's official length. These two rivers join to form the Ucayali River; the Amazon River proper is said to begin at the confluence of the Ucayali and Marañón rivers (the latter rises in the central Peruvian Andes) upstream from Iquitos. In Brazil, however, the section of the river between here and the confluence with the Rio Negro at Manaus, the largest city on the river, is known as the Solimões River.

After flowing generally eastwards, at one point forming part of the border between Colombia and Peru, the Amazon eventually empties into the Atlantic Ocean near the city of Macapa. What exactly constitutes the river's mouth is a matter of dispute, with estimates of its width ranging from 64 km (40 miles) to more than 320 km (199 miles).

The region around the mouth appears to have once been a gulf of the Atlantic Ocean. This gulf has been filled in with sediment and is now characterized by a cluster of half-submerged islets and shallow sandbanks, and channels called *furos* that link the Amazon to the Pará River. Between these two rivers lies Marajó Island, the world's largest combined river/sea island, a lowland a little larger than Denmark.

The Amazon empties into the turbulent waters of the Atlantic Ocean, whose wave and tidal energy around the river's mouth are such that most of its sediment – which amounts to more than 1 million tonnes (984,206 tons) per year – is washed out to sea, which is why the river doesn't possess a true delta. Instead, coastal currents sweep the river's sediment northward to be deposited along the coasts of northern Brazil and French Guiana.

The river's tributaries can be classified as either blackwater, whitewater or clearwater. The dark colour that gives blackwater rivers their name is caused by the presence of humic acids derived from the decomposition of organic matter. They tend to be slow moving and to flow through forested swamps and other wetlands, where they pick up a large concentration of dissolved tannin, which turns the water

The world's longest river?

The long-running debate over whether the Amazon or the Nile is the world's longest river remains unresolved. The historical consensus among geographical authorities has handed the title to the Nile, but recent studies have muddied the river waters. In July 2008, the Brazilian Institute for Space Research published an article that claimed that the Amazon was 6,992 km (4,345 miles) in length. Using the same techniques, the length of the Nile was determined to be 6,853 km (4,258 miles) – longer than previous estimates but shorter than the Amazon. However, the following year, a new paper gave a length of 6,575 km (4,085 miles) for the Amazon and 7,088 km (4,404 miles) for the Nile. The Amazon has a highly complex and ever-changing streambed, which makes obtaining an accurate measurement extremely difficult, so the river's length remains open to interpretation and continued debate.

the colour of black tea. Clearwater rivers contain less humic acid and have a higher mineral content. They tend to originate on the Brazilian Plateau or the Guiana Shield (the geological landmass centred around Venezuela, Guyana, Surinam, French Guiana, and northeast Brazil) and flow through regions with sandy soils and ancient, crystalline rocks that are already heavily weathered, so they accumulate little in the way of sediment. Whitewater rivers are pale and muddy, containing high levels of suspended sediment, which they pick up as they flow down from the Andes. Some rivers alternate, flowing as clearwater during the wet

Located at the mouth of the Amazon, Marajó is the world's largest combined river/sea island, with an area of more than 40,000 sq km.

The confluence of the muddy, tan-coloured Solimões or Upper Amazon and the 'black' water of the Rio Negro near the Brazilian city of Manaus.

season and blackwater during the dry. For more than 6 km (3.7 miles) from the confluence of the blackwater Rio Negro and the whitewater Solimões/Amazon, the dark water of the former and the sandy-coloured water of the latter flow side by side without mixing.

The Amazon exhibits an extraordinarily slight gradient. Where it crosses the Peruvian border, some 3,200 km (1,988 miles) from its mouth, it is less than 90 m (295 ft) above sea level. The river flows at an average velocity of about 2.5 km/h (1.6 mph), but that speed increases significantly when the river is in flood. In places, the river divides into multiple channels, or anabranches, that are connected by a complicated system of natural canals that divide the adjacent land, which rarely rises more than 5 m (16 ft) above the river, into numerous islands.

During the wet season, some 350,000 sq km (135,136 sq miles) of the Amazon basin are flooded, compared to about 110,000 sq km (42,471 sq miles) during the dry. The river's upper course experiences two annual floods, triggered by rainfall in the Peruvian Andes from October to January and the Ecuadoran Andes from March to July. These two seasons of high flow gradually merge, causing the river's rise to progress slowly downstream in a gigantic wave from November to June.

During the flood season, the Amazon often completely fills its floodplain, spreading out to a width of some 55 km (34 miles) or more. The river's level can rise by more than 12 m (39 ft), inundating the surrounding forests, which are known as *várzea* ('flooded forests'); the Amazon's flooded forests are the world's most extensive example of this habitat type, covering about 180,000 sq km (69,498 sq miles) of the Amazon basin. The water that floods the forests is high in nutrients and, consequently, *várzea* forests are among the most productive habitats in Amazonia, serving as important breeding grounds for fish and other animals.

The Amazon is synonymous with steamy jungles that teem with wildlife. For much of its length, the river flows through a vast tropical rainforest that resounds with the calls of myriad colourful birds, the chatter of monkeys and the throbbing whine of insects. Along the river itself, turtles bask on fallen trees, their shells adorned with brightly coloured butterflies, while caiman and alligators patrol the shallows.

More than two-thirds of the Amazon basin is covered by rainforest. So dense and impenetrable is the jungle that, until relatively recently, the Amazon was the only means of access into the forest. Covering

Left: *Flooded forest, or* várzea.

from the inundated trees. Other species migrate to spawn, swimming from blackwater and clearwater systems onto whitewater river floodplains, whose higher nutrient levels and thus higher productivity offer better conditions as nursery areas. A few species migrate the entire course of the river. The Dorado catfish, for example, has a life-cycle migration of about 11,600 km (7,208 miles) – the longest strictly freshwater migration in the world – moving between hatching areas in the Andes and nurseries in the lower Amazon and estuary.

Geological evidence suggests that, for millions of years, the Amazon flowed in the opposite direction, before the rise of the Andes blocked its flow to the Pacific and caused it to reverse direction and head towards the Atlantic. The Andes began to rise about 15 million years ago, blocking the river and causing the Amazon basin to fill with water and become a vast inland sea. Then, between 11 and 10 million years ago, water began to flow eastwards out of the basin. When the sea level dropped during glacial periods, water drained from the lake even faster, entrenching the Amazon as a river.

Tidal effects can be felt almost 1,000 km (621 miles) upstream at Óbidos. Towards the end of the northern latitude winter, as the tide rises, a breaking wall of water up to 7.6 m (25 ft) high, travelling at speeds of up to 24 km/h (15 mph), makes its way upstream with a rising roar. This wave is the leading edge of the *pororoca*, an undular tidal bore that forms as the incoming waters from the Atlantic are funnelled into the Amazon delta. The wave can travel as much as 800 km (497 miles) inland.

Shell mounds suggest that people were living in the Amazon basin as long ago as 7,500 BCE. The areas surrounding the river eventually hosted large-scale indigenous societies living in populous towns and cities. It's thought that by the time of the Spanish conquest of South America, more than three million people lived in the Amazon basin in highly developed civilizations.

In March 1500, the Spanish conquistador Vicente Yáñez Pinzón made the first documented journey up the Amazon by a European. He named the river Río Santa María del Mar Dulce, which was later shortened to Mar Dulce ('Sweet Sea'), a reference to the enormous plume of freshwater it creates in the ocean. In 1541, the Spanish soldier Francisco de Orellana became the first European to

an area of more than 5.4 million sq km (2.08 million sq miles), the Amazon rainforest is one of the world's most biodiverse habitats, containing more than a third of all known species, among them more than 3,000 fish species, with about 50 new species discovered each year. They include a number of important commercial species, such as the pirarucu, one of the world's largest freshwater fish, that reaches a length of 3 m (10 ft).

Most of the Amazon basin's fish species are migratory. Some undergo short migrations of only a few kilometres between habitats on the main river and the floodplains. Many frugivorous species, for example, move onto the floodplain during the flood season to benefit from the newly available habitat, feeding on fruits falling

A blue-and-yellow macaw.

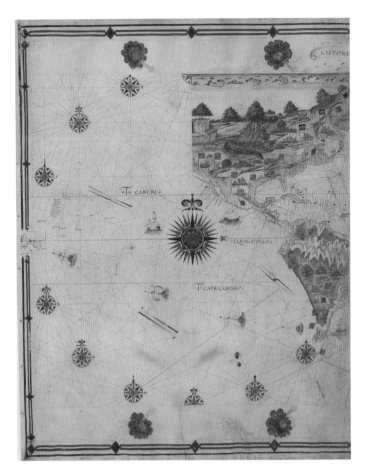

travel from the origins of the upstream river basins in the Andes to the river's mouth. It was he who gave the river its modern name, following battles with tribes of female warriors, whom he likened to the Amazons of Greek mythology. It wasn't until the 1630s that a European travelled up the entire river – a feat managed by the Portuguese explorer Pedro Teixeira, who arrived in Quito in 1637. Around this time, numerous colonial and religious settlements were established along the river's banks, for trade with, and the evangelization of, the local indigenous inhabitants.

The steamboat trade on the river began around the 1850s and exploded a decade or so later as the rubber boom kicked off. The internationally driven demand for rubber, which grows naturally in the Amazon basin, saw the river port cities of Iquitos and Manaus thrive and expand, but also brought diseases, such as typhus and malaria, which are believed to have killed as many as 40,000 indigenous Amazonians.

In 2005, the Manaus region experienced a devastating drought that saw parts of the river completely dry up, making transportation difficult, depleting drinking supplies and leaving millions of rotting fish in the riverbed.

Although the Amazon itself is undammed, there are more than 400 dams on its tributaries. There are no bridges that span the entire width of the river; crossings are made on ferries.

Left: *A 16th-century map showing Francisco de Orellana's journey from Quito to the mouth of the Amazon.*

The Port of Manaus on the Rio Negro, an important commercial centre for ocean-going vessels navigating the Amazon.

The Colorado River

One of the principal rivers of the southwestern USA, the Colorado River is best known for three things: geological wonders, white-water adventures and ecological disasters.

As monuments to the erosional power of rivers go, the Grand Canyon is difficult to top. Over a period of more than 5 million years, the Colorado River and its tributaries have carved their way down through rocks that formed as long as 2 billion years ago to form the canyon, which is almost 450 km (280 miles) long, up to 29 km (18 miles) wide and as much as 1,857 m (6,093 ft) deep. In the process, the river has carried away some 4.2 trillion cubic metres (148 trillion cubic ft) of rock and soil.

From its source in the Rocky Mountains of Colorado, the river flows generally west and south. In its upper reaches, the river is mostly a swift white-water stream, with a width of up to 150 m (492 ft) and a depth of 2–30 m (6.5–98 ft), although in a few areas, including the marshy Kawuneeche Valley near the headwaters, it exhibits a braided character.

As it makes its way into Utah and across the more arid Colorado Plateau, the river begins to cut deeper and deeper into the rock, forming the impressive gorges that characterize the river for some distance. In Utah, the Colorado flows through some of the most inaccessible terrain of the continental USA, a region, known as 'slickrock' country, of narrow canyons and unique 'folds' created by the tilting of sedimentary rock layers along faults. Forced between rock walls, the river becomes a treacherous maelstrom, tumbling over dangerous washing machine rapids. Near Moab, the river exits the Moab Valley via the Portal, a canyon flanked by 300 m (984 ft) sandstone cliffs.

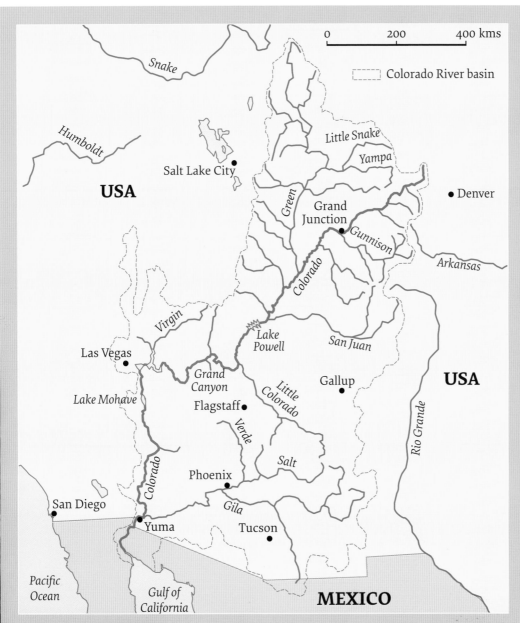

0   200   400 kms

- - - Colorado River basin

Snake

Humboldt

USA

Salt Lake City

Little Snake

Yampa

Green

Grand
Junction

Gunnison

• Denver

Arkansas

Colorado

Virgin

Lake
Powell

San Juan

Las Vegas

Grand
Canyon

Little
Colorado

Gallup

USA

Lake Mohave

Flagstaff

Verde

Salt

Colorado

Phoenix

San Diego

Gila

Yuma

Tucson

Rio Grande

Pacific
Ocean

Gulf of
California

MEXICO

At a glance
Length: 2,330 km (1,448 miles)
Watershed: 637,000 sq km (245,947 sq miles)
Annual mean discharge: 600 cubic metres per second (21,189 cubic ft per second)
Vertical drop: 3,104 m (10,184 ft)
Main tributaries: Green, Gila, Gunnison and San Juan rivers
Countries: USA, Mexico
Cities: Grand Junction, Yuma, San Luis Río Colorado

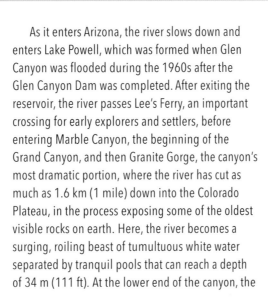

As it enters Arizona, the river slows down and enters Lake Powell, which was formed when Glen Canyon was flooded during the 1960s after the Glen Canyon Dam was completed. After exiting the reservoir, the river passes Lee's Ferry, an important crossing for early explorers and settlers, before entering Marble Canyon, the beginning of the Grand Canyon, and then Granite Gorge, the canyon's most dramatic portion, where the river has cut as much as 1.6 km (1 mile) down into the Colorado Plateau, in the process exposing some of the oldest visible rocks on earth. Here, the river becomes a surging, roiling beast of tumultuous white water separated by tranquil pools that can reach a depth of 34 m (111 ft). At the lower end of the canyon, the river widens out as it enters Lake Mead, the largest reservoir in the USA, formed by the Hoover Dam. After leaving the canyon, the river emerges from the Colorado Plateau and flows on to the Lower Colorado River Valley.

The river then turns to the south, first forming the Arizona–California state border and then, from Los Algodones, defining about 39 km (24 miles) of the Mexico–USA border. And finally, after passing through the Colorado River Delta, a vast alluvial floodplain that stretches across about 7,800 sq km (3,012 sq miles), and a large estuary, the river empties into the Gulf of California in northwestern Mexico. Since 1960, however, this final stretch of the Colorado is typically either dry or little more

than a desultory trickle formed by return flows from the many adjacent irrigation schemes.

The Colorado River basin encompasses parts of seven US states and two Mexican states, and takes in a wide range of natural environments, from alpine tundra and coniferous forests in its headwaters and upper elevations through semi-arid plateaus and canyons supporting piñon pine, juniper and sagebrush, to true arid landscapes dotted with creosote bush and other desert plants in the lower basin and delta (the lower Colorado is flanked by the Mojave and Sonoran deserts).

The formation of the Rocky Mountains 50–75 million years ago led to the birth of the Colorado River as a west-flowing stream draining the southwestern portion of the range. Prior to about 5–12 million years ago, when the Gulf of California formed, the Colorado emptied into the Pacific, possibly at Monterey Bay on the coast of California, where it may have played a role in the formation of the Monterey submarine canyon. The formation of the modern Sierra Nevada, which began about 10 million years ago, diverted the Colorado southwards towards the Gulf of California. About 5 million years ago, the Colorado Plateau reached roughly its present height and it was around this time that the Colorado River established its present course into the gulf. The plateau's continued rise over the next 2.5 million years or so saw the river begin to carve out the Grand Canyon, eventually sending tens of thousands of cubic kilometres of sediment down river and creating a vast delta that walled off the northernmost part of the gulf.

Humans first arrived on the Colorado Plateau about 12,000 years ago and began to form agricultural societies around the start of the early centuries CE. In Chaco Canyon in northwestern New Mexico, the Ancient Puebloan or Anasazi people developed a complex system to divert water from the Colorado for drinking and irrigation, and, between 600 and 700 CE, people of the Hohokam culture began to employ large-scale irrigation. During the 14th century, a megadrought hit the region, leading to the collapse of the ancient civilizations.

Two centuries later, explorers from Spain began to map and claim land within the Colorado basin. Early contact with the local indigenous groups mostly involved trade in furs in the headwaters and some trade along the lower river. Following Mexico's independence from Spain in 1821, the Colorado basin became part of that country, but the US invasion of 1846 saw most of the basin become part of the USA. Around this time, large-scale settlement began in the lower basin. Steamboats carried passengers from the Gulf of California to landings along the river that linked to dusty wagon roads into the interior.

In 1869 and 1871–72, John Wesley Powell became the first person to run the Grand Canyon's rapids. His dangerous yet spectacular exploration of the Colorado River canyons was the first to concentrate directly on the river and the information he collected during his expeditions was later used to develop it for navigation and water supply.

Today, the river's immense power has been drained away by dams and over-extraction. The Colorado is one of the world's most controlled and

A so-called entrenched meander, Horseshoe Bend is located near the town of Page, Arizona, on the eastern rim of the Grand Canyon. The site is a popular tourist destination, hosting more than two million visitors a year.

litigated rivers; every drop of its water and more has been allocated. Before humans began to fool around with its flow, the Colorado River discharged some 20 cubic km (4.8 cubic miles) of water into the Gulf of California each year, or an average of 640 cubic metres per second (22,601 cubic ft per second); since 1960, it has rarely reached the sea. Irrigation, industrial and municipal diversions, evaporation from reservoirs (which consumes more than 15 per cent of the river's natural runoff), natural runoff and climate change have all substantially reduced its flow.

Today, more than 29 major dams, most of which were built between 1910 and 1970, and hundreds of kilometres of canals divert water from the river to thirsty cities including Las Vegas, Los Angeles, Denver and Phoenix. Often referred to as the 'Lifeline of the Southwest', the Colorado provides drinking water for one in ten Americans. It also provides irrigation water to some 1.6 million ha (3.95 million acres) of farmland – the lower half of the river waters nearly 90 per cent of the USA's winter vegetables – and generates more than 12 billion kWh of hydroelectricity each year. Estimates suggest that each drop of the river's water is used an average of 17 times in a year. Reservoirs within the Colorado basin are capable of holding four times the river's annual flow.

Among the earliest water projects in the basin, begun in 1890 and completed in 1936, was the Grand Ditch, a canal 26 km (16 miles) long that diverts water from the Never Summer Mountains that would naturally have drained into the headwaters of the Colorado. This was followed by several other inter-basin water transfers, also known as transmountain diversions, which transport water from one side of the Continental Divide to the other – an attempt to deal with the fact that roughly three-quarters of the state of Colorado's precipitation falls west of the Rocky Mountains while 80 per cent of the population lives to the east of the range.

In 1922, seven of the states in the Colorado River basin signed the Colorado River Compact, which outlined their water rights. However, when the compact was drafted, it was based on barely 30 years of streamflow records, which, it turns out, were probably the wettest years in the past 500–1,200 years. Hence, more water is being allocated to river users than actually flows through the Colorado. A later treaty, signed in 1944, allocated water to Mexico. These and numerous other compacts, federal laws, decrees, agreements and regulatory guidelines under which the river are managed and operated are collectively known as the Law of the River.

The river's once-powerful, once-copious flow and steep gradient made it perfect for generating hydroelectric power. Hoover Dam, which is located in the Black Canyon, was completed in 1936. At the time, it was the world's tallest dam and had the world's largest hydroelectric power plant. Behind the dam sits Lake Mead, the USA's largest artificial lake, capable of holding more than two years of the Colorado's flow. The dam's construction represented a major step towards stabilizing the river's lower channel, stored water for irrigation, provided much-needed flood control and opened the door for rapid development on the river's lower reaches.

The last major US diversion is at the Imperial Dam, which was completed in 1938 and diverts virtually all of the Colorado's flow into two irrigation canals. One of these, the All-American Canal, is the world's largest irrigation canal. It supplies water to Southern California's Imperial Valley, helping it to become one of North America's most productive agricultural regions, growing two-thirds of the USA's winter vegetables. Very little of the water that remains in the river beyond the dam makes it past Yuma, Arizona, and the confluence with the intermittent Gila River.

The Colorado is mostly fed by melting snow from the Rocky Mountains of Colorado and Wyoming, which begins to enter the river in April and peaks during May and June, and makes up between 85 and 90 per cent of the river's discharge. A large part of the remainder comes from summer monsoon storms, which often produce heavy, highly localized floods on the river's lower tributaries. Before engineering works smoothed things out, the river's flow regime varied considerably, from summer peaks at Topock, Arizona, of more than 2,800 cubic metres per second/98,881

A large pottery jar dating from 950–1125 made by the Hohokam people, who developed an extensive irrigation system on the Colorado Plateau.

Above: A kiva – a round, sunken space used by Puebloan people for rites and political meetings – in Pueblo Bonito in Chaco Canyon, New Mexico.

Right: John Wesley Powell's 11-man team prepares to set out on his second expedition, which produced the first reliable maps of the Colorado River, in May 1871

We are three-quarters of a mile in the depths of the Earth, and the great river shrinks into insignificance, as it dashes its angry waves against the walls and cliffs, that rise to the world above; they are but puny ripples, and we but pigmies, running up and down the sands, or lost among the boulders.'

— John Wesley Powell's journal, August 1869

Ancient dams and colossal waves

Between 1.8 million and 10,000 years ago, volcanic eruptions caused at least 13 lava dams to form in the Grand Canyon, the largest of which was more than 700 m (2,297 ft) high, causing the river to back up for nearly 800 km (497 miles) to present-day Moab, Utah. The dams only lasted a few decades before collapsing or being washed away, leading to catastrophic floods that were among the largest ever to occur in North America. Mapping of flood deposits indicate that crests as high as 210 m (689 ft) passed through the Grand Canyon.

Completed in 1936 during the Great Depression, Hoover Dam in Nevada impounds Lake Mead, the largest reservoir in the USA by volume when full.

cubic ft per second (reaching 10,900 cubic metres per second/384,920 cubic ft per second in 1884) to a winter low of less than 71 cubic metres per second/2,507 cubic ft per second (dropping to 11.9 cubic metres per second/420 cubic ft per second in 1935). By way of contrast, the discharge on the lower Colorado River below Hoover Dam now typically ranges from 110 cubic metres per second (3,885 cubic ft per second) to about 1,000 cubic metres per second (35,315 cubic ft per second).

By the time the river reaches the northernmost point of the Mexico–USA border, its average flow is only a fifth of the natural flow. All of this water is then diverted to irrigate the fertile agricultural land of the Mexicali Valley; below Morelos Dam, the riverbed is generally dry, with the odd trickle of irrigation drainage water. Since 1963, the river has only reached the ocean during El Niño events in the 1980s and 1990s. During the early- to mid-1980s, record-breaking precipitation and snowmelt saw the river reach the sea over several consecutive years.

To make matters worse, since the beginning of the millennium, the Colorado River basin has been in the grip of the most severe drought on record; runoff has only reached normal or above-average levels in four years between 2000 and 2012.

The Colorado takes its name from its reddish colour, which is imbued upon the river by its natural sediment load; however, the damming of the river has given it a green hue, probably because a significant amount of sediment is being lost in the resultant reservoirs. Historically, the Colorado transported up to 91 million tonnes (89.56 million tons) of sediment to the Gulf of California each year – among North American rivers, only the Mississippi carried more. Nutrients from the sediment once provided nourishment for the wetlands and riparian areas found in its extensive delta, which was once North America's largest desert estuary, and elsewhere along its lower course. Today, however, most of the sediment is deposited at the upper end of Lake

The Colorado River flows through the Kawuneeche Valley in Rocky Mountain National Park, not far from its source.

A tree-like pattern of channels in the mudflats of the Colorado Delta.

Powell and most of the remainder settles out in Lake Mead.

The reduction in the river's flow has had devastating ecological consequences for its delta, which once acted as an important breeding ground for aquatic species, including fish, shrimp and sea mammals, in the Gulf of California. Today's shrunken, desiccated delta no longer provides a suitable habitat, and populations of many species have declined dramatically. The river itself boasts more than 30 endemic fish species; however, half of all the native fish in the Colorado basin have either gone extinct or are considered vulnerable.

The reduction in the river's flow has also caused salinity to become a problem in its lower reaches. In its natural state, the salt content in the lower Colorado was about 50 parts per million (ppm), but by the 1960s, it had increased to well over 2,000 ppm. Currently, high salinity levels in the Colorado River Basin cause an estimated US$300–400 million per year in economic damages across the US agricultural, municipal and industrial sectors. Pesticides in agricultural runoff have also become concentrated in the lower river, sometimes leading to extensive fish kills.

Much of the abstraction (the technical name for a river's loss of water) takes place in the Colorado's lower reaches, and the river remains one of the USA's most popular white-water rafting destinations. Famed for its dramatic rapids and canyons, the Grand Canyon section alone is run by more than 22,000 people each year. Recreation along the river is estimated to employ about 250,000 people and to contribute US$26 billion a year to the local economy.

The Mississippi River

North America's second-longest river, the mighty, unruly Mississippi looms large in the USA's cultural and economic development.

Arguably the USA's most important river, the Mississippi has played a defining role in the nation's growth, from the industrial revolution to the present day. One of the world's great commercial waterways, it is a capricious creature, prone to catastrophic floods and efforts to tame its unruly nature have transformed the river into an extensively engineered canal.

Lake Itasca in northern Minnesota has traditionally been considered the river's source, although the lake is, in turn, fed by several smaller streams. From there it flows generally south, its course memorably likened by Mark Twain to 'a long, pliant apple-paring', before passing through its extensive delta and into the Gulf of Mexico.

The elevation of the upper river, which is largely a clear, fresh multi-thread stream dotted with sandbars and islands, has dropped by more than half by the time it reaches Saint Paul, Minnesota. Between there and St Louis, Missouri, it flattens out, controlled and managed as a string of pools created by 26 locks and dams. Between Minneapolis, Minnesota and Dubuque, Iowa, the river is entrenched, flowing between high limestone bluffs. Above the confluence with the Missouri, the Mississippi's water is relatively clear, but this ends with the arrival of the turbulent, flotsam-laden Missouri. The middle Mississippi, between St Louis and its confluence with the Ohio River, is relatively free-flowing.

At a glance

Length: 3,770 km
(2,343 miles)

Watershed: 3 million sq km
(1.16 million sq miles)

Vertical drop: 450 m
(1,476 ft)

Main tributaries: Missouri,
Ohio, Illinois, Arkansas and
Red rivers

Mean annual discharge:
17,000 cubic metres per
second (600,349 cubic
ft per second)

Countries: USA

Cities: St Louis, New
Orleans, Minneapolis,
Memphis, Baton Rouge

The lower Mississippi is a classic example of a meandering alluvial river, extravagantly looping and curling, twisting and turning across its broad, flat floodplain, leaving behind meander scars, cut-offs, oxbow lakes and swampy backwaters. It reaches its full grandeur after Cairo, Illinois, where it is joined by the mighty Ohio River, whose flow is actually greater than the Mississippi's at this point and thus swells the latter to more than twice its size. Often more than 2 km (1.2 miles) from bank to bank, the Mississippi is transformed into a brown, languid river as it slowly descends towards the Gulf of Mexico.

This final part of the river's course has shifted every 1,000 years or so as deposits of silt and sediment clog the main channel, raising the river's level and causing it to eventually find a steeper, more direct route to the ocean. The abandoned distributaries slowly diminish in volume, forming what are known as bayous.

The Mississippi once carried about 400 million tonnes (394 million tons) of sediment to the gulf each year, but much of it is now captured by dams – there are an estimated 8,000 dams in the Mississippi's drainage basin – and the river's sediment load has more than halved. Consequently, the delta, which has an area of more than 28,500 sq km (11,004 sq miles), is shrinking at the rate of roughly one football field of land per hour; over the past 60 years, the total land area lost has been about 50,000 ha (123,553 acres).

Even before dam construction began, the Mississippi never actually carried enough sediment to sustain the whole of Louisiana's deltaic coastline at any one time. Instead, along one part of the coast, a section

Above: *Monk's Mound at Cahokia was built by the Mississippian culture from around 900–950 CE.*
Left: *A Mississippian culture bowl from the 11th–14th century.*

of the delta that was being supplied with new sediment, known as a lobe, grew in size, while coastal processes, such as subsidence and erosion, were eating away at older abandoned delta lobes. At any given time over the past 7,500 years, up to 40 per cent of the coast was growing and the remainder was retreating.

Most of the sediment in the river originates in the rolling expanses of the Great Plains. Heavy rainfall between April and September flows into tributaries such as the Arkansas, Kansas, Platte and Missouri rivers, which rise in the foothills of the Rockies and enter the Mississippi from the west, bolstering their erosive powers and helping them to scour away the sandy sediment. The rivers that flow in from the east drain the Appalachian Mountains system, whose rocks are generally harder and less easily eroded.

The Mississippi is thought to be as much as 70 million years old. The river's current course was mostly locked in during the last two ice ages, following channels carved out by the great ice sheets that spread out over North America and the meltwater that flowed south from them.

Native American hunter-gatherers first settled along the banks of the Mississippi about 6,000 years ago. Some groups eventually grew into prolific agricultural and urban civilizations, and the river basin was one of the few independent centres of plant domestication in human history. Between about 200 and 500 CE, cultural practices were shared along a network of trade routes that ran the length of the river,

referred to as the Hopewell interaction sphere. After around 1,000 CE, an advanced agricultural society known today as the Mississippian culture arose along the river, trading widely and building increasingly large settlements. At its peak, the most prominent of these, now called Cahokia, had more inhabitants than London, England, did at the time. The river's name is said to come from the French rendering of its Algonquin name, Misi-ziibi ('great river').

The first European known to have reached the Mississippi was the Spanish explorer Alonso Álvarez de Pineda, who mapped the river's mouth in 1519. The richness of the Mississippi's resources eventually sparked a territorial battle as Britain, Spain and France all laid claim to land bordering it. In 1682, the French explorer René-Robert Cavelier canoed the lower Mississippi River from the mouth of the Illinois River to the Gulf of Mexico and subsequently claimed the entire Mississippi River Valley for France, naming the surrounding region La Louisiane, for King Louis XIV.

The Mississippi came to act as a vital transport and communications link between France's settlements in the Gulf of Mexico and Canada. French traders established settlements along the upper river, including the town of St Louis. In 1718, Jean-Baptiste Le Moyne, Sieur de Bienville, established New Orleans on the Mississippi's banks, 160 km (99 miles) from the mouth.

During the 18th century, the river acted as the main western boundary of the nascent USA, first with France and then with Spain. Then, in 1803, the USA effectively secured control of the river as part of the Louisiana Purchase, which saw the transfer of 2.1 million sq km (810,815 sq miles) of territory from France to the USA.

A painting by George Catlin from 1847–48 depicts French explorer René-Robert Cavelier, Sieur de La Salle at the mouth of the Mississippi River claiming Louisiana for France in 1682.

In December 1811, the *New Orleans* became the first steamboat to travel the length of the Lower Mississippi, ushering in the golden age of steamboats. Between 1814–19, the number of steamers that stopped in New Orleans rose from 21 to 191; by 1850, thousands of steamboats were chugging up and down the river. Road and rail links in the Louisiana Purchase had yet to be developed, so the river was the best option for travel and trade, and the shallow-draught steamboats carried both freight – cotton, timber, livestock and farm produce, and Appalachian coal – and passengers. Steamers travelled all the way from Montana, down the Ohio, Missouri and Tennessee rivers, and along the main channel of the Mississippi. Shifting sand bars made navigation difficult and the steamboat pilots banded together to run a common information service about changing conditions along the channel.

The steamboats ushered in an era of unprecedented prosperity along the river. Towns proliferated along the river's banks, acting as ports for the shipment of local produce and vying with each other to provide services such as refuelling and warehousing. Plantations with river frontage maintained their own landings so they could ship crops directly. New Orleans became one of the country's busiest ports, acting as the trans-shipment point to ocean-going ships. The steamboat era also brought a flourishing tourist trade to the river. The arrival of the railroads during the 1880s saw steamboat traffic begin to tail off, but the boats remained a feature until the 1920s.

Perhaps unsurprisingly, the river also played a pivotal role in the American Civil War. In 1863, Ulysses S. Grant's successful siege of the Confederate stronghold at Vicksburg, aided by fortified gunboats and armoured steamers, gave the Union control of the river, dealing the Confederacy a heavy commercial and strategic blow, and hastening the Union victory. Following the victory, President Abraham Lincoln, himself a former Mississippi flat-boatman, reported that 'the Father of Waters flows unvexed to the sea'.

Work on the first levees on the Mississippi began in 1727, when the governor of French Louisiana, Étienne Perier, launched a large public works effort using enslaved African labourers aimed at protecting the infant city of New Orleans. After the USA gained control of the river, the growing traffic along its length required a clear channel, whose maintenance became the responsibility of the US Army Corps of Engineers, which was established in 1802. Early projects included the

A Midnight Race on the Mississippi shows a race between the steamboats Natchez *and* Eclipse *in 1854.*

The day the Mississippi flowed backwards

Starting on 16 December 1811, the region around the town of New Madrid, located near the Mississippi River in present-day Missouri, was struck by three powerful earthquakes and thousands of smaller tremors. The largest, which took place on 7 February 1812, is thought to have been the most powerful in US history. The quake created temporary waterfalls in the Mississippi; the river's water darkened and whirlpools developed suddenly above depressions created in the riverbed; many of the small riverine island, which were often used as bases by river pirates, permanently disappeared; large lakes were created nearby as river water filled newly created depressions. Most startlingly, eyewitnesses described the river flowing backwards for several hours. The earthquakes took place on a thrust fault that crossed the river in three locations and uplift along the fault formed 'cliffs' in the river, creating the waterfalls and also damming of the river, causing it to back up and reverse its flow.

removal of snags, rocks and sandbars and the closing off of secondary channels to increase the flow in the main channel, which would then scour off bottom sediments, deepening the river and, in theory, decreasing the frequency of flooding. These were followed by the construction of a series of 29 locks and dams on the upper Mississippi, which helped to make the river deeper and wider. Canals were also built to bypass rapids and connect to other waterways. In 1848, the river was connected to Lake Michigan via the Illinois and Michigan Canal, which was then replaced in 1900 by the Chicago Sanitary and Ship Canal. As its name suggests, this waterway served a double purpose, used for both shipping and the disposal of waste from Chicago that would otherwise have ended up polluting Lake Michigan, the source of the city's drinking water.

The catastrophic flood of spring 1927, when the river broke its banks in 145 places and about 65,000 sq km (25,097 sq miles) of land in the lower Mississippi valley was flooded to a depth of up to 9 m (29.6 ft), killing at least 250 people, proved to be the trigger for significant engineering works on the river, the federal government deciding that it was time to take the recalcitrant, unruly river by the scruff of its neck. (The Ohio River is the main instigator of floods on the lower Mississippi, usually triggered by rain on the Great Plains or a sudden hot spell in early spring that melts snow in the north.)

Today, continuous dredging increases the river's potential volume; levees constrain the river; mattresses of concrete slabs increase the channel's stability; floodways and improved channels move water past danger areas; spillways and so-called fuse plugs – specially weakened sections of levee that burst when the river is high – divert water into marshes and reservoirs; dams and locks on tributaries impound contributary floodwaters. Between the river's source and St Louis, 43 dams moderate its flow. The dams are supplemented by thousands of wing dykes along the river's length. In all, more than 3,200 km (1,988 miles) of the Mississippi watershed have been leveed; between Cape Girardeau, Missouri, and the Gulf of Mexico, the river is essentially 'walled in' by a long line of levees and has effectively been turned into a 'pipe'.

While this work has reduced the frequency of damaging floods, it has also severed the river's connection to the surrounding countryside, leaving many former riverbank towns high and dry, devastating natural wetland habitats such as swamps and marshes, and threatening wildlife.

Below: *An aerial view of a farm submerged by the Great Mississippi flood of 1927, the most destructive river flood in the history of the USA.*

The Old River Control Structure, a floodgate system on a branch of the Mississippi in central Louisiana designed to prevent the river from changing course by regulating the flow of water into the Atchafalaya River.

During the 1950s, US government scientists determined that the Mississippi's path was beginning to switch to the channel of the Atchafalaya River, a distributary that follows a much steeper path to the Gulf of Mexico and through which 30 per cent of the river currently flows. Should the Atchafalaya capture the Mississippi, it would leave New Orleans isolated on a side channel. Were it not for the efforts of the US Army Corps of Engineers, which actively works to keep the Mississippi within its present channel, the Atchafalaya would probably have captured all of the river's flow by now.

Today, the Mississippi provides drinking water for millions and supports a US$12.6 billion shipping industry that employs some 35,000 people. It represents one of the world's great liquid highways. The Little Mississippi, as the section above the Ohio River confluence is known, carries half of the USA's corn and soybean production.

The USA's cultural fabric could be said to be woven from the common thread of the Mississippi River, which provides the backdrop to countless iconic novels and plays, from the *Adventures of Huckleberry Finn* to Tennessee Williams' *The Glass Menagerie*. However, as rich as the literary tradition that grew up along the Mississippi is, the river's musical legacy is arguably even more profound. The blues, ragtime, jazz, rhythm and blues, rock and roll, and soul can all trace either their origins or a significant part of their development to places along the Mississippi, especially cities such as New Orleans, Memphis and St Louis.

Known as the 'mother fauna' of North American fresh water, the Mississippi basin's highly diverse aquatic fauna includes some 375 known species; a quarter of all fish species in North America have been recorded in the basin. However, the river's ecosystems have deteriorated to the point where it was described in a 2010 *St Louis Dispatch* editorial as 'a giant barge canal, mostly devoid of animal life'. Nutrients and chemicals from agricultural runoff in the Mississippi are the primary contributor to the Gulf of Mexico dead zone, a region of low oxygen that can kill fish and other marine life near the seafloor that can cover an area of more than 16,000 sq km (6,178 sq miles).

The Missouri River

The longest river in North America, the Missouri was one of the main conduits along which European settlers spread as the westward expansion of the USA took place during the 19th century.

For millennia, the Missouri River has played a central role in human migration in North America, from the first humans to settle on the continent to the 19th-century pioneers who opened up the American West.

The river starts life high in the Rocky Mountains, where three streams rise to form its headwaters. It officially begins at the confluence of the Jefferson and Madison rivers near Three Forks, Montana. It then flows east and south, its banks mostly populated by cottonwoods, willows and sycamores, before eventually emptying into the Mississippi River about 16 km (10 miles) north of St Louis, Missouri (the Missouri accounts for almost half of the Mississippi's annual flow past St Louis; when combined, the two rivers form the world's fourth-longest river system). Along the way, it drops over the Great Falls of the Missouri, a series of five substantial waterfalls, and winds through a scenic region of canyons and badlands known as the Missouri Breaks.

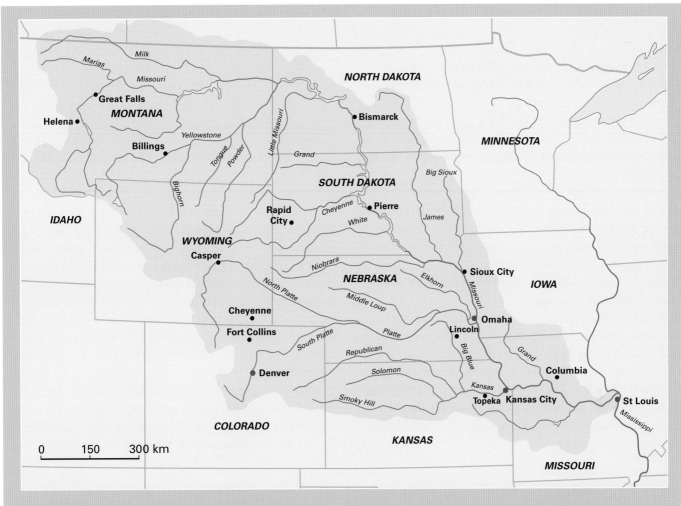

At a glance

Length: 3,767 km (2,341 miles)

Watershed: 1.4 million sq km (540,543 sq miles)

Vertical drop: 2,629 m (8,625 ft)

Main tributaries: Yellowstone, Platte, Kansas, James and Milk rivers

Mean annual discharge: 2,400 cubic metres per second (84,755 cubic ft per second)

Countries: USA

Cities: St Louis, Kansas City, Lexington, Omaha, Sioux City

About 12,000 years ago, towards the end of the last ice age, as humans were spreading out across the Americas, many used the Missouri to make their way south. While most passed through, eventually settling in the Ohio and lower Mississippi valleys, many remained along the Missouri, spawning the peoples of the Great Plains, who led a mostly nomadic existence, following the huge bison herds and using the Missouri and its tributaries as a source of sustenance and transportation. Some of those who lived along the river on its great southward bend in the Dakotas region formed walled villages on bluffs and islands that had populations in the thousands and later served as trading posts for early French and British explorers and fur traders.

In late June 1673, the French-Canadian explorer Louis Jolliet and the French explorer Jacques Marquette became the first Europeans to lay eyes on the Missouri, which was in full flood at the time. However, it wasn't until 1714 that the river was formally explored, when an expedition led by Étienne Veniard de Bourgmont reached at least as far as the mouth of the Platte River. Bourgmont's book of the trip, *The Route to Be Taken to Ascend the Missouri River*, published later that year, was the first known document to use the name 'Missouri River'.

In 1723, Bourgmont established Fort Orleans near present-day Brunswick, Missouri, the first European settlement of any kind on the river. The settlement only lasted three years, however, either abandoned or its small contingent massacred by Native Americans. Around this time, French fur trappers were beginning to explore the region, blazing trails that were later followed by westward-travelling pioneers. (The major trails that were used to open up the American West, including the California, Mormon, Oregon and Santa Fe trails, all began on the

Missouri River. Between the 1830s and 1860s, more than half a million people headed west from the river town of Independence, Missouri.)

The river passed through Spanish and French hands before becoming part of the USA in 1803, when a cash-starved Napoleon sold 2.1 million sq km (810,815 sq miles) of territory to President Thomas Jefferson for US$15 million – less than 3¢ per acre – thereby doubling the size of the nascent USA. That year, Jefferson instructed the explorer Meriwether Lewis to investigate the Missouri and search for a river route to the Pacific Ocean.

The famed Lewis and Clark Expedition of 1804–05 was the first to survey the river from its mouth to its headwaters. The explorers' glowing reports of abundant populations of fur-bearing animals prompted Spanish fur trader Manuel Lisa to mount an expedition up the Missouri and Yellowstone rivers in 1807, which led to a thriving fur trade with the local indigenous tribes, and the establishment of trading posts on the Missouri in Dakota and Nebraska.

Transport of the pelts – mostly from beavers and bison – required ships, which provided the primary motive for the start of river transport on the Missouri. During the height of the fur trade, steamboats and keelboats travelled nearly the river's entire length, from its mouth to the Missouri Breaks. They were joined by the Missouri River mackinaw, a light, open sailboat specifically developed to carry furs. Effectively capable only of travelling downriver, they were dismantled and sold for lumber upon arrival in St Louis.

There is only one river with a personality, a sense of humour and a woman's caprice; a river that goes travelling sidewise, that interferes in politics, rearranges geography, and dabbles in real estate; a river that plays hide and seek with you today and tomorrow follows you around like a pet dog with a dynamite cracker tied to his tail. That river is the Missouri.'

– George Fitch

The first 150 years of European settlement along the river saw little in the way of development, but that all changed at the beginning of the 20th century, as the Missouri was extensively engineered for irrigation, flood control, navigation and the generation of hydroelectric power. In 1912, the US Army Corps of Engineers (USACE) was given the go-ahead to begin constructing levees and wing dams to direct the river's flow into a straight channel and prevent sedimentation, and to dredge a deep-water channel from Kansas City to Sioux City. In all, attempts to improve navigation by cutting off meanders and channelizing the river itself have reduced its length by about 320 km (199 miles).

Construction of the Fort Peck Dam in Montana, the first dam on the upper Missouri, began in 1933 as part of the Depression-era New Deal. One of the world's largest earth-fill dams, it represented a significant step forward in reducing flood risk in the lower Missouri, but as it only

In this 1839 aquatint by Swiss-French artist Karl Bodmer, Mandan women use bull boats on the Missouri overlooked by the summer village of Mih-Tutta-Hangkusch.

Fur Traders Descending the Missouri *by George Caleb Bingham, 1845. The animal at the front of the boat is a black fox, whose pelt was particularly highly prized.*

controls run-off from 11 per cent of the river's watershed, it had little effect on a severe snowmelt flood that struck the lower basin ten years later, submerging manufacturing plants in Omaha and Kansas City, and greatly delaying shipments of military supplies for the Allies' efforts in Europe and Asia at the height of World War II.

The following year, primarily in response to flooding along the Mississippi–Missouri river system, the US Congress passed the Flood Control Act, which opened the way for the USACE to develop the Missouri on a massive scale. Today, there are 15 dams on the Missouri and hundreds more on its tributaries. The six reservoirs of the Mainstem System are among the largest in the world by volume, holding up to 91.4 cubic km (22 cubic miles) of water in total – more than three years' worth of the river's flow.

Much of the Missouri basin is semi-arid, so its discharge is much smaller and more variable than those of other North American rivers of comparable length. Before it became punctuated by dams, the river flooded twice a year; melting snow on the plains created the so-called 'April Rise' or 'Spring Fresh', while the considerably more destructive 'June Rise', when the river's flow could increase to more than ten times its normal discharge, was the result of snowmelt and summer rainstorms in the Rockies.

Nicknamed, the Big Muddy, the Missouri has one of the highest sediment loads of any North American river, picking up huge quantities of sand and silt as it meanders across its floodplain, eroding tonnes of soil and rock from its banks each time it changes course. Before it was developed, it transported as much as 290 million tonnes (285 million tons) per year, but channelization and the construction of dams and levees has reduced this to about 20 million tonnes (19.7 million tonnes). However, the river remains the primary source of the silt that the Mississippi carries into its delta and out into the Gulf of Mexico.

Fort Peck Dam in Montana, the highest of six major dams along the Missouri, is more than 6,400 metres long and 75 metres high. It's the largest hydraulically filled dam in the USA and creates Fort Peck Lake, the nation's fifth-largest artificial lake. The dam was built as part of the New Deal for hydroelectric power generation, flood control and water quality management

The Orinoco River

The third-largest river in the world by discharge volume, the Orinoco drains more than 2,000 rivers, including some 200 major and 600 minor tributaries.

At the beginning of August 1498, during his third voyage to the Americas, Christopher Columbus sailed from the island of Trinidad into the Gulf of Paria, which separates the island from the South American mainland. There he encountered such an enormous volume of freshwater that he believed that he had entered the outer reaches of the earthly Paradise, the Garden of Eden.

After planting the Spanish flag on the Paria Peninsula and exploring the nearby river delta, he realized that this newly discovered land must be a continent, for the volume of water entering the ocean couldn't be flowing from an island. The river was the Orinoco and the volume of water flowing from its mouth was indeed prodigious – the third greatest of any river on earth.

Scale: 0 — 150 — 300 km
Orinoco River basin

Caribbean
Sea

Guárico

Orinoco
Delta

Tigre
Tucupita
Zuata
Ciudad Guayana
Orinoco
Curiapo
Ciudad Bolívar

Apure

Cuchivero
Aro
VENEZUELA
Guri
Reservoir

Arauca   *Capanaparo*

COLOMBIA
Suapure
Caroní

Meta   Puerto Páez
Puerto
Carreño
Tomo   Puerto Ayacucho
Caura

Ventuari

Vichada   *Orinoco*

San Fernando de Atabapo

Guaviare

Inírida

Orinoco   **BRAZIL**

GUYANA

BRAZIL

At a glance

Length: 2,736 km (1,700 miles)
Watershed: 948,000 sq km (366,025 sq miles)
Vertical drop: 1,047 m (3,435 ft)
Average annual discharge: 33,000 cubic metres per second (1,165,384 cubic ft per second)
Main tributaries: Caroní, Apure, Caura, Guaviare, Meta and Ventuari rivers
Countries: Venezuela, Colombia
Cities: Puerto Ayacucho, Ciudad Guayana, Ciudad Bolivar

From the outskirts of Eden, the Orinoco then morphed into the pathway to riches. In 1531, the Spaniard Diego de Ordaz became the first European to explore the river, where he heard tales of the fabled golden city of El Dorado, tales that were to tempt the Spanish governor of Trinidad, Antonio de Berrio, and the English statesman Sir Walter Raleigh, to explore the river in 1584 and 1590, and 1595 respectively.

The Orinoco also played a crucial role in Latin America's wars of independence. In 1817, the legendary military leader Simón Bolívar set up a base far up the Orinoco in the interior of Venezuela, from which he began to recruit an army. The following year, he established his revolutionary capital in the Orinoco port town of Angostura (now Ciudad Bolivar) and then, in 1819, he and a small force used cowhide boats to cross a succession of flooded tributaries of the Orinoco before crossing

Atures Rapids in Venezuela, which obstruct navigation along the Orinoco, were a major point of confluence for local Indigenous groups.

the Andes and attacking Bogotá, Colombia.

The Orinoco flows in a sweeping ellipsoidal arc from its source in the Guiana Highlands, around the Guiana Shield, a 1.7-billion-year-old geological formation topped with several low mountains, and on to its mouth on the Atlantic Ocean. It rises near Cerro Delgado Chalbaud, at the southern end of the jungle-cloaked Sierra Parima range, which forms part of the boundary between Venezuela and Brazil. Spring-fed streams that flow down the western slopes of the Parima eventually give rise to the Orinoco.

Below the town of Esmeralda, an arm of the Orinoco splits off and flows south into the Casiquiare River, which eventually joins the mighty Amazon (see box). After the bifurcation, the river bends to the northwest,

flowing in great meandering curves as it leaves the rainforest-clad highlands and begins to cross the savanna-covered plains of the Llanos. It then flows northward and forms the border between Venezuela and Colombia, passing through an area known as the Region of the Rapids, where it's constrained by numerous huge granite boulders and falls through a succession of rapids, culminating in the Atures Rapids. The area around the rapids was once a meeting place for local Indigenous tribes – an ethnic, linguistic and cultural convergence zone – and some of the surrounding rocks bear huge panels of petroglyphs that date back several thousand years.

As it makes a great sweeping bend to the east across the Llanos,

A pair of Orinoco crocodiles.

the Orinoco slows down and widens, reaching about 8 km (5 miles) across. Several tributaries from the Andes join the river here, bringing sediment that forms abundant shoals and alluvial islands, some of which divide the river into narrow channels.

Where the river meets the Atlantic in the Gulf of Paría it forms an enormous, distinctive, triangular delta – some 200 km (124 miles) long and 370 km (230 miles) wide, and covering an area of about 22,500 sq km (8,687 sq miles) – known as the Delta Amacuro. Hundreds of rivers and waterways branch off the main channel at the head of the delta, flowing away through a vast coastal swamp forest, home to a rich bird fauna, with more than 175 species identified, and several threatened and endangered species, including the Orinoco crocodile – one of the world's rarest and largest reptiles (indeed, it's the largest predator in South America), which is found only in the middle and lower Orinoco Basin – the Amazon river dolphin and the giant river otter.

The Orinoco basin experiences a tropical climate, with pronounced wet and dry seasons driven by the north–south meandering of the intertropical convergence zone, a low-pressure trough that sits between the easterly trade winds. As the zone moves northward in what's described locally as the winter (April–October/November), it brings heavy rains that can cause the river to swell to a breadth of 22 km (14 miles) and a depth of 100 m (328 ft).

In the Llanos, the rains signal the end of a severe annual drought that typically lasts from January to April, and the beginning of extensive floods that usually last from June to October and can submerge lowland areas adjacent to the river under 20 m (66 ft) of water. The important towns in the increasingly urbanized Llanos are built on high ground to escape these annual floods.

Most of Venezuela's Indigenous people live within the Orinoco Basin, using the river and its tributaries as a source of food and for communication; during the rainy season floods, boats are the only viable means of travel throughout much of the basin.

Basin theft

The Amazon River is slowly stealing about 40,000 sq km (15,444 sq miles) of the Orinoco's drainage basin. The two rivers' watersheds are separated by the 320-km-long (199-mile) Sierra Parima. Below the mountains, the Casiquiare River splits off from the Orinoco, diverting about a quarter of the latter's water into the Rio Negro, a major tributary of the Amazon. The link, which is the only such connection between two major river basins, has existed for centuries.

The terrain on the Amazon side of the divide is more than twice as steep as the flat valley through which the Orinoco flows below the bifurcation and a recent study found that the Casiquiare is eroding more rapidly than the Orinoco, deepening its channel. The Orinoco's flow, on the other hand, is slowing due to the build-up of sediment in its streambed. These conditions make it likely that the Casiquiare will eventually completely capture the Orinoco's flow and divert it into the Amazon Basin.

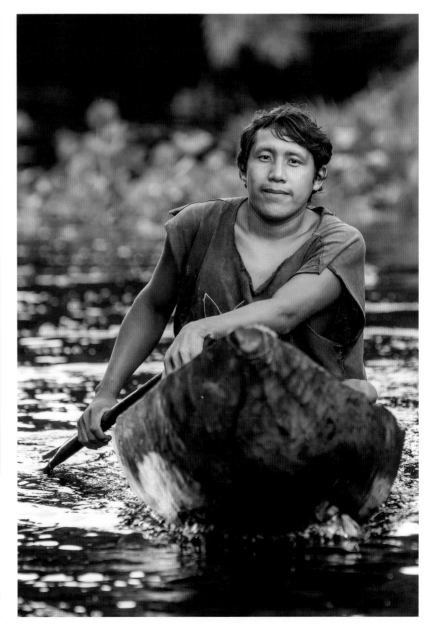

An Indigenous fisherman paddles his wooden canoe on the Orinoco in Venezuela.

The Paraná River

South America's second-longest river, the Paraná is a vital waterway for commercial shipping, provides drinking water for millions of people, powers hydroelectric plants and supports a rich biodiversity.

For the small South American nation of Paraguay, the Paraná River means two things: trade and energy. Paraguay is one of the world's leading exporters of agricultural commodities, but it's also landlocked; 96 per cent of its exports travel by river. And because much of the Paraná is navigable, it serves as a vitally important commercial waterway, linking cities in Brazil, Paraguay and Argentina with the ocean. Almost all of the more than 60 or so cities that are located on the river operate deep-water ports and, each year, the world's third-largest fleet of tug-steered barges transports billions of dollars' worth of agricultural and other commodities, including soybeans, corn, wheat and Brazilian iron ore downriver to the maritime ports of Buenos Aires and Montevideo about 1,300 km (808 miles) away and then on to countries around the world. Meanwhile, Argentine petrol and containers filled with Chinese-manufactured products travel upstream.

0	200	400 kms

⌐ ⌐ Parana River basin

At a glance

Length: 4,880 km (3,032 miles)

Watershed: 2.8 million sq km (1.1 million sq miles)

Vertical drop: 1,148 m (3,766 ft)

Main tributaries: Tietê, Paranápanema, Iguaçu, Salado and Paraguay rivers

Average annual discharge: 17,000 cubic metres per second (600,349 cubic ft per second)

Countries: Brazil, Paraguay, Argentina

Cities: Paraná, Rosario, Buenos Aires

The river also supplies most of Paraguay's electricity – as well as a healthy chunk of its income. Paraguay is the world's largest exporter of hydroelectric power and the fourth-largest exporter of electricity overall; in 2017, it exported US$2.1 billion worth of electricity, which represented 7.1 per cent of its GDP, with neighbouring Argentina and Brazil receiving the majority.

Much of this power is produced by the massive Itaipú dam, located on the Paraná near the border with Brazil. Completed in 1982 and incorporating a staggering 12.3

million cubic metres (434.4 million cubic ft) of concrete and enough steel and iron to build 380 Eiffel Towers, Itaipú is the world's second-largest hydroelectric plant (after the Three Gorges Dam on China's Yangtze River), with an installed capacity of 14,000 MW. It provides roughly 17 per cent of the energy used in Brazil and 76 per cent of the energy consumed in Paraguay. The dam holds the world record for annual power generation, producing more than 103 TW hours in 2016.

The enormous, shallow reservoir that formed behind the dam flooded Guaíra Falls, where the Paraná

Itaipú Dam on the Paraná River, located on the border between Brazil and Paraguay, is the world's third-largest hydroelectric dam.

once fell 114 m (374 ft) over a series of 18 cataracts clustered in seven groups spread out over 3 km (1.86 miles). Located at a point where the river was forced through a narrow, funnel-like gorge in which its width dropped from about 380 m (1,247 ft) to about 60 m (197 ft), the falls were said to rival the world-famous Iguazu Falls to the south and discharged a larger volume of water than Niagara and Victoria falls, creating a roar that could be heard 30 km (18 miles) away.

Rising on the plateau of southeast-central Brazil, the Paraná officially begins at the confluence of the Paranáíba and Rio Grande rivers in southern Brazil. Flowing generally southwest, it forms a section of the Paraguay–Brazil border round 200 km (124 miles) long before being joined by the Iguazú River. The point of confluence is known as the Triple Frontier, a tri-border area where Argentina, Brazil and Paraguay come together. The Paraná then carries on as the frontier between Paraguay and Argentina.

Below the Yacyreta Dam, which is shared by Paraguay and Argentina, the river becomes significantly braided, as sediment eroded from its banks in Brazil is deposited and piled up into islands and braid bars. After flowing for about 1,300 km (808 miles) through Argentina, the Paraná merges with the Uruguay River to form the Río de la Plata, which empties into the Atlantic Ocean; the Paraná accounts for about three-quarters of the Río de la Plata's total outflow.

Downstream from the city of Diamante, the river splits into several arms, dividing again and again as it flows into its delta. Roughly 18 km (11 miles) wide at its upper end and 65 km (40 miles) wide at its lower end, the delta region is a vast mosaic of wetlands brimming with biodiversity; it's considered to be one of the world's premier

The Triple Frontier, where the borders of Paraguay, Argentina and Brazil converge and the Iguazú River (in the foreground) enters the Paraná.

The sun sets over the Paraná Delta in Argentina, which consists of a number of islands known as the Islas del Paraná.

birdwatching destinations. Recently, however, changes to the river's flow patterns, mostly due to dam construction and climate change, have seen the delta increasingly being transformed into a productive dryland area. The reduced flow has also contributed to an increase in the frequency of wildfires in the region.

In its hot, humid upper reaches, the river flows through the Alto Paraná Atlantic Forest, which is a centre of endemism; half of its plant species and 90 per cent of its amphibians are found nowhere else. In the river's lower reaches, which receive much less rainfall, the Atlantic Forest gives way to savanna.

In 1527, the Venetian explorer Sebastian Cabot became the first European to travel up the river. He had been appointed to lead a four-ship Spanish expedition to carry out astronomical observations, strengthen Spanish territorial claims and develop trade with the Orient, but after hearing reports of fabulous wealth in the Río de la Plata region he diverted the expedition. In February 1527, after a disastrous journey in which he

became becalmed in the doldrums, Cabot ran his flagship aground off Santa Catarina Island and marooned several of his officers on the island for questioning his command. He then sailed into the wide Río de la Plata. He spent five months exploring the estuary and in August established the fort of San Salvador at the confluence of the Uruguay River and the Río San Salvador, the first Spanish settlement in what would become Uruguay. He then sailed up the Paraná River with an exploring party in search of gold, establishing a small fort at the confluence of the Río Carcarañá, the first Spanish settlement in present-day Argentina (not long after, it was overwhelmed and burnt by the local indigenous population).

In recent years, the Paraná has been severely affected by cyclical droughts. Dwindling rainfall upriver in Brazil has meant that at some points, the Paraná's flow is just over half the long-term average. In 2021, its level dropped to a 77-year low, forcing cargo vessels to reduce their loads, sometimes by as much as half. Consequently, goods are increasingly being moved over land.

The Rio Grande

One of the principal rivers of the southwestern USA and northern Mexico, the Rio Grande forms much of the controversial border between the two nations.

For almost two centuries, the Rio Grande, which marks part of the border between the US state of Texas and Mexico, has meant hope for multitudes of people seeking a better life. Today, it is people crossing the river from the south, hoping to escape persecution or poverty, but during the early 1800s the river offered a potential escape route for enslaved people fleeing south to Mexico, which had abolished slavery in 1829, when Texas was still part of America. This act was a significant factor in the decision of white, slave-holding immigrants to fight for independence in the 1835 Texas Revolution; once they formed the Republic of Texas in 1836, they made slavery legal again. Estimates suggest that as many as 10,000 people escaped bondage in Texas and other southern US states into Mexico.

At a glance

Length: 3,051 km (1,896 miles)

Watershed: 470,000 sq km* (181,468 sq miles)

Vertical drop: 3,700/3,890 m (12,139/12,762 ft)

Main tributaries: Conchos, Pecos, Devils, Chama, Puerco, Salado and San Juan rivers

Mean annual discharge: 75 cubic metres per second (2,649 cubic ft per second)

Countries: USA, Mexico

Cities: El Paso, Ciudad Juárez, Albuquerque, Nuevo Laredo, Las Cruces

The river's entire watershed covers about 870,000 sq km (335,909 sq miles), but about half of this area is arid or semiarid and doesn't contribute significantly to the river's flow.

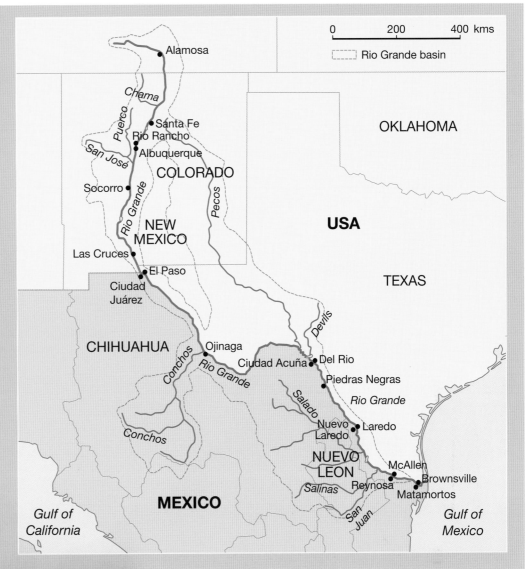

After Texas joined the USA as a state in 1845, the Rio Grande marked the disputed border between Mexico and the nascent state (in American minds, that is; according to Mexico, it was located along the Nueces River to the northeast). The disagreement provided part of the rationale for the US invasion of Mexico in 1846, triggering the Mexican–American War. The Treaty of Guadalupe Hidalgo, signed in 1848 at the end of the war placed the international border along the middle of the Rio Grande's deepest channel, from the twin cities of El Paso, Texas, and Ciudad Juárez, Chihuahua, to the Gulf of Mexico.

However, the river, and hence the border, is ever-shifting, as erosion, siltation and the formation of sandbars causes the river channel to meander, forcing the two countries to spend a considerable amount of money and time adjusting the boundary. (In Mexico, the river is known as the Río Bravo del Norte, or simply Río Bravo; in Spanish, *bravo* has several meanings, including 'furious' and 'agitated'.) The border's official length ranges from 1,431–2,008 km (889–1,248 miles).

The river's habit of meandering regularly and flooding occasionally has also meant that, in Texas, the border wall built during the Trump administration is often located some distance – in some cases more than a kilometre – to the north of the river, effectively turning thousands of hectares of US territory between the water and the wall into no man's land.

The limestone walls of Santa Elena canyon in Big Bend National Park rise almost 500 metres (1,640 ft) above the river.

The Rio Grande flows through a mixture of forest, steppe and desert, providing water for bountiful cropland as it makes its descent from the Rocky Mountains to the Gulf of Mexico. The river rises as a clear, snow-fed mountain stream more than 3,700 m (12,139 ft) above sea level in the western part of the Rio Grande National Forest in the San Juan Mountains, in southwestern Colorado, and for much of its length it continues to flow at a high elevation.

From the Continental Divide, it passes through a number of valleys and gorges that support forests of spruce, fir and aspen, irrigating farmland and providing water for the desert cities of Albuquerque and Las Cruces. Irrigated agriculture is found along most of the river's course, but is particularly extensive in the subtropical Lower Rio Grande Valley. In New Mexico, the river flows through an area known as the Rio Grande rift, making its way from one sediment-filled basin to another through canyons that it has cut in the basins' rims.

East of El Paso/Ciudad Juárez, the river flows through desert, entering more open terrain, the vegetation shifting from piñon pine, juniper and sagebrush to mesquite, creosote bush, cactus, yucca and other desert plants. Shortly before it enters the Gulf Coastal Plain, the river cuts three canyons up to 520 m (1,706 ft) in depth across the faulted area occupied by the 'big bend', here the river changes from running east-southeast to north-northeast. After meandering sluggishly across the Gulf Coastal Plain, the river forms a small, sandy, fertile delta and then empties into the Gulf of Mexico.

Today, vast quantities of the river's water are consumed by irrigation and cities in the region, and held back in numerous reservoirs and diversion dams. Its flow is punctuated by multiple dams and a considerable amount of hydroelectricity is produced within its basin; however, diversion for irrigation has the greatest impact on the river's flow. The river provides water for more than 850,000 ha (2.1 million acres) of cropland, slightly more than half of which is in Mexico, on which a wide variety of crops are grown, including potatoes, alfalfa, cotton, pecans, grapes and citrus fruits.

Abstraction for irrigation has severely decreased the river's flow and, in some sections, it occasionally dries up completely. Since the mid-20th century, only a fifth of the Rio Grande's water reaches the Gulf of Mexico; in mid-2001, the river completely failed to reach the ocean for the first time in recorded history, after a 100-m-wide (328 ft) sandbar formed at its mouth. In 2020, the river only flowed between March and September. Along its length, the river's depth can vary from 18 m (59 ft) to nothing at all.

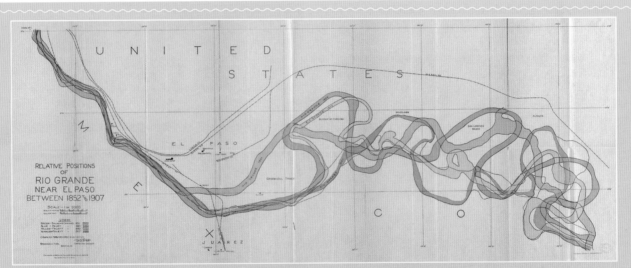

The channel of the Rio Grande moved several times between 1852 and 1907, triggering a dispute between the USA and Mexico

The Chamizal Dispute

The Rio Grande's ever-shifting channel was almost responsible for the combined assassinations of the US and Mexican presidents. According to the terms of the Treaty of Guadalupe Hidalgo, signed in 1848 at the end the Mexican–American War, the border between the two countries ran along the middle of the Rio Grande's deepest channel. Between 1852 and 1868, that channel shifted south, making a particularly large jump during a flood in 1864. By the early 1870s, about 2.4 sq km (1 sq mile) of land, known as El Chamizal, had been transferred to the northern bank of the river, effectively transferring part of Mexico to the USA. Mexico sued to have the land returned, but it was eventually incorporated into El Paso. In 1899, a channel dug by both countries for flood control created an 'island' of Mexican land that jutted into US territory. Claimed by both countries but properly administered by neither, what became known as Cordova Island developed into a haven for crime and illegal crossings. In 1909, at a presidential summit aimed at ending the dispute attended by Porfirio Díaz and William Howard Taft, a would-be assassin was captured, disarmed and arrested just a few feet from the two leaders. Eventually, in October 1967, the USA formally returned most of the territory to Mexico. The USA kept about 0.8 sq km (0.3 sq mile) of Cordova Island and the two nations agreed to share the cost of creating a concrete channel designed to prevent the Rio Grande from ever blurring the international boundary again.

The St Lawrence River

Canada's second-longest river, the mighty St Lawrence drains the heart of North America before emptying into the ocean through the world's largest estuary.

The St Lawrence River was born at the end of the last ice age. The river flows through an ancient geological depression that contains the Canadian Shield and the Appalachian Mountains. During the glacial period of the Pleistocene up to 2.58 million years ago, the depression was filled with glaciers. As the vast northerly ice sheets receded, it allowed the sea to rush in, flooding the depression and forming the Champlain Sea, essentially a huge inlet of the Atlantic Ocean. However, with the weight of the glacial ice gone, the underlying ground began to rise up, causing the sea to drain away again. By about 6,000 years ago, a residual river-like watercourse – the St Lawrence – had been established.

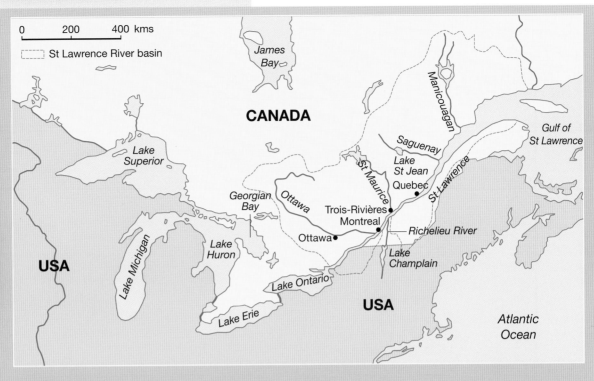

At a glance

Length: 1,197 km (744 miles)

Watershed: 1.3 million sq km (807,783 sq miles)

Vertical drop: 75 m (246 ft)

Main tributaries: Saguenay, Ottawa, Saint-Maurice, Richelieu, Saint-François and Chaudière rivers

Mean annual discharge: 16,800 cubic metres per second (593,286 cubic ft per second)

Countries: Canada, USA

Cities: Montreal, Quebec City

During the 11th century, Norse mariners became the first Europeans to explore the river's vast estuary. They were followed during the 15th and early 16th centuries by more European seafarers, including the Italian explorer John Cabot, the Portuguese brothers Gaspar and Miguel Corte-Real, and a procession of Basque whalers and fishermen, who traded with the local indigenous people and established a number of small settlements on the nearby Atlantic coast.

In 1535, while searching for the fabled Northwest Passage between the Atlantic to the Pacific, the French navigator and explorer Jacques Cartier became the first European known to have sailed up the river itself. Arriving in the estuary on 10 August – St Lawrence's feast day – he named it the Gulf of St Lawrence. The river went on to serve as the main route for European exploration of the North American interior, first pioneered by the French explorer Samuel de Champlain, who, in 1608, established Quebec City on high bluffs close to the river's mouth. This region became the cradle of Canada's French-speaking population.

The river's drainage basin is home to the Great Lakes, the world's largest lake system, containing about a fifth of the world's freshwater resources. While the river runs for 3,058 km (1,900 miles) from its farthest headwater – the North River in the Mesabi Range at Hibbing, Minnesota – to its mouth, it officially begins at the eastern outflow of

The Thousand Islands is an archipelago of 1,864 islands in the St Lawrence River where it emerges from the northeast corner of Lake Ontario.

Lake Ontario, 1,197 km (744 miles) from the Atlantic. From here to the city of Cornwall, about 180 km (112 miles) downstream, the river forms the border between Canada and the USA. In this part of the river, sudden breaks in the gradient of the riverbed have created what's known as the International Rapids section of the river. Due to the need for a navigable route upriver to the Great Lakes, as well as the regional need for power, several dams, hydroelectric power stations, canals and a major part of the St Lawrence Seaway (see box) have been built in this section of the river.

In the region of the Quebec lowlands, the river is dotted with numerous islands, one of which, the Island of Montreal at the confluence with the Ottawa River, is home to Montreal, Canada's second most populous city. Development of the city's port, which lies at one end of the St Lawrence Seaway, required the deepening of the river channel through a mixture of dredging and canalization, engineering projects that were begun during the 18th century. The river is at least partially ice covered for most of the winter, and icebreakers are required to open up the main channel for shipping.

At the Île d'Orléans, the river becomes tidal as it broadens out to a width of about 100 km (62 miles), first as the St Lawrence estuary and then as the oval-shaped marine region known as the Gulf of St Lawrence, a vast inland sea comparable to the Mediterranean. The tides are amplified as they enter the river, reaching about 7 m (23 ft) in range during the largest spring tides in the upper estuary at Saint-Joseph-de-la-Rive. Lower down, near the confluence with the Saguenay River, the St Lawrence's bed exhibits a significant break in gradient; within 16 km (10 miles) of the confluence, the depth increases from about 25 m (82 ft) to 349 m (1,145 ft) as the river passes down a drowned glacial valley known as the Laurentian Channel.

Throughout its length, the St Lawrence displays a great natural beauty. In its upper reaches, the river flows through a subarctic zone that supports a vast coniferous boreal forest as it moves into a more temperate region. This boreal character is lost and the river is bordered by broadleaf deciduous forests of birch, maple, oak, beech and cedar; some of these cedars are among the oldest trees in eastern North America, having been around for almost 800 years. As the river flows further east, the climate returns to a subarctic level.

Most of the input from tributaries occurs downstream of the international portion of the river; upstream from Cornwall, Ontario,

The St Lawrence is a haven for whales.

99 per cent of the discharge originates from Lake Ontario. The water in the river tends to be poorly mixed from bank to bank, with clear water from the Great Lakes occupying the central portion of the channel and the more sediment-laden water entering from tributaries hugging their respective shorelines for up to 100 km (62 miles). The St Lawrence transports the smallest quantity of suspended sediment of the world's major rivers.

The river is a significant seasonal food source for birds such as ducks, bustards and geese, which gather on its sandy banks and in the adjacent wetlands during the warmer months. The river's sandbanks and reefs also provide a staging area for huge flocks of migratory birds, including almost all of the world's snow geese. Abundance typically peaks around September, at which time several hundred thousand birds can be in attendance.

The river's lower reaches and estuary also play host to 13 species of whale – including a year-round population of endangered beluga whales – which come to feed on the abundant plankton that thrive in the nutrient-rich water that wells up along the Laurentian Channel. The river is home to 87 freshwater and 18 migrating (diadromous) species of fish, including the world's healthiest surviving stocks of Atlantic salmon and populations of the Atlantic sturgeon, which can grow to 4.3 m (14 ft) and weigh 360 kg (794 lb).

A container ship passes through the Welland Canal, a section of the St Lawrence Seaway that connects Lake Ontario and Lake Erie, enabling ships to bypass Niagara Falls.

The St Lawrence Seaway

The discovery of vast iron ore deposits in Quebec and Labrador in Canada, needed to feed hungry US steel mills, led to the construction of the St Lawrence Seaway, a massive navigational project involving an extensive system of canals and locks that extends for some 3,766 km (2,340 miles), linking Duluth, Minnesota, at Lake Superior's westernmost point, to the Atlantic. Undertaken jointly by Canada and the USA, and officially opened on 26 June 1959, the seaway opened up North America's industrial and agricultural heartlands by allowing deep-draft ocean vessels to reach the Great Lakes. Its completion involved the clearing of a throughway along a 299-km (186-mile) stretch of the St Lawrence River between Montreal and Lake Ontario. Today, the Great Lakes–St Lawrence system is one of the world's most heavily used international trade routes, carrying some 140 million tonnes (138 million tons) of cargo annually – mostly grain from the prairies of Canada and the US Midwest, Canadian iron ore, coal from US mines, and imported iron and steel.

The Yukon River

Flowing through the vast pine forests of northern Canada and then into Alaska, the Yukon is one of the world's last great free-flowing rivers.

Today, the name Yukon is inextricably linked with a romantic ideal of frontier existence, a connection forged during the 18th and 19th centuries as fur trappers and gold miners ventured deep into North America's remote and forbidding Arctic wilderness.

Black and grizzly bears still roam the region's thickly forested river valleys, as do caribou, deer and moose, and predatory timber wolf packs. The Yukon River itself is home to muskrats and beavers, which engineer the river with their dams and consume plant life along its banks. Many of these and other mammal species were important to the river's early human development, their furs supporting lucrative trade networks, first established by the region's indigenous communities and then exploited by entrepreneurial European settlers.

For millennia, indigenous peoples used the Yukon River as both a bountiful food source and a communication and trade conduit. They mostly travelled in birchbark canoes, but also paddled up- and downriver in moose-skin boats and on rafts that could carry entire households.

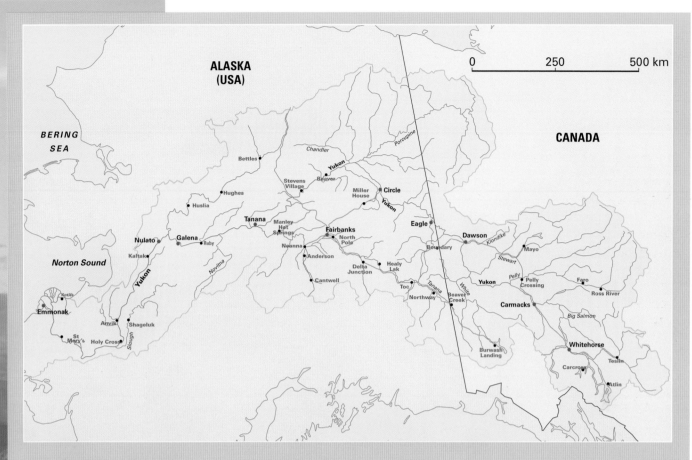

At a glance

Length: 3,185 km (1,979 miles)

Watershed: 833,000 sq km (321,623 sq miles)

Vertical drop: 669 m (2,195 ft)

Main tributaries: Teslin, Pelly, White, Stewart, Porcupine, Tanana, and Koyukuk rivers

Mean annual discharge: 6,500 cubic metres per second (229,545 cubic ft per second)

Countries: Canada, USA

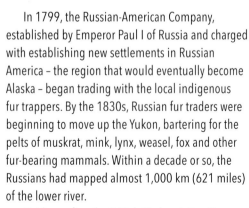

In 1799, the Russian-American Company, established by Emperor Paul I of Russia and charged with establishing new settlements in Russian America – the region that would eventually become Alaska – began trading with the local indigenous fur trappers. By the 1830s, Russian fur traders were beginning to move up the Yukon, bartering for the pelts of muskrat, mink, lynx, weasel, fox and other fur-bearing mammals. Within a decade or so, the Russians had mapped almost 1,000 km (621 miles) of the lower river.

Not long after, the British Hudson's Bay Company moved into the region, establishing trading posts at Fort Yukon, at the junction of the Porcupine and Yukon rivers in 1847, and Fort Selkirk a year later at the junction of the Yukon and Pelly rivers. However, after the latter was attacked, looted and burned down in 1852 by Chilkat Tlingit First Nation warriors, who resented the interference with their traditional trade with the Athabaskan First Nations of the interior, Europeans withdrew from the upper Yukon basin for two decades. (The fort was eventually rebuilt about 40 years later and became an important supply point along the Yukon River.)

After the USA purchased Alaska from Russia in 1867, the Alaska Commercial Company acquired the assets of the Russian-American Company and started to build more trading posts on the river. In order to supply these outposts, and to bring furs out to market, in 1869 the company brought in the steamboat *Yukon*, the first paddle-wheeler on the river.

Another valuable natural resource then spurred the next chapter in the river's development as prospectors and miners began to arrive in its watershed during the mid-1880s and quickly made

The steamboat Flora, *loaded with prospectors, navigates Five Finger Rapids on the Yukon during the Klondike gold rush c. 1898.*

a series of gold strikes. In 1896, a particularly big find on a tributary of the Klondike River known as Rabbit Creek (soon to be renamed Bonanza Creek in celebration of this and later strikes) triggered a full-scale gold rush that transformed the Yukon, into which the Klondike flows.

Although the main mining operations were located on Yukon tributaries, Dawson City, the territory's principal settlement, sat at the confluence of the Klondike and Yukon rivers. As more and more prospectors arrived, steamboat traffic on the latter expanded considerably (between June and September 1898, 57 registered steamboats, carrying about 11,000 tonnes/10,826 tons of supplies,

docked at Dawson City) and the Yukon took on the role of busy liquid highway.

During the May–September navigation season, the sternwheelers would take on freight and supplies, as well as fur traders and prospectors, at the port of Saint Michael, Alaska, near the river's mouth and ferry them up to Dawson City and beyond. The journey was extremely hazardous, the steamboat captains forced to contend with low water, shifting channels and submerged sand bars, not to mention mechanical failures, boiler explosions and collisions with logs and submerged rocks.

The end of the gold rush in 1899 and the completion of the railroad line between Skagway, Alaska, and Whitehorse, Yukon, the following year led to a decline in the use of water transport on the river. The completion of the Alaska Highway in 1942 was the final nail in the coffin; the paddle-wheel riverboats stopped running about a decade later.

The Llewellyn Glacier in British Columbia is generally considered to be the river's source. Its headwater tributaries flow out of a semicircle of high mountains in the province's northwest corner where it borders the Yukon territory. Downstream from Whitehorse, the river widens to form Lake Laberge, before entering a broad, flat-bottomed glacial valley. Here, its banks are low and the river meanders lazily across the valley floor. Numerous sandbars and small wooded islands dot the channel and its long, wide stretches are bordered by pine forests that slope up to high mountains.

At Fort Selkirk, the Yukon transforms from a clear, gentle river into something more substantial as its volume is swelled considerably by the inflow of the Pelly River, followed not long after by the White River, which adds large quantities of silt eroded from the mountains to the southwest, dramatically changing the river's clarity.

Past Dawson City, the valley narrows and then, as it enters Alaska, it widens again as it enters the broad, low interior plateau that slopes down across the state. Known as the Yukon Flats, this 28,500-sq-km (11,004-sq-mile) expanse of tundra, forest and wetlands contain some 40,000 small lakes, ponds and streams. Here the river frays into myriad channels that thread their way among numerous islands and sandbars.

At the flats' western end lies a narrow gorge that passes through a low mountain barrier known as the Ramparts, which coaxes the river into becoming a rushing, frothing torrent, before it finally empties into the Bering Sea via the 129,500-sq-km (50,000-sq-mile) Yukon–Kuskokwim Delta, whose area exceeds that of the Mississippi Delta.

The large quantities of glacial debris in the Yukon Basin results in the river carrying a much higher suspended sediment load than the great Siberian Arctic rivers, transporting about 60 million tonnes (59 million tons) of sediment annually to the Bering Sea, with another 20 million tonnes (19.6 million tons) deposited on the floodplains and braided reaches of the river each year.

Although the Yukon has considerable potential for the generation of hydroelectric power, few attempts have been made to harness it, mainly because demand for power is negligible in the region due to its sparse population. There is only a single, small plant at Whitehorse, as well as two even smaller ones on Yukon tributaries.

Except when swollen by spring snow-melt, the Yukon is generally a slow-moving, relatively shallow river with a complex, ever-shifting braided channel. In its upper reaches, the river is bordered by alpine tundra, which slowly gives way to boreal forest. For much of the river's length, the valley floors are dominated by coniferous forests of spruce, fir and pine, which peter out at about 1,000 m (3,281 ft) on the surrounding mountains. Alder and willow trees often line the banks.

The long run

For millennia, the Yukon has hosted one of the world's longest salmon runs, as Chinook, coho and chum salmon return to their terminal streams each year in summer. Salmon don't eat during their spawning migration, so those in the Yukon have particularly large fat reserves to sustain them on their long journey and are known for their rich, oily flesh. Local indigenous people have long relied on the salmon for sustenance, as have the local bald eagle and grizzly and black bear populations. Recently, however, salmon numbers have been dropping precipitously for reasons that are, as yet, unclear.

Lake Laberge, a widening of the Yukon north of Whitehorse, freezes over each winter.

CHAPTER THREE

Rivers of
Asia

Home to the world's highest mountains, Asia hosts some of the planet's most powerful and important rivers, which help to support more than half of the world's population. The Tibetan Plateau (sometimes described as Asia's water tower) alone is the source of 12 major rivers, ten of which are more than 2,000 km (1,243 miles) long. Together these rivers provide drinking water for more than a billion people and convey more than half of the world's riverine sediment to the ocean.

Asia's rivers have birthed great civilizations and continue to play a central role in the continent's prosperity. For millennia, several of these rivers have been considered sacred by those who live along them, including the much-revered Ganges. Many are swollen each year by torrential monsoonal downpours that have, in the past, fuelled some of the most devastating floods in human history.

In recent decades, Asia's burgeoning population has placed great pressure on the continent's rivers, which are among the most polluted on the planet; ten rivers carry more than 90 per cent of the plastic that enters the oceans, and eight of those rivers are in Asia.

Si Phan Don, or the 4,000 islands, on the Mekong River.

The Amur River

Situated on the frontier between China and Russia, the Amur has long been an important symbol of, and geopolitical factor in, relations between the two nations.

Deep in the hinterland of Mongolia, not far from the birthplace of Genghis Khan, rises one of the last major free-flowing rivers on earth – a river with a blood-soaked history, a river that has, for centuries, acted as the frontier between two of the world's most formidable nations: China and Russia.

The river proper begins where the Shilka and Argun rivers come together in the mountains of northeastern China. Flowing through the Lesser Hinggan Range via a narrow gorge where its depth and speed increase dramatically, it emerges into a vast marsh dotted with lakes and ponds, where it transforms into a classic braided river.

At a glance

Length: 2,824 km* (1,755 miles)

Watershed: 1.9 million sq km (733,595 sq miles)

Vertical drop: 303 m (994 ft)

Main tributaries: Zeya, Bureya, Amgun, Songhua, Ussuri, Huma He and Anyui rivers

Annual discharge: 9,800 cubic metres per second (346,084 cubic ft per second)

Countries: Russia, China

Cities: Blagoveshchensk, Heihe, Khabarovsk, Amursk, Nikolaevsk-on-Amur

4,440 km (2,759 miles) if its source river, the Argun, is included.

The Amur's largest tributary, the Songhua, enters near Nizhneleninskoe-Tongjiang, flooding the river, which until then is relatively clear, with yellow, silt-laden water. Swollen by the additional water, the lower Amur flows out across an area of flat, marshy ground, forming a labyrinth of branches, channels, offshoots, former riverbeds, islands, sandbanks and spits. When the flow is particularly heavy, this region is transformed into a vast lake. After turning to the southeast, the river flows in a wide arc before eventually entering the Sea of Okhotsk near Nikolayevsk-na-Amure through a wide, bell-shaped estuary and a mouth 16 km (10 miles) wide.

For much of its length, the Amur flows through the taiga, a vast forest dominated by spruce, fir and larch, home to several large mammal species, including the critically endangered Amur tiger and Amur leopard. Elsewhere, the landscapes within its watershed include desert, steppe grasslands and tundra, often underlain by a layer of permafrost.

Right: *An Amur tiger.*

'I'm in love with the Amur and would be happy to stay here for a couple of years. It is beautiful, with vast open spaces and freedom.'
– Anton Chekhov

Since time immemorial, fishing has been the primary economic activity along the Amur. The river supports at least 120 species of fish from 23 families, including several endemic species – the most of any Russian river. Among them is the kaluga, a type of sturgeon that can reach lengths in excess of 5.5 m (18 ft). The river is also a spawning ground for the salmon stocks of the Sea of Okhotsk and the Japan Sea, a fishery targeted by both commercial fishers and indigenous people. Following flooding in 2013, however, the population of chum salmon – the main species caught in the river – crashed, and conservationists and indigenous groups have been pushing Russian authorities to ban salmon fishing in the river in order to give the fish stocks a chance to recover.

During winter, polar air masses bring dry, cold conditions to the river, with average temperatures as low as –33°C (–27.4°F) in the north; in contrast, subtropical maritime air masses raise average summer temperatures in southern parts of the basin as high as 22°C (71.6°F). Towards the end of October, ice begins to form on the river. By the beginning of November, the upper reaches are usually frozen over; by the second half of the month, the lower reaches are too. When the ice breaks up in spring, ice jams often form where the river takes a sharp turn, causing water to rise upriver to as much as 15 m (49 ft). If these dams burst, it can cause catastrophic flash flooding downstream.

When the river is ice free, it is navigable throughout its entire course and there are numerous trading ports along its length and on some of its tributaries. During the period of Sino-Soviet tensions in the latter half of the 20th century, the Amur's importance as a waterway diminished, but it increased again following the break-up of the Soviet Union as China and Russia began to undertake joint projects to improve navigation, drain marshland for agriculture and develop the basin's considerable hydroelectric potential.

The Amur River basin was originally populated by nomadic peoples who supported themselves by hunting, raising cattle and fishing in the river and its tributaries. Among them were the Jurchen people, who formed China's Great Jin dynasty during the 12th century.

The Manchu people of the lower Amur, who established the Qing dynasty during the 17th century, considered the river sacred. Around the beginning of the dynasty, Russian explorers and traders began to enter the region north of the Amur and Russian Orthodox missionaries were proselytizing to the indigenous peoples along the Amur, behaviour that was viewed as a threat by the Qing. Albazin, the first Russian settlement on the Amur, was also depriving the Manchu rulers of local tributes of sable pelts. Consequently, after they had conquered China, the Qing sent military expeditions upstream, leading to fierce battles between the Manchu-Chinese and Cossack-Russians. In 1685, Albazin fell and hostilities ended a few years later with the signing of the Treaty of Nerchinsk in 1689, under which Russia ceded control of the entire Amur valley to China.

As the lone Siberian river to flow eastward to the Pacific Ocean, the Amur took on geopolitical significance for the Russian Empire during the mid-19th century. The Russian government saw the possibility of using the river as a supply route to the Pacific to support the naval defence of Siberia's east coast, while also harbouring fears that the British would occupy the river mouth. Consequently, during the 1850s, Russia established a number of forts and towns along the Amur,

The kaluga is native to the Amur and can grow up to 5.5 m (18 ft) in length.

California on the Amur

In 1883, the discovery of gold near the Albazikha River, a tributary of the Shilka, itself a tributary of the Amur, drew Chinese and Russian prospectors from far and wide. An illegal settlement, known as Zheltuga, formed on the right bank of the Amur itself. Nicknamed 'California on the Amur', the settlement was home to some 12,000 prospectors at its peak. The Russian government turned a blind eye, but about a year after its founding the Chinese government caught wind of the settlement and sent a detachment of 1,600 soldiers to raze it. The Russians were allowed to leave, but the Chinese were massacred as they tried to escape across the river's frozen surface.

Left: Horsemanship Competition for the Shunzhi Emperor, *from 1662, documents an event accompanying the emperor's arrival in Beijing shortly after the fall of the Ming dynasty to the Manchus.*

Below: *The frozen Amur River in Mohe, the northernmost county in China.*

including at its mouth, in what China considered to be its territory.

At the end of the decade, the Russian Empire annexed some 910,000 sq km (351,353 sq miles) of Chinese territory – the land north of the Amur and east of the Ussuri – through a series of unequal treaties forced upon the Qing, including the 1858 Treaty of Aigun and the 1860 Convention of Peking, which placed the border between the two countries along the river itself. Today, the river forms the frontier for about 400 km (249 miles) from its beginning to the confluence with the Ussuri.

One of the darkest stains on the river's history took place in 1900, when the booming border town of Blagoveshchensk witnessed an anti-Chinese pogrom. After Chinese Boxer troops shelled the Russian side of the border, Russians in the town began to view their Chinese neighbours as a 'fifth column'. Mobs attacked Chinese residents, blaming them for lost work after the fighting caused trade to falter. In

July, the order was given to expel the Chinese. Cossacks, members of local militias and ordinary townsfolk dragged Chinese residents from their homes and forced them into the river, telling them to swim back to China. As they began to drown, those still on the bank refused to enter the water and were either shot or hacked down by axe-wielding militia members. The last few survivors were eventually forced into the river by a bayonet charge. Historians estimate that as many as 9,000 people lost their lives.

The Amur again became a regional flashpoint during the mid-20th-century Sino–Soviet political split. In March 1969, long-simmering tensions in the area erupted into armed conflict along the Ussuri; roughly 1,000 soldiers were killed. As relations thawed, the Amur border became a trade gate between the two neighbours, although the relationship remains tense and uneasy, tainted with lingering mistrust.

The Brahmaputra River

One of Asia's most powerful and sediment-laden rivers, the Brahmaputra is the lifeblood for millions of people on the Indian subcontinent.

The Brahmaputra is a prodigious river, carrying enormous quantities of both water and sediment. The combined Ganges-Brahmaputra system has the third-largest average discharge of the world's rivers – roughly 31,000 cubic metres per second (1,094,755 cubic ft per second) – and their combined suspended-sediment load of about 1.8 billion tonnes (1.77 billion tons) per year is the world's highest.

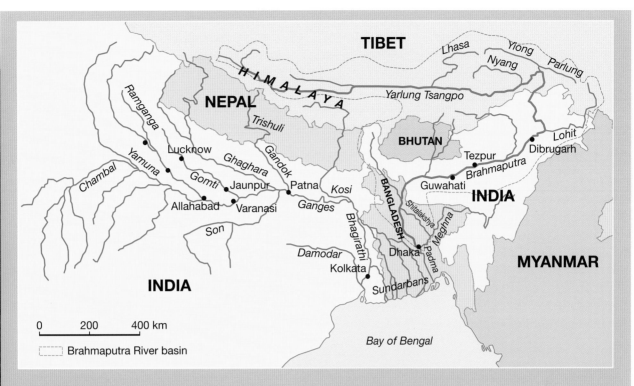

At a glance

Length: 3,848 km (2,391 miles)

Watershed: 650,000 sq km (250,966 sq miles)

Vertical drop: 5,150 m (16,896 ft)

Main tributaries: Subansari, Lohit, Dibang and Siang rivers

Mean annual discharge: 19,800 cubic metres per second (699,230 cubic feet per second)

Countries: Tibet, China, India and Bangladesh

The river rises in the Kailash Mountains on the northern side of the Himalaya, where meltwater from the Chemayungdung and Angsi glaciers forms streams that ultimately merge to give birth to the great river, which then flows generally eastwards for almost 1,100 km (683 miles), bordered to the south by the main range of the Himalaya and to the north by the Kailash Mountains. Here, it is generally known as the Yarlung Tsangpo ('Purifier'). Descending rapidly, the river breaks through the Himalaya in a series of deep, narrow, rapid- and cascade-filled gorges, including the spectacular Yarlung Tsangpo Grand Canyon, whose walls rise some 5 km (3 miles) and more on each side of the river, before flowing out onto the plains of the Indian state of Arunachal Pradesh, where it becomes known as the Siangor Dihang.

At the head of the Assam Valley, the river is joined by the Dibang and Lohit rivers. Below its confluence with the Lohit, about 1,450 km (901 miles) from the Bay of Bengal, the river is finally officially known as the Brahmaputra. It now widens significantly, reaching 20 km (12.4 miles) from bank to bank in places, and becomes complexly braided. Here, the river is mighty, even in the dry season, bolstered by several rapidly flowing Himalayan streams. At Guwahati, near the ancient pilgrimage centre of Hajo, the river has cut deeply into the bedrock of the Shillong Plateau and is at its narrowest, stretching 1 km (0.6 miles) from bank to bank.

Crossing into Bangladesh, the Brahmaputra is joined by one of its largest tributaries, the Tista, before splitting into two south-flowing distributary branches. The larger, western branch continues due south as the Jamuna and merges with the lower Ganges, which at this point is known as the Padma. The Padma then flows into the Meghna River near Chandpur, which then finally flows out into the Bay of Bengal.

The combined delta is the world's largest, sprawling over some 59,570 sq km (23,000 sq miles). This low-lying region of farms and forests is regularly scoured by tropical cyclones and associated tidal surges, which sweep in from the Bay of Bengal, causing widespread destruction and loss of life. A cyclone in 1970 is estimated to have killed as many as half a million people.

As it makes its journey from mountain to sea, the river flows through several climatic zones, from the harsh, cold, dry conditions in Tibet to the generally hot and humid conditions that prevail in Assam and Bangladesh. The former region lies in the rain shadow cast by the Himalaya, so precipitation is relatively light. Lower down, rainfall increases, becoming very heavy on the Bengal Plain.

Main image: *As the sun sets, a boat floats on the Brahmaputra near the city of Guwahati in Assam, India.*

As it flows across the high Tibetan Plateau, the river is bordered largely by xerophytic (drought-resistant) shrubs and grasses. The increase in precipitation as the river descends into India and then Bangladesh supports the growth of semi-evergreen forests and bamboo thickets, which eventually give way to the tall reed jungles that grow in the swamps and depressed water-filled areas (known as jheels) of the floodplains.

The Brahmaputra is a restless river, its course continually shifting; from year to year, it is never in exactly the same place. Over the past 250 years, the river's course has moved westwards by about 80 km (50 miles). The most spectacular of these shifts took place in 1787, when an exceptionally high flood in the Tista saw that river move eastward and the Jamuna develop a new channel. Prior to 1843, the lower Brahmaputra passed through Bangladesh's Jamalpur and Mymensingh districts, and some water still flows through that course, which is now known as the Old Brahmaputra.

The river exhibits two periods of high water, one in late spring or early summer, when the snow in the mountains melts, and another towards the end of summer as torrential monsoon rainfall swells its flow. Both periods of high water regularly spawn catastrophic floods; in most years, the Brahmaputra valley experiences extensive flooding during the summer monsoon.

In Tibet, the river is fed by tributaries that cross the hard rocks of the geologically old plateau to the south and its waters are clear; however, as soon as it enters Arunachal Pradesh, its sediment load becomes much heavier as several fast, high-volume tributaries laden with silt eroded from the slopes of the Himalaya flow in from the north.

Due to its strong current, the scarcity of riparian vegetation and weak banks made of loosely connected sand and silt, the Brahmaputra experiences high levels of bank erosion and channel migration, making the building of permanent structures close to the river problematic. When the river is in flood, the banks have a tendency to collapse in large slabs. At present, the banks are eroding at a rate of about 30 m (98 ft) per year – down from 150 m (492 ft) per year in 1973–92. The loss of land is such that it has made some 700,000 people homeless.

Millions of people are reliant on the Brahmaputra. The delta alone is home to 130 million people and some 600,000 people live on islands within the river's main stream. These people, most of whom are farmers, rely on the regular annual floods to hydrate the soil and bring fresh, fertile sediment to the floodplains. Many rural populations also rely on fish caught both on the floodplain during floods and in the many ponds that dot the floodplain for most of their protein.

Majuli

Situated between two channels of the Brahmaputra – the northern Kherkutia channel and the southern Brahmaputra channel – in Assam, India, that re-join about 100 km (62 miles) downstream, Majuli is the world's largest riverine island, with an area of about 350 sq km (135 sq miles). The island is home to almost 200,000 people, most of whom make their living by growing rice (as many as 100 varieties are grown on Majuli) or fishing. The island is steadily eroding – at the beginning of the 20th century it had an area of 1,255 sq km, (485 sq miles) – and is expected to disappear completely within 20 years.

Majuli, the world's largest riverine island.

The Euphrates River

The longest and one of the most historically important rivers in western Asia, the Euphrates, along with the Tigris, is one of the two defining rivers of Mesopotamia, the 'Land Between the Rivers'.

For millennia, the Euphrates River has sustained human populations in one of the world's harshest environments. Transporting life-giving water through the desert and regularly replenishing the fertile soils on its floodplain, together with the Tigris River it nurtured some the first human civilizations.

At a glance

Length: 2,780 km (1,727 miles)

Watershed: 440,000 sq km (169,885 sq miles)

Vertical drop: 693 m (2,274 ft)

Main tributaries: Sajur, Khabur, Balikh, Kara Su and Murat rivers

Mean annual discharge: 360 cubic metres per second (12,713 cubic ft per second)

Countries: Turkey, Syria, Iraq

Cities: Fallujah, Karbala, Hit, Ramadi

Originating in the Armenian highlands in northeastern Turkey, the Euphrates (known in Turkey as the Firat) descends through a series of valleys and gorges to the uplands of Syria and northern Iraq, and then out onto the alluvial plain of central Iraq before joining the Tigris River to form the 200-km (124-mile) Shatt al-Arab, which empties into the Persian Gulf. The river's headwaters are formed by the Kara Su and Murat Su rivers, which both rise northwest of Lake Van, at elevations of 3,290 m (10,794 ft) and 3,520 m (11,549 ft) respectively. The two rivers join to form the Euphrates upstream from Keban, where the Keban Dam now spans a deep gorge.

Downstream from Baghdad, the land is particularly flat. As the Tigris and Euphrates rivers enter the region, their velocity slows and the sediment they carry begins to settle, building their beds up above the level of the plain and making them prone to overflow their banks, change course and split into multiple branches. Over time, this has led to the creation of an inland delta populated by a mosaic of shallow, almost interconnected freshwater lakes and permanent and seasonal marshes. During flood periods, the whole area is inundated. The Mesopotamian Marshes were historically the largest wetland ecosystem of Western Eurasia. The world's first epic poem, the *Epic of Gilgamesh*, mentions the marshlands: 'Ever the river has risen and brought us the flood.'

Together with the Tigris, the Euphrates played a central role in the development of human civilization. The region around these two rivers is considered to be among the longest continually inhabited areas in the world. People began to move into the upper reaches of the Euphrates basin – the region popularly known as the Fertile Crescent – in around the 11th millennium BCE, as hunter-gatherers and then early farmers began to establish permanent villages in the Taurus Mountains and the upper part of the Euphrates valley in what is now Syria.

The development of irrigation during the 6th millennium BCE enabled the occupation of lower Mesopotamia – the fertile plain between the Tigris and Euphrates rivers – where rainfall is insufficient for dry agriculture. Only below Kut is the Tigris high enough above the surrounding plain for flow irrigation to be possible. In contrast, the

Euphrates has built its bed up much higher than the alluvial plain and consequently has been the primary source for irrigation in Mesopotamia throughout history. Clay boat models from the 5th millennium BCE indicate that the rivers were being used for transport at that time. Over the next few thousand years, urban settlements were established along the river and the canals attached to it, some of them growing into cities that covered more than 100 ha (247 acres).

Eventually, the Euphrates basin spawned multiple empires, including the Sumerians, Babylonians, Assyrians and Hittites. The Sumerian civilization, considered

A statue of Gudea, a Sumerian ruler.

The partially excavated ruins of the city of Uruk, located beside a dried-up ancient channel of the Euphrates.

to be the world's first, arose in Mesopotamia around 3000 BCE. The Sumerians dug a series of ditches to control the seasonal flooding of the Tigris and Euphrates, and then developed a system of irrigation agriculture, using water from the two rivers, controlled by canals, channels, dykes, weirs and reservoirs, to exploit the fertile alluvium they had deposited. The surplus output from their crops – barley, chickpeas, lentils, wheat, dates and onions among others – enabled them to form urban settlements that eventually grew into city states. Uruk, located in southern Mesopotamia on what is now a dry former channel of the Euphrates, is considered to be the world's first true city. Later described as 'Venice in the desert', the city was criss-crossed by a network of canals that connected it with both maritime trade and the surrounding fields. At its peak, the city had a population of between 40,000 and 80,000 people. It's thought that its eventual decline may have been precipitated by a shift in the Euphrates' course.

The ancient city of Babylon, capital of the Babylonian Empire, which achieved regional dominance between the 19th and 15th centuries BCE, and again between the 7th and 6th centuries BCE, was built along both banks of the Euphrates just south of present-day Baghdad. Where it passed through the city, the river was constrained by steep embankments, built to contain the river's seasonal floods. Numerous other important ancient cities, including Nippur, Ur, Adab, Kish, Mari, Eridu and Sippar, were located along the river's course.

During the 1st century BCE, the north–south-flowing upper reaches of the Euphrates, from its headwaters in Armenia to the plains of northern Syria, came to represent a negotiated boundary between the Romans to the west and the Parthian Empire to the east, and largely remained so until the overthrow of the Parthians by the Sassanian Empire during the 3rd century CE. During this period, the main river crossing was a pontoon bridge located at Zeugma in modern-day Turkey, the site of a Roman legionary base, one of three built to defend the frontier. The crossing helped to make Zeugma an important trade centre, acting as a useful staging post on the Silk Road, which connected China to Rome. Even after the defeat of the Parthians, the Euphrates generally demarcated the boundary between the Roman and Persian spheres of influence until the Islamic conquest of the mid-7th century CE.

The Euphrates is mostly fed by winter rainfall and spring snowmelt in the Armenian Highlands. Its volume usually peaks in April and May; discharge at this time represents more than 40 per cent of the annual total. From year to year, the total

A mosque in the town of Halfeti in Turkey rises from the waters of the Euphrates, having been partially submerged following the building of Birecik dam.

discharge is highly variable, swinging from a low of 15.3 cubic km (3.75 cubic miles) in 1961 to a high of 42.7 cubic km (10.24 cubic miles) two years later. Three intermittent spring-fed rivers join the Euphrates in Syria, but they add comparatively little water; some 90 per cent of the water in the river originates in Turkey. Once the Euphrates enters Iraq, it receives no further natural tributaries, although it does receive some water from the Tigris via a number of man-made canals.

It's believed that before human settlement in the region, the Euphrates valley supported a riverine forest populated by Oriental plane, the Euphrates poplar, tamarisk, ash and a variety of wetland plants. From source to mouth, the amount of rainfall experienced along the river drops steadily and today, the vegetation along its banks changes accordingly. In its upper reaches, as the Euphrates flows through the mountains and foothills of southeast Turkey, it's flanked by oak and pistachio trees, and members of the Rosaceae family, along with the wild variants of many cereals, including einkorn wheat, emmer wheat, oat and rye. South of this zone, the vegetation transitions into mixed woodland and steppe vegetation, and then into true steppe, characterized by white wormwood and chenopods, although heavy overgrazing by sheep and goats has greatly diminished the plant cover. Southeast of the border between Syria and Iraq, the river flows into true desert, often flowing through areas devoid of vegetation.

The first modern water diversion structure built in the Tigris–Euphrates river system was the Hindiya Barrage in Iraq, which was completed in 1913. It was followed by a number of structures designed to regulate the river's flow and discharge excess flood water into what is now Lake Habbaniyah. The Haditha Dam, an earth-fill dam 9 km (5.6 miles) long that provides electricity to Baghdad, is Iraq's largest dam on the Euphrates. Its reservoir submerged the ancient town of ʿĀnah and dozens of smaller settlements, as well as a major part of the agricultural base of

the middle Euphrates. Iraq has also created an intricate network of canals that connect the Euphrates with lakes and reservoirs that can be used to store excess floodwater. The largest of these is the 565-km-long (351-mile) Third River or Main Outfall Drain, which was constructed between 1953 and 1992 in order to prevent soil salinization from irrigation by draining the area between the Euphrates and the Tigris south of Baghdad. It also allows large freight barges to navigate up to Baghdad.

Under the 1923 Treaty of Lausanne, which partitioned the Ottoman Empire and redrew the borders of southwest Asia, the three riparian states of the Euphrates – at that time Turkey, France for its Syrian mandate and the UK for its mandate of Iraq – set the rules for use of the Euphrates' water and the construction of dams and other river infrastructure. This was followed by a 1946 agreement between Turkey and Iraq that required the former to tell the latter about any hydraulic changes it made to the Tigris–Euphrates system. It also gave Iraq permission to construct dams on Turkish territory to manage the flow of the Euphrates.

Syria and Turkey completed their first dams on the Euphrates during the 1970s – first the Tabqa Dam in Syria in 1973 and then the Keban Dam in Turkey a year later. Right around this time, severe drought settled over the area, greatly diminishing the river's flow and triggering an international crisis. Starved of water by the combination of drought and upstream damming, Iraq threatened to blow up the Tabqa Dam. Saudi Arabia and the Soviet Union intervened and an agreement between Syria and Iraq was eventually reached. In 1981, tensions arose once more, after Turkey halted the river's flow in order to refill the Keban Dam reservoir, which was almost empty as the water had been used to temporarily increase the production of hydroelectricity. From 1984, Turkey, Syria and Iraq began to sign agreements that specified the amount of water that flows from one country to the next.

The Tabqa Dam is Syria's largest and Lake Assad, its reservoir, is an important source of water for irrigation and also supplies most of Aleppo's drinking water. Syria has dammed the Euphrates twice more since the Tabqa was built and plans to build a fourth dam – the Halabiye Dam – between Raqqa and Deir ez-Zor.

During the 1970s, Turkey launched the Southeastern Anatolia Project, an ambitious plan to harness the Tigris-Euphrates for irrigation and hydroelectricity generation. Consisting of 22 dams and 19 power plants, when completed the project will affect some 75,000 sq km (28,958 sq miles) and about seven million

The construction of Keban Dam on the Euphrates in Turkey's Elazığ province, completed in 1974, resulted in the displacement of about 25,000 people.

A mosaic from the ancient city of Zeugma, which was flooded when Birecik dam was built, on display in the Zeugma Mosaic Museum in Gaziantep, Turkey.

people, produce an estimated 27 billion kWh of hydroelectric power annually and provide irrigation water to 1.7 million ha (4.2 million acres) of agricultural land, more than half of which will be located in the Euphrates basin. The largest of the dams is the Atatürk Dam, 184 m (604 ft) high and 1,820 m (5,971 ft) long, completed in 1992, whose reservoir is Turkey's third-largest lake, with a maximum capacity of 48.7 cubic km (11.7 cubic miles) – large enough to hold the Euphrates' entire annual discharge – and feeds a huge irrigation project. The dam construction – in both the Euphrates and Tigris basins – has affected 382 villages and almost 200,000 people have had to be resettled elsewhere. The project was scheduled to be completed in 2010, but the World Bank withheld funding because Turkey has thus far neglected to sign an official agreement on water sharing with the downstream states on the Euphrates and the Tigris.

Dam building and the large-scale abstraction of water for irrigation and other uses has had a significant effect on the Euphrates' discharge regime, much to the detriment of the Mesopotamian Marshes, while also causing the river's salinity to increase, making its water less potable. The creation of large reservoirs and irrigation areas has also increased the rate of evaporation on the river by as much as 50 per cent; an estimated 8 cubic km (1.9 cubic miles) of water evaporates from reservoirs along the Euphrates each year. Dam construction has also led to the flooding of numerous archaeological sites and other places of cultural significance in the Euphrates valley, including the ancient Roman town of Zeugma, which was known for its unique mosaics.

Between 2014 and 2017, while the Syrian civil war raged, much of the territory along the Euphrates was controlled by Islamic State. Having captured the Nuaimiyah Dam near Fallujah, in April 2014 the militants closed its floodgates, cutting off the water supply to the south and causing extensive upstream flooding. The water inundated land up to 100 km (62 miles) away and submerged the town of Abu Ghraib under up to 4 m (13 ft) of water. More than 10,000 houses and about 200 sq km (77 sq miles) of fertile farmland were flooded, destroying crops and killing livestock; as many as 60,000 people were displaced. The floods also forced government troops to retreat and lift the siege on its stronghold of Fallujah and caused electricity shortages in towns south of Baghdad as hydroelectric power stations were starved of water. Not long after, the militants re-opened five of the dam's floodgates, apparently fearing their strategy would backfire by flooding Fallujah.

Unsurprisingly, given the importance of the river to the lives of people in the Middle East, the Euphrates has great sacred significance in Islam, Christianity and Judaism. Each religion regards the river's depletion as a portent of the Day of Judgement. Once known as Perat, it appears in the Biblical Book of Genesis as one of the four rivers that flowed out of the Garden of Eden and it's also mentioned in the hadiths of the Prophet Muhammad.

Agriculture makes up more than 70 per cent of water use in the Euphrates basin and, as a result, water quality has become a serious issue for the Euphrates, with return flows from agricultural drainage leading to problems with salinity. The dumping of untreated sewage into the river and its tributaries has exacerbated the problem.

The Ganges River

Flowing through one of the world's most fertile and densely populated regions, the sacred Ganges is blighted by staggering levels of pollution.

According to Hindu culture and mythology, the Bhagirathi River, which rises in a subglacial meltwater cave at the foot of the Gangotri Glacier at Gomukh in the western Himalaya, is the source of the Ganges. The cave is a sacred site for Hindu pilgrimage; in Hindu mythology it's said to reside among the matted locks of the god Shiva. However, the Alaknanda River, which rises about 50 km (31 miles) north of the Himalayan peak of Nanda Devi, is generally considered to be the Ganges' true source due its greater length.

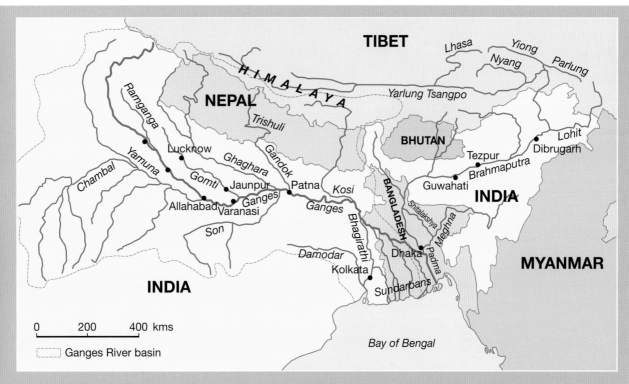

The map shows the Ganges River basin with labels: TIBET, Lhasa, Yiong, Nyang, Parlung, Yarlung Tsangpo, HIMALAYA, NEPAL, Trishuli, BHUTAN, Lohit, Tezpur, Dibrugarh, Ramganga, Lucknow, Ghaghara, Gandok, Brahmaputra, Guwahati, INDIA, Yamuna, Chambal, Gomti, Jaunpur, Patna, Kosi, BANGLADESH, Shitalakshya, Meghna, Allahabad, Ganges, Ganges, Varanasi, Bhagirathi, Padma, Dhaka, Son, MYANMAR, Damodar, Kolkata, Sundarbans, INDIA, Bay of Bengal

0 200 400 kms

☐ Ganges River basin

At a glance

Length: 2,525 km (1,569 miles)

Watershed: 1.1 million sq km (424,712 sq miles)

Vertical drop: 830 m (2,723 ft)

Main tributaries: Son, Chambal Kosi, Ghaghara and Yamuna rivers

Mean annual discharge: 16,650 cubic metres per second (587,989 cubic ft per second)

Countries: India, Bangladesh

Cities: Lucknow, Allahabad, Patna, Kanpur, Kolkata and Varanasi

The river officially begins at Devprayag in the Indian state of Uttarakhand, at the confluence of the Bhagirathi and Alaknanda rivers. It flows first through a narrow Himalayan valley before emerging from the mountains at Rishikesh and then debouching onto the broad Gangetic Plain at the sacred pilgrimage town of Haridwar in northern India. Here, a dam diverts some of the river's flow into the Ganges Canal, which irrigates the Doab region of Uttar Pradesh. As it flows across the plain, it's joined by the Yamuna River, which also rises in the Himalaya. At the confluence, the Yamuna is actually the larger river, contributing almost 60 per cent of the combined flow. Several more tributaries soon join from Nepal, greatly swelling the Ganges' flow.

After the river enters Bangladesh, it's joined by the Brahmaputra and becomes known as the Padma. The Padma is then joined by the Jamuna and Meghna rivers, and the converged flow takes on the Meghna's name as it enters its delta. After flowing through the delta in a complex collection of innumerable channels – the largest of which is known as the Meghna estuary – the river finally empties into the Bay of Bengal.

Stretching 400 km (248 miles) along the bay, and with an area of about 64,000 sq km (24,719 sq miles), the Meghna/Ganges-Brahmaputra Delta is the world's largest. On the eastern, seaward side of the delta, the deposition of silt leads to the rapid development of new areas of the mainland, known as chars, and new islands. During the monsoon, most of the region lies under at least a metre of water. Consequently, local villages and homesteads are built on artificially raised land.

Along the seaward side of the delta lies a vast stretch of tidal mangrove forests and swamps known as the Sundarbans. Criss-crossed by a network of rivers, canals and creeks with widths that vary from a few metres to several kilometres, the mangrove forest is the world's largest, covering an area of about 10,000 sq km (3,861 sq miles). Much of the area is protected and it supports a population of about 180 endangered Bengal tigers, as well as some 290 bird, 120 fish, 42 mammal, 35 reptile and eight amphibian species.

Where the Meghna enters the Bay of Bengal, the combined rivers' sediment has formed the Bengal Fan, the world's largest submarine fan – an underwater geological formation composed of silt deposits. Covering an area of roughly 1,430 x 3,000 km (888 x 1,864 miles), with a maximum thickness of 16.5 km (10 miles), it's thought to contain as much as a fifth of the world's store of buried organic carbon. The sediment has been accumulating for at least 20 million years.

The Ganges is arguably the most religiously important of all the world's rivers, revered by Hindus as *Ganga Maiya* (Mother Ganga). Thanks to the sustenance provided by its waters and its fertile silt, the river became associated with fecundity early in ancient Indian culture and was imbued with magical qualities.

The Sundarbans host the world's largest single block of mangroves.

As early as the 5th century CE, the Ganges had become a goddess in her own right, revered in anthropomorphic form and surrounded by an elaborate mythology.

The Ganges is sacred to Hindus along its entire length. They believe that casting the ashes of the dead into the river confers salvation upon the deceased and direct passage to heaven. Consequently, ghats, temples that sit atop riverside steps and are used either for bathing in the river or as sites for cremation of the dead, punctuate the banks of the Ganges along much of its length (within the city of Varanasi alone, there are 88 ghats). Bathing Hindus pay homage to their ancestors and to the gods by cupping water in their hands, lifting it and releasing it so that falls back into the river. Floral offerings floating in shallow clay dishes filled with oil and lit with wicks are regularly cast off into the river.

Pilgrimage to sacred sites along the Ganges plays a central role in Hinduism. The most sacred of all the pilgrimages is the Kumbh Mela. Held four times every 12 years at four different sites, and attended by thousands of holy men and women, and tens of millions of other devotees, the mela is the largest gathering of people in the world.

Main image: *Ghats line the banks of the Ganges in Varanasi, India.*

'The Ganga is the river of India, beloved of her people, round which are intertwined her racial memories, her hopes and fears, her songs of triumph, her victories and her defeats. She has been a symbol of India's age-long culture and civilization, ever-changing, ever-flowing and yet ever the same Ganga.'

– From the will of Indian nationalist leader Jawaharlal Nehru

In Hindu culture, the waters of the Ganges are both pure and purifying, believed to reclaim order from disorder. Moving water is said to absorb spiritual impurities and take them away. Hence the swiftly moving waters of the Ganges' upper reaches, where bathers must hold tightly to anchored chains to avoid being swept away, are considered to be particularly purifying.

Sadly, in reality, the river's water is far from pure. The Ganges basin is among the world's most densely inhabited regions, hosting hundreds of millions of people; today, the sacred waters of the Ganges are so polluted that they represent a severe health risk to those who bathe in them. Varanasi is home to about a million people and the city releases roughly 200 million litres (44 million gallons) of untreated human sewage into the river each day in 32 separate streams. Before the river even reaches Varanasi, levels of faecal coliform bacteria from human waste are more than 100 times the Indian government's official limit. Downstream, levels can rise to 25,000 times the official limit.

The river is also a dumping ground for industrial waste, agricultural runoff, the remnants of partially burned or unburned bodies from funeral pyres, religious offerings wrapped in non-degradable plastic and animal carcasses. In the past, un-cremated bodies were thrown into the Ganges in their thousands during cholera epidemics, causing the disease to spread even more widely. Each year, about two-thirds of those who use the river's waters for bathing and other domestic uses develop water-borne and enteric diseases including cholera, dysentery, hepatitis A and typhoid. Rates of cancer among those who live along the river's banks are also higher than those in other parts of India. Estimates suggest that cleaning up the river would require an investment of at least US$1.5 billion.

The Gangetic Plain, which extends over an area of some 700,000 sq km (270,271 sq miles), has acted as the cradle of several empires, from the Mauryan empire of Ashoka in the 3rd century BCE to the 16th century Mughal Empire, and many former imperial capitals are located on its banks and the banks of its tributaries. The plain's alluvial mantle, which may only be about 10,000 years old, is more than 1.8 km (1 mile) thick in places. This fertile soil has been instrumental to the agricultural economies of both India and Bangladesh. The Ganges basin has long been intensively cultivated, and although the forests of the lower Gangetic Plain remained largely intact until the early 20th century, today little of the original natural vegetation remains. The plain is extremely flat – over the final 1,600 km (994 miles) of its course, the river's elevation only drops by a little more than 200 m (656 ft) – so the river flows slowly.

Despite its importance, the Ganges is relatively short compared to the world's other great rivers. For most of its course, it is wide and sluggish, but the Ganges-Brahmaputra-Meghna system still has the third-largest discharge of the world's rivers and the combined sediment load, amounting to some 1.8 billion tonnes (1.77 billion tons) per year, is the world's highest.

The river's flow is highly seasonal. From April to June, it is fed by snow melting in the Himalaya; however, its flow is primarily governed by the vagaries of the Southwest Monsoon. About 85 per cent of the total rainfall across the river basin falls during the monsoon, from July to September, and the flow then is about six times greater than it is during the dry season. At this time, powerful tropical cyclones that sweep in from the Bay of Bengal can bring further torrential rain (as well as causing widespread devastation; in November 1970, some 500,000 people lost their lives as a result of one such storm). This strong seasonal variation can result in both drought and floods, particularly in Bangladesh.

Although the hydroelectric potential of the Ganges and its tributaries is huge – as much as 129,000 MW, 40 per cent in India and the remainder in Nepal – it has been little exploited. However, there are hydroelectric developments on several of the river's tributaries.

Use of the Ganges' water for irrigation, either when the river is in flood or by means of gravity canals, dates back more than 2,000 years, and dams and canals were common across the Gangetic Plain by the 4th century BCE. From the 12th century onward, during the period of Muslim rule, it was developed further, with the Mughal kings later constructing numerous canals. The British further extended the canal system. At the time of its opening in 1854, the Ganges Canal was the largest canal ever built. Today, the Upper and Lower Ganga canals and their branches have a combined length of almost 18,000 km (11,185 miles).

For thousands of years, the Ganges acted as an important transportation route. However, large-scale water transport began to decline during the mid-19th century as the increasing abstraction of water for irrigation affected navigation and the burgeoning railway

network took over the heavy lifting. Today, river traffic is mostly insignificant outside West Bengal and Bangladesh, which continue to transport jute, tea, grain and other agricultural and rural products on the waterways.

The Farakka Barrage, located at the head of the delta, just before the border with Bangladesh, diverts half of the river's flow into a feeder canal linked to the Hooghly River in order to keep the water relatively silt-free and thus restore navigability at the port of Kolkata. Completed in 1975, the barrage sparked a water-sharing dispute between India and East Pakistan (now Bangladesh) some 14 years earlier when India released its plans for the project. The dispute was ultimately resolved in December 1996 with the signing of the 30-year Indo-Bangladesh Ganges Water Treaty.

Abstraction is increasingly leading to water shortages and parts of the river now dry up completely. In March 1997, the river's flow in Bangladesh dropped to its lowest-ever level: just 180 cubic metres per second (6,357 cubic ft per second). The river's level is also dropping: around Varanasi, the average depth was once 60 m (197 ft), but in places it may now reach only 10 m (33 ft).

Main image: *The Ganges flows beneath Lakshman Jhula bridge, overlooked by the 13-storey Tera Manzil Temple at Rishikesh in Uttarakhand, India.*

Right: *A painting of an evening concert from the Mughal period, c. 1650–70.*

The Indus River

One of Asia's most important rivers, the Indus has aided the rise of a number of great cultures.

Flowing through the driest and hottest part of the Indian subcontinent, the Indus River acted as a lifeline for several major civilizations and is, today, a critical factor in the lives and economies of more than 260 million people in Pakistan, India and Afghanistan, supporting one of the world's largest irrigation systems. However, there are fears for the river's future in a warming world.

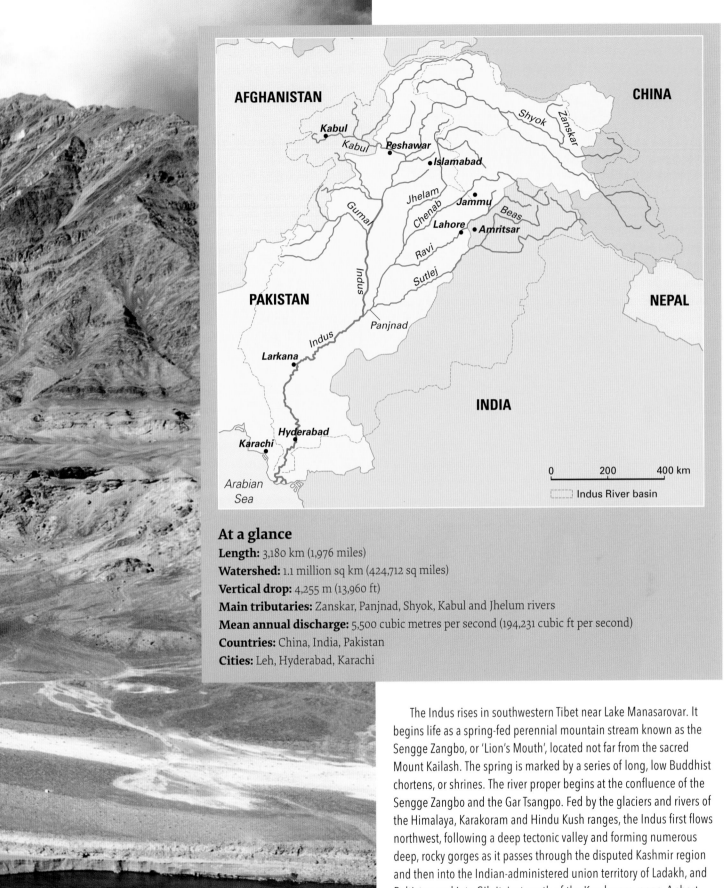

At a glance

Length: 3,180 km (1,976 miles)

Watershed: 1.1 million sq km (424,712 sq miles)

Vertical drop: 4,255 m (13,960 ft)

Main tributaries: Zanskar, Panjnad, Shyok, Kabul and Jhelum rivers

Mean annual discharge: 5,500 cubic metres per second (194,231 cubic ft per second)

Countries: China, India, Pakistan

Cities: Leh, Hyderabad, Karachi

The Indus rises in southwestern Tibet near Lake Manasarovar. It begins life as a spring-fed perennial mountain stream known as the Sengge Zangbo, or 'Lion's Mouth', located not far from the sacred Mount Kailash. The spring is marked by a series of long, low Buddhist chortens, or shrines. The river proper begins at the confluence of the Sengge Zangbo and the Gar Tsangpo. Fed by the glaciers and rivers of the Himalaya, Karakoram and Hindu Kush ranges, the Indus first flows northwest, following a deep tectonic valley and forming numerous deep, rocky gorges as it passes through the disputed Kashmir region and then into the Indian-administered union territory of Ladakh, and Baltistan and into Gilgit, just south of the Karakoram range. A short distance beyond Leh, the river is bolstered by the inflow from the Zanskar River, which actually has a greater volume of water than the Indus itself before that point.

The river then gradually bends to the south and, after cutting across the Salt Range near Kalabagh, it enters the Punjab plain, the northern part of the Indo-Gangetic plain. As the river moves slowly across the sandy plain, much of the sediment it's carrying is deposited on its bed, causing it to rise above the level of the adjacent land. Here it receives its most notable tributaries – the five rivers that give the Punjab its name ('Land of Five Rivers'). Their input swells the river, which can be several kilometres wide during the flood season (July–September). As it flows across the plains, the river becomes slow and highly braided before splitting into multiple distributaries as it enters its delta to the south of Thatta in Pakistan's Sindh province.

The delta, which covers an area of about 7,800 sq km (3,012 sq miles) and extends along the coast for about 210 km (130 miles), is criss-crossed by a network of active and abandoned channels. The river eventually empties into the Arabian Sea near the port city of Karachi, where it has formed the Indus submarine fan, the second-largest sediment body on earth, consisting of about 5 million cubic km (1.2 million cubic miles) of material eroded from the Karakoram in northern Pakistan and India, and the Himalaya, mostly by the large rivers of the Punjab.

From its source to its mouth, the Indus passes from freezing high-mountain regions where coniferous trees abound and most precipitation falls as snow down to arid semi-desert areas dominated by thorny acacia forests and sand in India's Sindh and Punjab provinces.

Some 45 million years ago, sand and silt from Tibet were being deposited in the Arabian Sea, implying that, at that time, an ancient Indus River was already flowing. Archaeological evidence suggests that humans began to settle along the river about 17,000 years ago. More recently, the river has seen the rise and fall of numerous civilizations and empires. During the 3rd millennium BCE, the Indus Valley Civilization, a major Bronze Age urban culture, arose along the river, eventually expanding to cover an area from northeast Afghanistan to Pakistan and northwest India, and featuring the great cities of Harappa and Mohenjodaro, which were among the largest human settlements of the ancient world. The civilization had its roots in irrigated agriculture and is believed to have been the first to domesticate cotton – and to spin and weave it. It's believed that the civilization's end was brought about either by a shift in the course of the Indus or a prolonged drought that slowly destroyed its irrigation systems.

The Indus's lower basin forms a natural boundary between the Iranian Plateau and the Indian subcontinent and, consequently, the river has witnessed numerous military incursions over the centuries. During the 6th century BCE, during the reigns of Cyrus the Great and Darius the Great, the Persian Achaemenid Empire became the first West Eurasian empire to annex the Indus Valley. Darius commissioned the Greek explorer Scylax of Caryanda to explore the river's course.

In 326 BCE, Alexander the Great crossed the river with his marauding Macedonian army, but after conquering the peoples living on the western bank he brought his Asian campaign to an end. Later, between the 8th and 16th centuries, the Muslim armies of Muhammad bin Qasim, Mahmud of Ghazni, Mohammed Ghori, Tamerlane and Babur all crossed the river and made incursions of varying distances and durations into the Indian subcontinent.

The Indus Valley is the birthplace of Hinduism and the Indus is one of the seven rivers considered to be sacred by Hindus. The word 'Hindu' itself is derived from the Sanskrit word for river, *sindhu*, which was also originally used as the name for the Indus River.

Since time immemorial, the Indus's waters have supported agriculture on the Indian subcontinent. The scarcity of rainfall in the lower Indus valley prompted the people of the Indus Valley Civilization to begin constructing irrigation canals, work that was continued by the engineers of the Kushan and Mughal empires. This

Left: A woman with two bulls from the late Harappan civilization, c. 2000–1750 BCE.

Opposite: *The Indus, surrounded by the mountains and foothills of the Karakoram in Pakistan.*

The Indus River and the irrigation system surrounding it allows for extensive agriculture in a region with limited rainfall.

network was made up of so-called inundation canals, which functioned only during periods of high river flow.

In 1850, the British East India Company began a stupendous irrigation project, building new canals and restoring old ones, eventually building one of the most extensive and complex irrigation networks in the world, helping to turn desert into fields in which sugarcane, wheat, cotton and rice are the major crops under cultivation. However, agricultural production is regularly disrupted by sediment clogging up poorly maintained canals.

The creation of Pakistan through the partition of British India in 1947 cut the irrigation system of the Bari Doab and the Sutlej Valley Project – originally designed as one scheme – into two parts, with the headwork in India and the canals in Pakistan, leading to a disruption in the water supply in some parts of Pakistan. The ensuing dispute was finally resolved in 1960 with the signing of the Indus Waters Treaty, which assigned the flow of the three western rivers of the Indus basin (the Indus, Jhelum and Chenab) to Pakistan and the flow of the three eastern rivers (the Ravi, Beas and Sutlej) to India.

Today, the Indus is Pakistan's primary freshwater source and the river's waters are key to the country's economy. Pakistan possesses the world's largest contiguous irrigation system and the river contributes towards a quarter of its GDP, providing water for almost 90 per cent of its food production, particularly in Punjab province, the country's breadbasket. The river also supports numerous heavy industries and provides most of Pakistan's potable water. Factories on the river's banks, agricultural drainage water and untreated sewage from Karachi and Lahore (which can amount to some 3 million cubic metres/106 million cubic ft per day) all contribute to its pollution and lead to the spread of numerous water-borne diseases in downstream areas.

The river has a prodigious flow - roughly twice that of the Nile and three times that of the combined Tigris and Euphrates rivers. It's largely fed by melting snow and glaciers in the great mountain ranges of the Himalaya, Karakoram and Hindu Kush; hence its flow diminishes significantly in winter (December–February). However, it regularly breaches its banks during the monsoon months (July–September) and devastating flash floods periodically sweep down from the mountains, the result of intense rainfall, mostly during summer storms. Very little water is added in the plains and the river's volume decreases considerably here due to evaporation and seepage.

Over the past 20 years, the construction of hundreds of kilometres of levees has seen the river aggrade rapidly, leading to breaches of barrages and inundation of large areas upstream. The various dams and barrages constructed on the river - not to mention abstraction for agriculture, notably cotton cultivation; estimates suggest that 97 per cent of the river's water goes towards producing crops - have also reduced its flow considerably, from an original average of about 180 billion cubic metres (6,357 billion cubic ft) to about 33 billion cubic metres (1,165 billion cubic ft) today. It has also reduced the amount of sediment that reaches the delta, from some 400 million tonnes (394 million tons) per year to about 100 million tonnes (98 million tons).

The Indus is a critical water source for millions of people in India and Pakistan, both for agriculture and drinking water. The basin of the Upper Indus contains the greatest area of perennial glacial ice outside of the polar regions - some 22,000 sq km (8,494 sq miles) and more than 7,000 known glaciers - and the area of winter snow cover is an order of magnitude greater. This ice and snow plays a central role in regulating the river's flow, acting as a natural storage reservoir during winter and then releasing meltwater in spring and summer; about half of the river's flow is derived from glacial melt. Global warming has led to an increase in flow as glacial melting has picked up pace, but there are fears for the future as the glaciers shrink.

Sukkur Barrage in Pakistan's Sindh province, built during the British Raj between 1923 and 1932, feeds water from the Indus into seven irrigation canals with a combined length of 9,923 km (6,166 mi).

The Irrawaddy River

Myanmar's largest river and most important commercial waterway, the Irrawaddy River flows through the country's historical, cultural and economic heartland.

Neatly bisecting Myanmar from north to south, the Irrawaddy (or, officially, Ayeyarwady) River has been the region's central artery, along which culture and commerce have flowed, since time immemorial. Navigable for most of its length, the river has long served as the country's major transportation route for communication, trade and warfare. Before colonization by Britain, it acted as the principal axis of the old Myanmar kingdom, thus shaping the country's history, settlement patterns and economic development. Control of the river

equated to power in the region as it was the key conduit for trade between China and India.

Civilization in the Irrawaddy valley is ancient – by 3,500 years ago, its inhabitants were farming rice, raising livestock and using bronze implements. When the Bamar, the ancestors of today's Burmese, arrived around the 7th century, they used the Irrawaddy to spread out onto the Kyaukse plain, where they began to cultivate rice, while also using the river to gain regional power through trade and transport on the

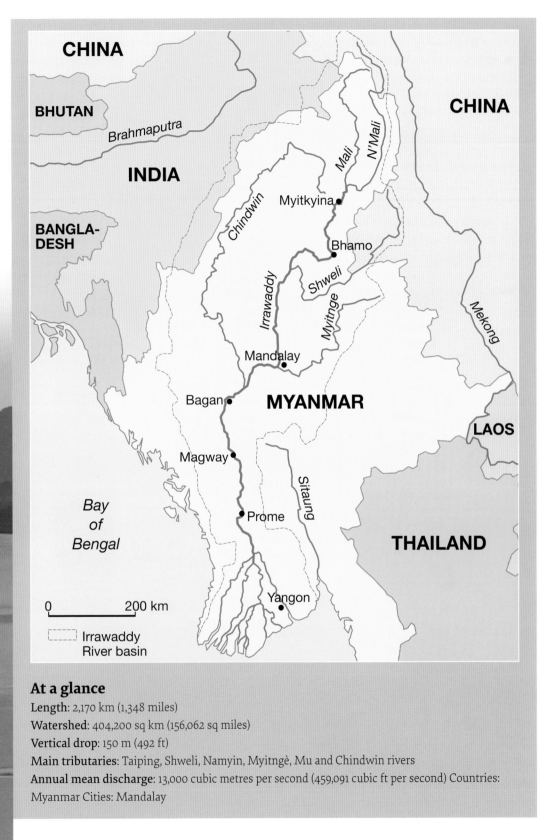

At a glance

Length: 2,170 km (1,348 miles)
Watershed: 404,200 sq km (156,062 sq miles)
Vertical drop: 150 m (492 ft)
Main tributaries: Taiping, Shweli, Namyin, Myitngè, Mu and Chindwin rivers
Annual mean discharge: 13,000 cubic metres per second (459,091 cubic ft per second) Countries: Myanmar Cities: Mandalay

China–India route. Having fortified the town of Pagan, located on a bend in the Irrawaddy about 290 km (180 miles) southwest of Mandalay, they formed the Pagan Empire, the first to unite the regions that would go on to constitute modern-day Myanmar, and eventually went on to build more than 10,000 religious monuments spread across 104 sq km (40 sq miles) of the Bagan plains.

During the 19th century, the Irrawaddy became a key part of Britain's imperial expansion into Asia. British traders began to set up trading ports along its banks, and after Britain annexed Lower Burma in

1855 it set about developing the port of Rangoon (now Yangon) and irrigation in the Irrawaddy Delta, whose rice exports eventually became vital to Britain's economic interests.

The Irrawaddy is sometimes referred to as the road to Mandalay, after Rudyard Kipling's famous poem of the same name, which alludes to its use as a transport conduit by British troops. In 1885, during the Third Anglo-Burmese War, some 9,000 British soldiers travelled upriver on rickety paddle steamers, requisitioned from the Irrawaddy Flotilla Company, to the combustible Burma–India border. On 1 January 1886, the British annexed the rest of Burma, which meant that it controlled shipping on the Irrawaddy and thus a direct trade route to China.

The Irrawaddy Flotilla Company, which began operating in Burma in 1865, monopolized inland river trade and passenger transport during the colonial period, at one time running the world's largest fleet of river vessels. Unlike on many other great riverine systems, the construction of railways in Burma during the second half of the 19th century didn't put the river steamers out of business, but rather complemented them by connecting services and assisting with the transhipment of goods.

Renamed Inland Water Transport in 1989, the company still carries passengers along this mighty waterway, operating more than 600 vessels, transporting about 15 million passengers and 2 million tonnes (1.96 million tons) of cargo annually. Navigators are kept on their toes by constantly shifting sandbars – deep channels can silt up and disappear over the course of a single day – and ships regularly run aground and can become stranded for days at a time.

Main image: *Some of the more than 2,200 surviving temples and pagodas on Bagan Plain, with the Irrawaddy visible in the distance.*

Today, the river retains an extraordinary, timeless quality. Among simple bamboo houses thatched with coconut-palm fronds and perched on stilts, each with a teak dugout canoe slung beneath for when the summer monsoon turns dirt lanes into waterways, villagers thresh rice while bullock-drawn carts piled with fodder pass slowly in the distance. Every few kilometres, rambling teak Buddhist monasteries topped with gold-painted pagodas overlook the languid river, where fisher families cast fine nets into the brown water, picking out their silvery catch as they draw the nets back into their rickety wooden boats. Flotillas of small, brightly coloured cargo boats moored on the riverbank bob up and down as large rafts of teak logs – of which Myanmar is the world's major exporter – slowly float downstream.

A boat on the Irrawaddy near Mandalay.

The Irrawaddy dolphin

A beakless cetacean with a high, rounded forehead, the Irrawaddy dolphin has, for centuries, collaborated with cast-net fishermen, who summon them by tapping the gunwales of their wooden canoes. The dolphins drive teeming schools of baitfish towards the canoe and then pluck snacks from the nets after the fisherman has entrapped the fish. Sadly, pollution and electric-shock fishing have reduced the dolphin's numbers and, today, it's found in a few discontinuous sub-populations in rivers, estuaries and coastal waters in the Bay of Bengal and Southeast Asia; fewer than 80 remain in its namesake river.

The river begins in Myanmar's northern highlands near the border with China at the confluence of the N'mai and Mali rivers – both of which are fed by Himalayan glaciers – and eventually empties into the warm bath of the Andaman Sea through a vast, fertile delta.

In its upper reaches, the river is swift and narrow. Between Myitkyinā and Mandalay, it flows through three defiles (narrow passages or gorges) overlooked by sheer limestone cliffs. Here, the suddenly constrained river speeds up and forms strong currents, treacherous eddies and swirling whirlpools as it races around mid-stream rocks.

The second defile, where the river narrows to a dark ribbon of water, reduced to a width of just 90 m (295 ft) by tree-topped hills and imposing, precipitous walls up to 90 m (295 ft) high, is the most dramatic. Before entering the defile's most treacherous section, boat captains consult a red-and-green-painted rock shaped like a parrot's head. If the parrot drinks from the water, or worse still, if it isn't visible at all, they know that they must turn back.

For about 180 km (112 miles) between Katha (the town in which the writer George Orwell was stationed during his service as a colonial

Golden pagodas sit atop the hills of Sagaing, capital of the Sagaing Kingdom, which was established beside the Irrawaddy near Mandalay during the 14th century.

policeman) and the ancient capital of Mandalay, the river follows a remarkably straight north–south course as it follows the Sagaing Fault, where the Indian and Sunda tectonic plates meet. It only deviates near Kabwet, where the Singu Plateau, a sheet of lava measuring 62 sq km (24 sq miles) laid down during the Holocene period up to 11,700 years ago, forces it to bend sharply westward.

The river leaves the plateau through the third defile at Kyauk Myaung, and then follows a broad, open, braided course across the alluvial flats of Myanmar's densely populated central 'dry zone' – the country's ancient cultural heartland – its banks sometimes more than 6 km (3.7 miles) apart. Between Mandalay and the ancient city of Pagan, the ruins of several old Burmese capitals, including Mingyun, Sagaing and Amarapura, line the banks. The temples of Pagan itself are visible from the river for more than 30 km (19 miles).

The Irrawaddy Delta begins about 93 km (58 miles) above Hinthada and extends for some 290 km (180 miles). As it flows into the delta, the river splits into nine main channels. The port of Yangon, Myanmar's former capital, is situated on the left bank of the delta's easternmost distributary, the Yangon River. Remarkably flat (much of it below 5 m/16 ft in elevation), the 35,000-sq-km (13,514 sq mile) delta is among Myanmar's most densely populated regions, home to more than seven million people, who mostly live in small farming and fishing communities, and market towns. On 2 May 2008, Cyclone Nargis battered the delta, causing a 3.7-m (12 ft) storm surge and killing at least 135,000 people and leaving another 2.5 million homeless.

The river basin experiences a humid tropical/subtropical climate, dominated by the South Asian summer monsoon, which brings heavy rains between May and October. The rapid melting of snow and glaciers in northern Myanmar during summer (March–May) also leads to a large influx of water. Consequently, the river's level exhibits significant seasonal variation – in places by as much as 11 m (36 ft) or more – making it necessary for ports along its length to have separate landing areas for low and high water. During the wet season, the river may resemble a vast, chocolate-brown lake; during the dry season, its level may drop so low that its bed looks like a desert of white sand dunes. Erosion of the riverbanks sometimes causes whole villages to collapse into the river and be swallowed up by the swirling brown water.

In May 2007, Myanmar's military junta signed an agreement with the China Power Investment Corporation for the construction of seven hydroelectric dams along the Irrawaddy, Mali and N'Mai rivers, with a combined capacity of 15,160 MW. The government hopes to export much of the power, mostly to China. The Myitsone Dam, due to be situated at the very start of the Irrawaddy, where the Mali and N'mai rivers join, has been particularly controversial. Flooding behind the dam wall is expected to affect an area of more than 750 sq km (290 sq miles) and force the evacuation of at least 47 villages. The dam is also located less than 100 km (62 miles) from the Sagaing Fault, a particularly active strike-slip geological fault, raising concerns about the likelihood of earthquakes.

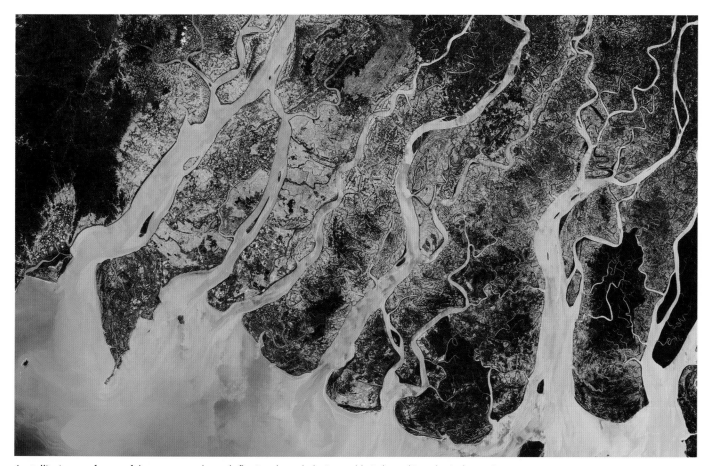

A satellite image of some of the numerous channels flowing through the Irrawaddy Delta and into the Andaman Sea.

The Jordan River

Flowing roughly north-south through the Middle East, the Jordan has long been an epicentre for both world religion and regional conflict

Flowing through the barren, desolate region that spawned several of the world's major religions, a land that has been mired in territorial conflict for thousands of years, the Jordan River's cultural, spiritual and political importance bely its relatively short length.

The river holds great significance to the three Abrahamic religions. According to the Bible, after years of wandering in the desert, the Israelites under Joshua crossed the river on dry ground near Jericho, entering the Promised Land while carrying the Ark of the Covenant. It's also said to be where John the Baptist anointed Jesus, and the Sea of Galilee (Lake Tiberius), through which the river flows, is where Jesus is said to have walked on water.

At a glance

Length: 360 km (224 miles)

Watershed: 18,500 sq km (7,143 sq miles)

Vertical drop: 950 m (3,117 ft)

Main tributaries: Baniyas, Dan, Jabbok, Hasbani and Yarmouk rivers

Mean annual discharge: 2 cubic metres per second (71 cubic ft per second)

Countries: Jordan, Israel, Syria, Palestine, Lebanon

Cities: Jericho

Many scholars have concluded that Jesus' baptism took place on the Jordanian side of the river, where the ruins of Al-Maghtas now stand. While along much of the river's length, water quality has deteriorated significantly due to a combination of high salinity, agricultural run-off and untreated wastewater, a small section of its lower reaches – the first 3 km (1.9 miles) or so below the Sea of Galilee – is kept as clean as possible to support local tourism and allow baptisms to take place.

The Jordan has three principal sources – the Ḥāṣbānī, Bāniyās and Dan rivers – all of which rise at the foot of Mount Hermon, which straddles the border between Syria and Lebanon. The three rivers come together in the Ḥula Valley, just inside Israel, in an area that was once occupied by a lake and marshes but was drained during the 1950s to create agricultural land. From here, the river drops quickly as it flows 75 km (47 miles) to Lake Hula, once an extensive water body surrounded by swamps but now much diminished.

At the Hula Valley's southern end, the river has cut a gorge through a barrier of basalt and from here it descends even more steeply as it travels 25 km (15.5 miles) before entering the northern end of the Sea of Galilee, where it drops much of the silt that it has been carrying. After leaving the lake, the river enters what is commonly referred to

Pilgrims being baptized in the Jordan River at Qasr el Yahud (Castle or Tower of the Jews), believed to be the site where Jesus was baptised by John the Baptist.

as the Jordan Valley. Part of the extensive East African Rift System, the valley is a long, narrow trough with an average width of about 10 km (6 miles) and sheer walls that rise up to 1,700 m (5,577 ft) from the valley floor and are broken only by the gorges of tributary wadis – seasonal watercourses that only run following heavy rain. Here the river meanders so extensively that its length is some 215 km (134 miles) compared to an as-the-crow-flies distance of only 105 km (65 miles).

At the valley's lower end lies the river's floodplain, known as the Zūr (or Zhor). The Zūr floods frequently and was once covered with thickets of reeds, tamarisk, willows and white poplars, but the land has since been converted to irrigated fields. The river only drops 210 m (689 ft) here, meandering languidly as it passes through a broad, gently sloping delta.

The Jordan has the lowest elevation of any of the world's rivers. It lies within an endorheic basin – that is, it doesn't have an external outlet – what's left of its flow eventually emptying into the Dead Sea, which, at 422 m (1,384 ft) below sea level, is the lowest land point on earth.

North of the Sea of Galilee, the river is within Israel, where it forms the western boundary of the Golan Heights; to the south, it acts as the border between Israel and the Israeli-occupied West Bank, and the

Kingdom of Jordan (both Jordan and the West Bank take their names from the river). After 1948, the river's eastern bank, from just south of the Sea of Galilee to the point where the Yābis River flows into it, formed the border between Israel and Jordan. However, since the Six-Day War in 1967, when Israeli forces occupied the West Bank, the Jordan has served as the cease-fire line as far south as the Dead Sea.

A mixture of groundwater (springs) and rain falling on the neighbouring plateaus feed the river, whose current is relatively swift; however, the high rate of evaporation and the seeping away of water through the river's porous bed diminish the natural rate of flow in its lower reaches. The river itself is relatively shallow; in places it resembles a creek – less than 10 m (33 ft) across and 2 m (6.6 ft) deep. This fact, combined with its precipitous upper course and the large seasonal fluctuations in its flow, make it effectively unnavigable.

Today, the river's flow is much diminished; some 70–90 per cent of its water is used for human purposes. Where once it discharged 1.3 billion cubic metres (46 billion cubic ft) of water into the Dead Sea each year, as of 2013 that amount was just 20–200 million cubic metres (706–7,063 million cubic ft) per year. Consequently, the Dead Sea, which has an extremely high

At more than 200 m (656 ft) below sea level, the Sea of Galilee, through which the Jordan River flows, is the world's lowest freshwater lake.

evaporation rate, exacerbated by the presence of evaporation ponds for the industrial extraction of salts, is rapidly shrinking.

Much of the abstracted water is used for irrigation, which has brought agriculture to the arid, desolate landscapes of the Jordan Valley, which is dotted with Arab and Jewish farming settlements. Overall, the total irrigated area within the river basin is about 100,000–150,000 ha (247,105–370,659 acres). A canal from the Sea of Galilee to Bet She`an enables the pumping of 320 million cubic metres (11.3 billion cubic ft) of the Jordan's waters to central and southern Israel each year, while the 69-km-long (43 miles) East Ghor irrigation canal, completed in 1967, enables the cultivation of oranges, bananas, vegetables and sugar beets on the Jordanian side of the valley. The rocks in the region have a high concentration of gypsum, which makes the water salty, which can have a detrimental effect on the soil when the water is used for irrigation.

Share and share alike

The question of water sharing in the Jordan River basin is inextricably linked to the ongoing conflicts between Israel and its neighbours, and threatens to inflame existing regional tensions. Conflict over the river's water contributed to the outbreak of the Six-Day War, when, in 1965, Syria began to try to divert some of its headwaters in collaboration with Lebanon and Jordan, potentially cutting Israel's overall water supply by about 11 per cent.

Syrian artillery on the Golan Heights during the Six-Day War.

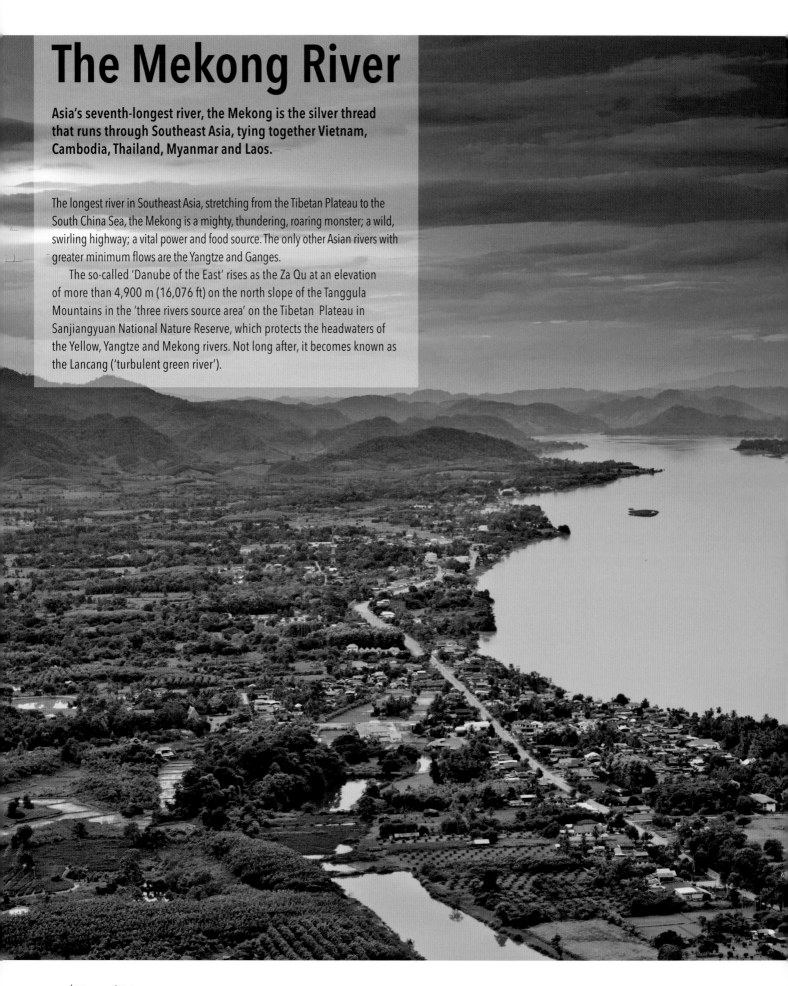

The Mekong River

Asia's seventh-longest river, the Mekong is the silver thread that runs through Southeast Asia, tying together Vietnam, Cambodia, Thailand, Myanmar and Laos.

The longest river in Southeast Asia, stretching from the Tibetan Plateau to the South China Sea, the Mekong is a mighty, thundering, roaring monster; a wild, swirling highway; a vital power and food source. The only other Asian rivers with greater minimum flows are the Yangtze and Ganges.

The so-called 'Danube of the East' rises as the Za Qu at an elevation of more than 4,900 m (16,076 ft) on the north slope of the Tanggula Mountains in the 'three rivers source area' on the Tibetan Plateau in Sanjiangyuan National Nature Reserve, which protects the headwaters of the Yellow, Yangtze and Mekong rivers. Not long after, it becomes known as the Lancang ('turbulent green river').

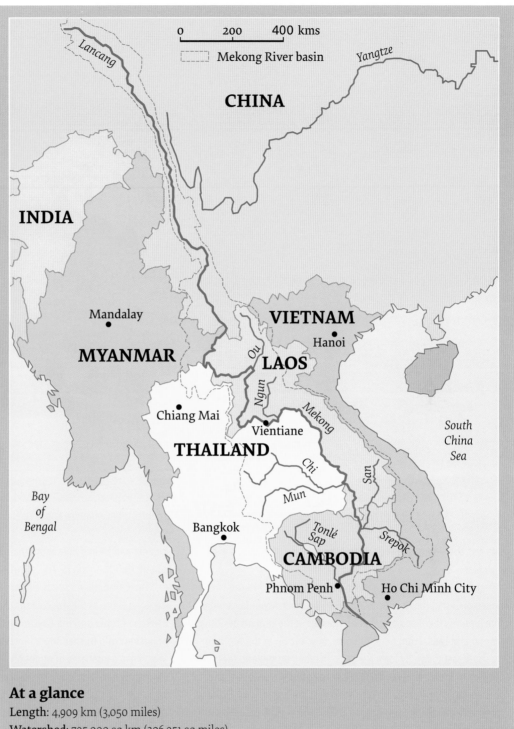

At a glance

Length: 4,909 km (3,050 miles)

Watershed: 795,000 sq km (306,951 sq miles)

Vertical drop: 4,900 m (16,076 ft)

Main tributaries: Tha, Ou, Ngum, Songkhram, Mun, Kading, Bangfai, Banghiang and Kong rivers

Mean annual discharge: 14,500 cubic metres per second (512,063 cubic ft per second)

Countries: China, Myanmar, Laos, Thailand, Cambodia and Vietnam

Cities: Vientiane, Phnom Penh, Ho Chi Minh City

In its upper reaches, the river drops 4,500 m (14,764 ft) in 2,200 km (1,367 miles). Here the basin is steep and narrow, and heavy rainfall causes substantial soil erosion, feeding the river with about half of its total sediment load. Thanks to the driving, turbulent flow, the streambed has cut deeply into the rugged landscape and the river is confined by narrow, deep gorges before the valley eventually

Stretching 10,783 m (35,376 ft) across the Mekong River in southern Laos, near the border with Cambodia, Khone Falls is the world's widest waterfall.

opens out, the floodplain widens and the river itself becomes wider and slower.

After flowing through the eastern part of Tibet and through Yunnan province in China, the river briefly marks the China–Myanmar border before it enters the notorious Golden Triangle at the tripoint of China, Myanmar and Laos. From here, the river, now known as the Mekong, turns southeast to briefly form the Laos–Thailand border and then southwest to form the Myanmar–Laos border. It then turns east and flows into the interior of Laos. When it meets the border with Thailand, it once more defines the frontier for some 850 km (528 miles) before entering Laos again.

The river crosses into Cambodia with a sudden plunge at Khone Falls. Stretching almost 11 km (6.8 miles) from one edge of their multiple channels to the other, the falls are the world's widest. They are located just downstream from an extensive archipelago of riverine islands known as Si Phan Don ('Four Thousand Islands'), half of which are submerged when the Mekong is in flood.

From Cambodia on, the terrain through which the river passes is generally flat and the river becomes more gentle. At Phnom Penh, the Sab River and lake system of Tonlé Sap join the Mekong on its right bank. When water levels in the Mekong are low, the Sab acts as a tributary, but when the Mekong floods, the flow reverses and the lake

can expand from a little more than 2,600 sq km (1,004 sq miles) to about 15,000 sq km (5,792 sq miles).

The Cambodian capital, Phnom Penh, marks the beginning of the Mekong Delta as the main channel divides first into two branches – the Mekong proper and the Bassac – just before both rivers enter Vietnam. They then split further into an increasing number of branches. The delta, which has a total area of about 65,000 sq km (25,096 sq miles) and is extremely flat, regularly experiences both drought and flood; during the rainy season, up to half is flooded. Crisscrossed by an elaborate system of canals, the delta is farmed intensively and little natural vegetation remains. In some delta towns, the river's waters host bustling floating markets where traders hawk fresh produce from bobbing boats.

In its upper reaches, the Mekong is fed largely by snow melting on the Tibetan Plateau, a volume of water sometimes described as the 'Yunnan component', which, even as far downstream as Kratie, makes up almost 30 per cent of the average dry season flow. In the lower basin, most of the river's flow comes from rainfall, which is strongly linked to the monsoon.

Between Chiang Saen, Thailand, and the capital of Laos, Vientiane, the river flows through forested mountains pockmarked by patches cleared for slash-and-burn agriculture, its hydrology dominated in both wet and dry seasons by the Yunnan Component. From Vientiane, the

Above: *Vietnamese Army troops in combat operations against Communist Viet Cong guerrillas in the marshy terrain of the Mekong Delta in 1961.*

Left: *The Mekong giant catfish, which is found only in the Mekong River, is one of the world's largest freshwater fish, capable of reaching a length of up to 3 m (9.8 ft) and a weight of up to 350 kg (770 lb).*

river's hydrology begins to change, as large left-bank tributaries begin to assert their influence. By the time the Mekong enters Cambodia near Kratie, more than 95 per cent of the flow from its tributaries has entered the river.

For much of its length, the Mekong flows through channels carved into the bedrock. There are only a few short stretches – around Vientiane and downstream from Kratie – where the river is free of the control exerted by the underlying rock and has been allowed to develop the alluvial stretches typical of mature rivers, such as meanders, oxbow lakes, cut-offs and wide floodplains.

The river played a pivotal role in the Vietnam War. It was used by the North Vietnamese army for transport and the resupply of troops fighting in the south in some of the war's fiercest battles, including the infamous Tet Offensive, which raged in the Mekong Delta after the North Vietnamese infiltrated from Cambodia. From 1965, the US Navy patrolled the delta's maze of channels in a fleet of small boats. During the 1970s, large quantities of explosives – in some cases entire barges loaded with military ordnance – were submerged in the section of the river that flows through Cambodia. Today, the material poses a risk to both fishermen and construction.

For thousands of years, small boats have been used to ferry goods and people among the numerous towns on the Mekong's banks. Today, smaller ocean-going vessels can sail upstream as far as Phnom Penh, but navigation further along the river is complicated by the presence of rapids and waterfalls, as well as the extreme seasonal variation in the river's flow; however, it still acts a major trade route between western China and Southeast Asia.

The Mekong boasts the highest biodiversity per hectare of any river, and no other river hosts as many species of very large fish, including the giant pangasius, giant barb and endemic Mekong giant catfish, all of which can grow to about 3 m (10 ft) in length and to a weight of 300 kg (661 lb), and the giant freshwater stingray, which can reach at least 5 m (16 ft) in length, with a 1.9-m (6.2 ft) wingspan.

The inland fisheries of the Mekong Basin are among the world's largest and most productive, with an estimated 2 million tonnes (1.96 million tons) of fish landed each year (about 15 per cent of the total global freshwater catch), together with about 2 million tonnes of farmed fish and almost 500,000 tonnes (492,103 tons) of other aquatic animals. The wild-capture fisheries alone have been valued at US$2 billion a year and are believed to employ some 40 million rural people – more than two-thirds of the rural population in the lower Mekong basin.

The Mekong is heavily dammed – mostly for hydropower generation – and many more dams are either under construction or in the planning stages; hydropower construction in the Mekong Basin is growing faster than in any other large river basin. China has constructed 11 hydropower dams along the mainstream in the Upper Mekong Basin, with another 11 dams, each with a production capacity of more than 100 MW, either planned or under construction.

The government of Laos has stated that its aim is to lift the nation out of poverty by making it 'the battery of Asia'. It has built two dams on the river's mainstream – exporting virtually all of the electricity they produce to Thailand and Cambodia – and plans to build nine more.

A fisherman casts his net as the sun rises over the Mekong.

The Ob River

Flowing through western Siberia, the Ob is one of Asia's greatest rivers.

The longest and westernmost of the three great Siberian rivers that flow into the Arctic Ocean, the Ob begins 25 km (15.5 miles) southwest of Biysk in the Altai Krai region at the confluence of the Biya and Katun rivers, which flow down from the Altai Mountains, near the border with Mongolia. Leaving the foothills of the Altai, the river flows in a zig-zag pattern, alternating between roughly west and roughly north before finally turning east and emptying into the ocean through the world's longest estuary, the 850-km (528 mile) Gulf of Ob, a forked indentation of the Kara Sea that separates the Yamal Peninsula from the Gyda Peninsula. The river delivers about 15 per cent of the freshwater that flows into the Arctic Ocean.

In its lower reaches, the Ob splits into braids as it crosses a vast floodplain, the world's second largest, before reforming as two main channels – the Great Ob and the Little Ob – which are themselves then reunited into a single stream that's up to 19 km (12 miles) wide and 40 m (131 ft) deep. And then, finally, the river splits again into two principal arms – the Khamanelsk Ob and the larger Nadym Ob – as it forms its delta.

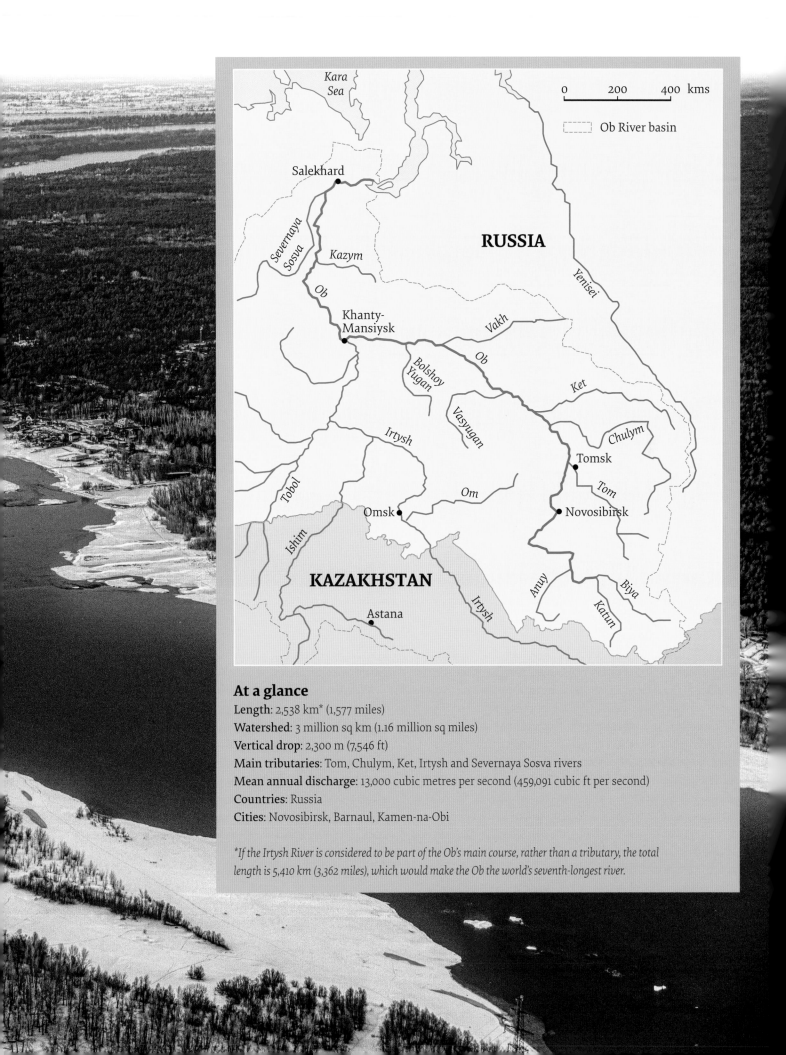

At a glance

Length: 2,538 km* (1,577 miles)

Watershed: 3 million sq km (1.16 million sq miles)

Vertical drop: 2,300 m (7,546 ft)

Main tributaries: Tom, Chulym, Ket, Irtysh and Severnaya Sosva rivers

Mean annual discharge: 13,000 cubic metres per second (459,091 cubic ft per second)

Countries: Russia

Cities: Novosibirsk, Barnaul, Kamen-na-Obi

*If the Irtysh River is considered to be part of the Ob's main course, rather than a tributary, the total
length is 5,410 km (3,362 miles), which would make the Ob the world's seventh-longest river.*

Founded on the right bank of the Ob in 1893, the Siberian city of Novosibirsk became a transport hub following the completion of a rail bridge over the river four years later.

The Ob basin hosts more than 1,900 rivers with an aggregate length of about 180,000 km (111,847 miles). Several ecological zones lie within the basin, ranging from semi-desert in the far south through steppe grassland, taiga (swampy coniferous forest), marshland and vast stretches of tundra in the north. In its middle reaches, it's often flanked by rich meadows that extend for several kilometres from the river's banks. The basin experiences short, warm summers, with temperatures soaring to as high as 40°C (104°F) in the arid south, and long, cold winters, during which temperatures can drop to below –30°C (–22°F) at the river's mouth and to –60°C (–76°F) in the Altai Mountains.

Unsurprisingly, given its location, the river is icebound for extended periods during winter. By the last week of November, the entire river is frozen. The thaw takes up most of May. The direction of the thaw is the same as the direction of the river's flow – south to north – frequently resulting in ice jams behind which the river, swelled by runoff from melted snow, builds up and sometimes breaks its banks.

The river and its gulf host more than 50 species of fish, with sturgeon, salmon and whitefish all spawning in the lower reaches. The Ob estuary represents one of the largest fisheries in the Russian Arctic; however, each winter, large numbers of fish are killed when the seasonal ice cover causes the depletion of oxygen in the water.

Modern humans are believed to have lived in the lower reaches of the Ob since the beginning of the Upper Palaeolithic, about 50,000 years ago. Today, most of the human population in the Ob basin is found along the river's valleys. The population density for the basin as a whole is only nine people per sq km, with most of those people concentrated in a few large cities clustered around the mineral wealth found beneath the river's southern watershed. Founded at the end of the 19th century, Novosibirsk, the largest city in Siberia and the third-largest in Russia, lies on the river's banks. It's here that the Trans-Siberian Railway crosses the Ob on a single-track bridge that opened in 1897.

The Ob has long been one of western Siberia's principal transportation arteries for both imports and exports, despite the fact that it's generally only navigable for about 190 days per year on its upper reaches and 150 days on its lower reaches. Since 1844, steamboats have navigated the Ob's middle reaches, but it wasn't until 1857 that steamboat shipping really started to develop in the Ob system. The river's importance diminished following the completion of the Trans-Siberian Railway, which was both more direct and more reliable, but together with the Irtysh – the Ob's chief tributary – it still acted as an important connection between remote regions and the major cities along the railway, including Novosibirsk and Omsk. Recently, navigation has been jeopardized by lower-than-average rainfall in the surrounding region, which has seen the river's depth drop to record lows.

Estimates place the Ob's hydroelectric potential at some 250 million megawatts. At present, there is only one large power station along its length, at Novosibirsk, and two on the Irtysh. In 1956, the building of the Novosibirskaya Dam to power the hydroelectric station led to the creation of the then-largest artificial lake in Siberia. Informally known as the Ob Sea, the reservoir is 160 km (99 miles) long and up to 22 km (14 miles) wide, and is a popular summer destination for Novosibirsk residents, who flock to its beaches and sail on its surface.

The Ob basin supports both agriculture – in the upper Ob valley, farmers grow grapes, melons and watermelons; and the steppe zone in the southern Ob basin is Russia's main producer of spring wheat – and industry; cities such as Omsk, Novosibirsk and Barnaul are all major industrial and manufacturing centres. The taiga and tundra zones of the middle and lower Ob host the largest and most important oil, coal and gas fields in Russia, contributing about two-thirds of the country's crude oil and natural gas output. The river represents an important means of transporting these raw materials.

Industrialization along the river has led to significant pollution of its waters. A combination of fallout from nuclear testing, poor storage of nuclear waste, the dumping of waste from weapons research and production, and a 1993 explosion at a nuclear power plant have resulted in what has been described as 'staggering' levels of radioactive contamination of the Ob and several of its tributaries. In June 2015, a leak in an oil pipeline blackened the river and contaminated tap water in the city of Nefteyugansk, while in March 2021 partially refined oil emerging from a burst underwater pipeline in a remote part of the Khanty-Mansiysk region caught fire on the ice of the frozen river.

A painting by Nikolai Nikolaevich Karazin shows Cossacks building a linear fortress on the Irtysh in the first half of the 17th century.

Soft gold

For centuries, the territory around the Ob was sparsely populated by nomadic peoples such as the Mansy, Khanty, Nenets and Samoyeds. By the late 1500s, after Russia's conquest of the khanate of Sibir, however, Russian trappers began to spread out across Siberia seeking the furs – 'soft gold' – of local mammals such as otters, foxes, beavers, ermine, mink and sable. At river junctions, the trappers and traders built fortified wooden stockades that eventually grew into towns and cities, such as Surgut, located on the Ob near the junction with the Irtysh, and Narym, near the Ob's confluence with the Ket River.

The Tigris River

The eastern of the two great rivers that define Mesopotamia, the Tigris has been a key source of irrigation, power and trade since the birth of some of the earliest-known civilizations.

Flowing through a parched region, one of the world's harshest environments, the Tigris River played a significant role in the growth of some of the earliest known civilizations by making the surrounding land both habitable and productive.

The river originates in Lake Hazer in the Taurus Mountains in eastern Turkey, about 30 km (19 miles) from the headwaters of the Euphrates. From here it flows 400 km (249 miles) across southeastern Turkey in a series of valleys and gorges before forming a section of the Syria–Turkey border 44 km (27 miles) long, the only part of the river that is located in Syria. After meandering its way through the Syrian and Arabian deserts on the plain of central Iraq, which it created with the Euphrates, it finally empties into the Persian Gulf downstream from Basra. Along the way, it passes through the centre of the Iraqi capital, Baghdad.

At a glance

Length: 1,750 km (1,087 miles)

Watershed: 472,000 sq km (182,240 sq miles)

Vertical drop: 1,150 m (3,773 m)

Main tributaries: Greater and Lesser Zab, Uzaym, Al-Adhaim, Diyala and Karkheh rivers

Mean annual discharge: 400 cubic metres per second (14,126 cubic ft per second)

Countries: Turkey, Syria, Iraq, Iran

Cities: Baghdad, Basrah, Mosul, Samarrah, Amarah

After rising in close proximity, the Tigris and Euphrates diverge significantly – near the Turkey–Syria border, they are separated by about 400 km (249 miles). They then gradually approach each other again in their middle courses, bounding a desert triangle known as Al-Jazīrah (Arabic for 'the Island') that sprawls over eastern Turkey, northern Iraq and northeastern Syria. Here the rivers have cut far down into the limestone bedrock, creating permanent channels that have undergone little change for millennia.

For much of its course, the Tigris flows roughly parallel with the Euphrates; according to historians, the two rivers once had separate outlets. Today, however, they join at Al-Qurnah in southeastern Iraq to form the Shatt al-Arab, which empties into the Persian Gulf. However, by then, seepage, evaporation and abstraction for irrigation have so diminished the rivers that they contribute only a small portion of the Shatt al-Arab's waters. The Shatt al-Arab is fringed by a narrow agricultural belt that represents the world's richest area of date palm cultivation.

At various points before they join, the rivers share their waters via both natural and man-made connections. For example, near Al-Fallūjah and Baghdad, the two rivers are only about 50 km (31 miles). During

The sun sets on a traditional reed house in the Mesopotamian marshes.

the Sāsānian period, five navigable canals linking them were built, allowing water from the Euphrates to flow into the Tigris. Similarly, at Qarmat ʿAlī, near Baṣrah, the main stream of the Tigris receives water from the Euphrates that has filtered through Lake Al-Ḥammār.

Just before the two rivers meet, the Tigris splits into several channels, a number of which feed the so-called Mesopotamian Marshes, an extensive area of wetlands that was traditionally home to the Maʿdān, otherwise known as the Marsh Arabs. Living in elaborate reed houses, the Maʿdān lived by fishing, hunting, cultivating rice and raising water buffalo. During the 20th century, upstream damming projects and deliberate draining of the wetlands by Saddam Hussein reduced the marshes to about 15 per cent of their original size. In recent years, though, more than half of the original area has been rehabilitated.

Despite their close proximity, the Tigris and Euphrates have quite different characters. Where they reach the Mesopotamian alluvial plain, the Tigris is the larger, faster, more silt-laden and less predictable of the pair; before modern dams began to alter the river's flow, estimates suggest that its mean annual discharge was 1,240 cubic metres per second (43,790 cubic ft per second) and its silt load was about one tonne per second – roughly twice the estimates for the Euphrates. Overall, the Tigris is shorter and carries more water and hence has a greater tendency to flood and to build natural levees. Being shorter than the Euphrates, the Tigris's annual flood period takes place a month earlier.

Oak, pistachio and ash forests once covered the mountains and foothills through which the upper Tigris passes. In the steppe zone to the south, most plants are ephemeral, bursting forth in the spring and then succumbing to the brutal heat of May and June; camel thorn and prosopis are among the only shrubs that can eke out a living in the driest areas. Among the most abundant plants, particularly in the marshes, are the narrow-leaved cattail and various types of reed. The giant mardi reed, which can reach a height of 8 m (26 ft), has been used for construction since antiquity. The Euphrates poplar and willow trees also grow in small belts beside the river; the former providing strong timber for construction and boat building. Date palms and liquorice grow in abundance, and tamarisk and mesquite thickets are common along the river's lower and middle courses.

Four strong tributaries – the Great Zab, Little Zab, ʿUẓaym and Diyālā rivers – all of which are mainly fed by snowmelt in the Taurus and Zagros mountains – feed the Tigris, their precipitous flow responsible for making the Tigris more susceptible to short-term flooding than the Euphrates; during March and April, floodwaters from the two Zab rivers double the Tigris's volume. Around Baghdad, the river is lined with artificial embankments, designed to reduce the risk of flooding.

When they are in flood, the two rivers may carry a combined silt load of as much as 3 million tonnes (2.95 million tons) per day. However, about 90 per cent of the water and silt that pass Baghdad and Al-Ramādī never reaches the gulf; the water either evaporates, is abstracted for irrigation or is absorbed in the marshes, while the silt

The kalak

The Tigris has long been an important transport route in a region dominated by desert. Shallow-draft vessels can travel as far as Baghdad, but only rafts can move farther upstream as far as Mosul. Traditionally, people travelling downstream on both the Tigris and Euphrates rivers would use a kalak – a raft made of the strongest reed or wood available and supported by several inflated goat skins tied beneath. Capable of carrying loads of up to 35 tonnes (34 tons), including people and donkeys, they could make the journey from Mosul to Baghdad in a few days. Upon arrival, the vessels were disassembled, the goods and timber sold, and the skins deflated and loaded on donkeys for the land-based return trip.

settles upstream from the Shatt al-Arab.

In their lower reaches, the Tigris and Euphrates form the boundary of the region known as Mesopotamia (Greek for 'land between the rivers'), part of the so-called Fertile Crescent, within which settled farming is believed to have first emerged. Considered to be the cradle of human civilization, from about 12,000 BCE, Mesopotamia witnessed some of the most pivotal developments in human history, including the invention of the wheel and glassmaking, the planting of the first cereal crops and the development of irrigation, writing, medicine, mathematics and astronomy. Several great civilizations and empires, including the Sumerians, Akkadians, Assyrians and Babylonians arose in Mesopotamia, and many of the great cities of antiquity, many of them imperial capitals, stood on or near the Tigris, including Nineveh, Calah, Ashur, Ctesiphon and Seleucia.

In modern times, Iraq and Turkey have both built dams along the Tigris, for hydropower, to provide water for irrigating the arid regions that border the river valley and to avert floods. Overall,

The Burney Relief, a Babylonian terracotta plaque believed to date from the 19th or 18th century BCE.

the last 30 years have seen discharges decrease by a third, primarily due to the construction of Turkey's Southeastern Anatolia Project.

In addition to affecting the river's flow, dam building has led to increasing conflict among the three co-riparian countries – Turkey, Syria and Iraq. Until 1960, use of the Tigris's water was relatively low and relations among the three nations were generally cordial. However, at the beginning of the 1960s, the unilateral, uncoordinated initiation of large-scale water development projects caused tensions to rise, almost triggering armed conflict between Iraq and Syria. Droughts, population growth and the increasing cultivation of water-intensive crops put greater demand on water, exacerbating the problems. By the turn of the millennium, relations had improved significantly, but cooperation eventually stalled and underlying tensions continue to simmer. Turkey has courted controversy by building several new dams on the Tigris.

Miraculously, despite about 7,000 years of use for irrigation, the quality of the Tigris's water is generally considered to be acceptable.

The Yangtze River

Asia's longest river, the third-longest in the world and the longest to flow entirely within a single country, the Yangtze has played a central role, both good and bad, in Chinese history.

The Yangtze is China's most important river, its principal waterway and an economic artery. It's among China's longest-inhabited regions and has played a central role in China's history, culture and economy. For millennia, the river has been used for drinking water, irrigation, sanitation, transportation, industry, boundary-marking and war. Its basin is the nation's great granary and contains nearly a third of its population. Thanks to its agricultural potential, the Yangtze region has been of significant economic importance to successive dynasties.

The Yangtze rises on the Tibetan Plateau as the Ulan Moron or Tuotuo River, which is initially fed by meltwater from the Jianggendiru Glacier on the southwest side of Geladandong Peak, the main pinnacle of the Tanggula Mountains in southern Qinghai province on the border with Tibet. It then flows in a generally easterly direction across central China before emptying in the East China Sea.

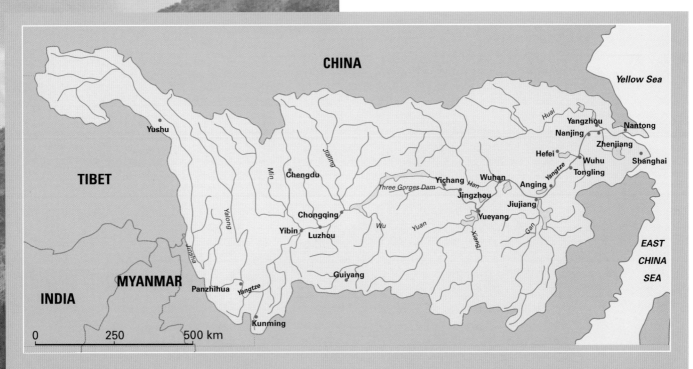

CHINA

Yellow Sea

Yushu

TIBET

MYANMAR

INDIA

Panzhihua
Yangtze

Kunming

Yalong

Jinsha

Min

Jialing

Chengdu

Chongqing

Yibin   Luzhou

Guiyang

Wu   Yuan

Xiang

Gan

Three Gorges Dam

Yichang   Han

Jingzhou

Wuhan

Yueyang

Jiujiang

Anging

Huai

Yangzhou

Nanjing

Hefei

Zhenjiang

Wuhu

Tongling

Yangtze

Nantong

Shanghai

EAST
CHINA
SEA

0   250   500 km

At a glance

Length: 6,300 km (3,915 miles)

Watershed: 1.8 million sq km (694,984 sq miles)

Vertical drop: 5,170 m (19,962 ft)

Main tributaries: Yalung, Min, Jialing, Han, Wu, Yuan, Xiang and Gan rivers

Mean annual discharge: 30,000 cubic metres per second (1.06 million cubic ft per second)

Countries: China

Cities: Chongqing, Yichang, Wuhan, Nanjing and Shanghai

In its upper reaches, the Yangtze – at this point known as the Jinsha in China – flows across the Tibetan Plateau among mountains that soar to heights of almost 5,000 m (16,404 ft), capped with glaciers and perpetual snow, and cut by gorges and deep valleys (more than three-quarters of the river's course runs through mountains). For more than 400 km (249 miles), the Yangtze, Mekong and Salween rivers all run close to and parallel to each other, separated by no more than 50 km (31 miles).

After the rivers diverge, the Yangtze turns east and passes through a steep, winding valley, swelling as it receives water from multiple tributaries. It then widens to between 300–400 m (984–1,312 ft) and passes through several narrow gorges as it turns southeast and then south, tumbling downhill over washing machine rapids. Over its first 2,600 km (1,616 miles), the river drops more than 5,000 m (16,404 ft).

The river's middle course crosses the hilly Sichuan province, separated from the Yellow River basin by the Qin Mountains. Here the river's flow is bolstered by several more voluminous tributaries. The current is still swift and the river's banks are frequently high and steep. As it passes through eastern Sichuan and into western Hubei, the river flows for some 200 km (125 miles) through the famous Three Gorges region, bordered by steep, sheer limestone cliffs that once rose 600 m (1,968 ft) or more above the river.

Often considered the most beautiful of the Three Gorges on the Yangtze River, Qutang Gorge, which separates Chijia Mountain to the north and Baiyan Mountain to the south, is also the shortest and narrowest of the three.

After passing through the gorges, the river debouches onto the extensive lowland plains of east-central China, which lie at an elevation of less than 50 m (164 ft). Here its current slows as it enters a complex system of lakes and marshes, and splits into multiple channels. For millennia, this vast region has served as a natural flood-regulation basin and represents China's most important rice-growing region. As it loops between the numerous lakes, which are among China's largest – although silting and land reclamation have caused many to shrink – the river widens and accepts water from three main tributaries (the Yuan, Xiang and Han rivers) and numerous smaller ones. These lakes help to regulate the effect of variations in the river's water level.

The Yangtze delta, which consists of numerous branches, tributaries, lakes, ancient riverbeds and marshes connected with the main channel, begins beyond Zhenjiang. When major floods occur, the delta is completely submerged. As it passes through the upper delta, the river's width may be less than 2 km (1.2 miles); farther downstream, the channel gradually widens and transforms into a large estuary with a width that exceeds 80 km (50 miles) near the river's mouth, site of the megacity of Shanghai. Sandbars at the mouth restrict its depth to a few metres. Tidal influences reach 400 km (249 miles) from the river's mouth. Two enormous parallel banks, faced with stone in most parts, protect the delta from the sea. Just before it empties into the sea, the Yangtze divides into two arms that flow either side of 1,267-sq-km (489-sq-mile) Chongming Island, home to about 700,000 people.

The Yangtze valley floodplain has long been a centre for agriculture and, by the 20th century, tens of millions of people lived on the plain, kept relatively safe from the summer floods by a series of dykes. However, periodically the river has risen to the point where it has overtopped the dykes – notably in 1931, 1954 and 1998. The first of these was among the deadliest natural disasters ever recorded (excluding pandemics and famines); estimates of the total death toll suggest as many as four million people lost their lives. Heavy, continuous monsoon rains across most of the middle and lower basin generated six huge flood waves in May–June that swept down the river and destroyed flood protections in two dozen places. More than 90,000 sq km (34,749 sq miles) of land were inundated, in places up to 6 m (20 ft) deep, and some 40 million people were left homeless. On average, catastrophic floods have occurred in the Yangtze basin every 50 years or so.

The Yangtze has played a central role in the cultural origins of both southern China and Japan. Humans have been living in the Three Gorges area for almost 30,000 years and the Central Yangtze valley was home to sophisticated Neolithic cultures. Archaeological evidence suggests that the lower Yangtze was the site for the first domestication of rice, around 10,000 years ago, by the Shangshan culture, triggering the rise of civilization along the river. By the beginning of the 1st century CE, the Yangtze region had become particularly important to China's economy, the establishment of irrigation systems and the building of dykes along the river making agriculture in the Yangtze lowlands more stable and productive.

Above: A scene from 10,000 Miles along the Yangtze River, a 16.5 m (54 ft) scroll that represents one of the earliest surviving paintings to depict the full length of the Yangtze.

Below: The 1.6 km (1 mi) double-deck road and rail Wuhan Yangtze Great Bridge, completed in 1957, was the first modern bridge designed and built in China without help from foreign architects.

During the 19th and early 20th centuries, the Yangtze was the focus of several foreign incursions into China. During the Opium Wars of the mid-1840s, the British sailed up the Yangtze and seized several Chinese tax barges, dealing a significant blow to the Imperial government, and, in 1865, the USS *Wachusett* sailed almost 1,000 km (621 miles) up the river to Hankow in an effort to track down bandits who were harming American interests. In 1876, the China Navigation Company was founded in London to conduct trade on the Yangtze from its base in Shanghai; located at the river's mouth, the city was an obvious site for foreign traders to set up their commercial headquarters.

Early in Chinese history, the Yangtze stood as a significant geographical barrier, dividing northern and southern China, and the river has consequently also acted as both a political and a cultural boundary. Climatically, to the north of the Yangtze, China is drier and cooler. The main grain grown in the north is wheat; in the south it is rice.

For millennia, the river could only be crossed by ferry or sometimes by pontoon bridges. However, following the founding of the Communist People's Republic of China in 1949, Soviet engineers began to assist with the design and construction of a road and rail bridge in Wuhan, which opened in 1957, the first to cross the river (between Yibin and Shanghai). Today, more than 100 bridges and six tunnels cross the river.

Although there are only two dams on the Yangtze itself – the Three Gorges and Gezhouba dams – the former is the largest power station in the world by installed capacity, at 22.5 GW, and the world's largest dam structure. Completed in 2006, the dam submerged large parts of the Qutang, Wu and Xiling gorges, an area of great scenic beauty, for some 600 km (373 miles) upstream and forced the relocation of about a million people. Power generation is only one of the dam's functions – it also feeds irrigation and one of its major objectives was flood control.

There are also several dams operating or being built on the Jinsha River – the upper portion of the Yangtze – including the Xiluodu Dam, the world's third-largest power station, and the Baihetan Dam, the second largest after the Three Gorges Dam. The river's total potential for hydropower represents about two-fifths of the total energy potential of all China's rivers.

While it's significantly less silty than the Yellow River, the Yangtze still carries a considerable quantity of sediment. In its upper reaches, as it flows across the Tibetan Plateau, the river is relatively clear, but downstream, its waters acquire the colour of milky coffee. Estimates suggest that the river carries about 500 million tonnes (492 million

The Three Gorges Dam.

tone) of sediment per year, about 300 million tonnes (295 million tons) of which are deposited at its mouth, causing the delta to extend into the sea by an average of about 1.5 km (0.9 mile) every 100 years.

During the 1950s, the Chinese government embarked on a programme of river engineering, installing dams and dykes for flood control, land reclamation, irrigation and the control of disease vectors such as the flukes that cause schistosomiasis (a serious infection caused by parasitic worms). The work saw more than 100 lakes cut off from the main river. Although gates were installed so that floodwaters could be diverted into the lakes, illegal encroachment by farmers and other settlers meant that it became impossible to open the gates as this would have caused significant destruction and loss of life, and many of the lakes eventually dried up. Since 2002, the Chinese government has been reconnecting some of the lakes to the Yangtze in the hope of increasing biodiversity and reducing the frequency and severity of floods.

The Yangtze has long been one of China's most important transportation arteries, connecting the interior with the coast, and in recent decades has become the world's busiest inland waterway, with cargo transportation reaching 3.53 billion tonnes (347 billion tons) in 2021. There is also significant passenger traffic. Ship locks incorporated into the Three Gorges Dam enable ships of up to 3,000 tonnes (2,953 tons) to travel as far upriver as Chongqing, while large ocean-going vessels up to 10,000 tonnes (9,842 tons) can reach as far upriver as Wuhan, almost 1,000 km (621 miles) from the ocean. However, a drought-induced drop in water level has recently meant that ocean-going ships can no longer reach upstream ports.

The 1,776-km (1,104-mile) Grand Canal, the world's longest, crosses the Yangtze near the city of Zhenjiang, connecting the river with the Yellow, Huai, Wei and Hai rivers, and several major cities, including Beijing, and the seaports of Hangzhou and Tianjin. It was mostly built during the 7th century (although the southernmost portion was probably in use as early as the 4th century) to enable the transport of grain from the Yangtze basin to the great northern capital cities.

The volume of water that flows down the Yangtze is stupendous. Even in its upper reaches, its average flow exceeds the discharge rate at the mouth of the Yellow River, China's second-longest river. Rainfall in the basin is dominated by the summer monsoon and, during the rainy season, the river's discharge can be more than double the average. The river's level typically begins to rise in May and peaks in August; the fluctuation in height is considerable, averaging about 20 m (66 ft).

Floods are typically triggered by torrential monsoon rains in the basin's middle and lower reaches, which usually begin in March or April, but can take place at any time during the following eight months. The most destructive floods occur when both the main channel and one or more of the major tributaries overflow at the same time. Because the river valley and floodplain are relatively densely populated, hosting a number of large, rich cities, floods are often particularly deadly and costly.

Flooding is often the result of silt building up on the river's bed. As it leaves the mountains and enters the plain, the river's current slows abruptly, causing much of the sediment that it's carrying to drop out onto its bed, which consequently rises. In some areas, this has raised the level of the bed above the level of the plain. In order to keep the river constrained, levees have been constructed along about 2,740 km (1,703 miles) of its banks.

The Yangtze basin comprises a fifth of China's land area, generates a similar proportion of its GDP and is home to nearly a third of its population. The basin is comparatively well irrigated and its economy is focused largely on agriculture, with almost half of China's crop production taking place there, including more than two-thirds of the total volume of rice. Among the other crops grown are cotton, wheat, barley and corn. With extremely fertile soil and favourable climatic conditions, the lower basin and the delta are particularly favourable to agriculture and have grown into some of China's most economically developed areas. The growing period here can extend to 11 months, enabling some areas to produce multiple harvests each year. However, the irregular nature of the rainfall means that even the areas of highest precipitation are often hit by severe droughts; floods are also a constant threat.

The river has a high species richness – one of the highest in Asia – with numerous endemic species, but many, including the river's two sturgeon species, are seriously threatened by human activities. More than 25 of the river's fish species have become important in fish farming and introduced widely outside their native range, including four species of carp. The largest fish in the river, the Chinese sturgeon, is among the world's largest freshwater fish, reaching 5 m (16 ft) in length. It was exceeded by the now extinct Chinese paddlefish, which is said to have reached a length of 7 m (23 ft). Fishing supports much of the population along the river. Other threatened species include the Chinese alligator and the narrow-ridged finless porpoise; the Yangtze river dolphin, or baiji, is now extinct.

Above: *Qiqi, the last known living Yangtze river dolphin or baiji, which died in 2002.*

Since 1950, as China's economy has developed, so too has the environmental degradation in the Yangtze basin. Pollution levels have risen, overgrazing and land clearing have increased erosion and hence silt loads, and land reclamation has seen lakes and wetlands shrink, and exacerbated seasonal flooding. More plastic pollution flows from the Yangtze into the sea than from any other river. In 2020, the Chinese government passed a sweeping law designed to protect the river's ecology, strengthening rules for hydropower projects, banning chemical plants within a corridor 1 km (0.62 miles) wide on either side of the river, relocating polluting industries, severely restricting sand mining and banning fishing.

Dating from 1770, this painting by court painter Xu Yang shows the Qianlong Emperor entering the city of Suzhou along the Grand Canal during his tour of southern China.

The Yellow River

China's second longest river, the Yellow River is both creator and destroyer: birthplace of Chinese civilization and progenitor of devastating floods.

One of the world's most dangerous and destructive rivers, the Yellow River has long been seen as both a blessing and a curse, a fact reflected in its many nicknames, which include 'the Ungovernable', 'China's Pride' and 'China's Sorrow'. Widely considered be the cradle of Chinese civilization, the river has played a central role in northern China's economic development.

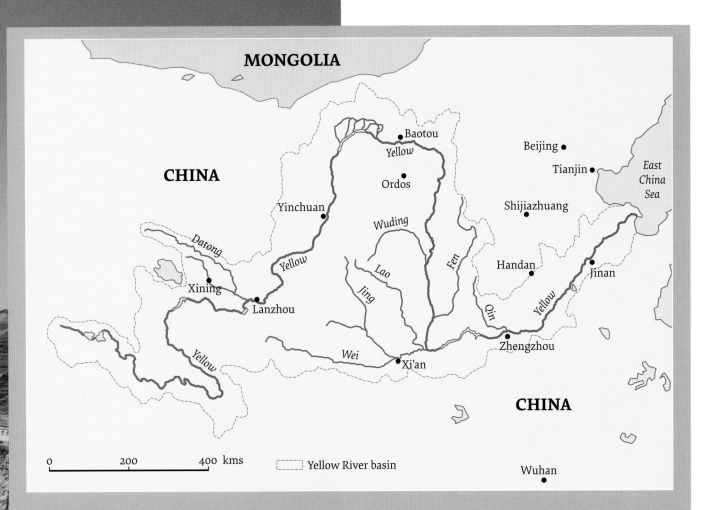

At a glance

Length: 5,464 km (3,395 miles)

Watershed: 750,000 sq km (289,577 sq miles)

Vertical drop: 3,496 m (11,479 ft)

Main tributaries: Wei, Fen, Qin, Tao and Huangshui river

Mean annual discharge: 2,100 cubic metres per second (74,161 cubic ft per second)

Countries: China

Cities: Lanzhou, Hohhot, Yinchuan, Jinan, Zhengzhou, Kaifeng

The river can be divided into three sections: the narrow, cold, tumultuous and mountainous upper course across the Tibetan Plateau, in which the river drops 3,496 m (11,470 ft) over a distance of 3,472 km (2,157 miles); the middle course across the Loess Plateau, where it picks up more than 90 per cent of the yellow silt that gives the river its name; and the lower course across the North China Plain, where the river is an ever-shifting, turbulent, silt-laden stream that regularly overflows its banks.

In common with the Yangtze and Mekong rivers, the Yellow River originates on the Tibetan Plateau, rising at an elevation above 4,600 m (15,092 ft) in the Bayan Har Mountains near the eastern edge of Tibet. Here, the river's water is clear and flows steadily, often constrained between steep cliffs of crystalline rock. After winding its way through some 20 deep gorges, the river leaves the Tibetan Plateau near the city of Lanzhou and begins to decelerate as it makes its way across the

The Hukou Waterfall, the largest waterfall on the Yellow River and the second-largest in China

Yinchuan and Hetao plains, vast alluvial flatlands once covered in desert and grassland but now among the most important irrigation areas along the river.

Entering its middle reaches, the river flows across the Zoige Basin, describing a wide arc – northwest then northeast then south – known as the Ordos Loop. Here the river flows across the Loess Plateau, where the underlying bedrock is covered by thick layers of fine-grained wind-blown soil, known as loess, which can stack up to a depth of 150 m (492 ft). The river has cut deep valleys through this loosely packed material, making the plateau one of the world's most highly eroded landscapes. The riverbed itself is particularly unstable, shifting regularly as it scythes through the easily eroded soil.

Finally, the river enters its lower reaches. After passing through Sanmen Gorge, where the Sanmenxia Dam has been built to prevent flooding and provide irrigation and hydroelectric power, the river descends onto the densely populated North China Plain, a wide, flat, virtually featureless alluvial fan formed over some 25 million years as the Yellow River and other waterways deposited silt, sand and gravel into the shallow sea that once covered the region. Here it slows considerably and begins to meander, confined to a levee-lined course. The silt collected on the Loess Plateau begins to drop out of the river here, elevating the river bed. The plain has long has been one of China's principal agricultural regions thanks to the fertile alluvium.

The Yellow River's marshy, reed-covered delta begins about 80 km (50 miles) from its mouth and spreads out over an area of about 5,400 sq km (2,085 sq miles). Until the late 20th century, the delta was among the world's fastest growing; however, dam construction has reduced the deposition of silt and, since 1996, it has reportedly been shrinking. In response, the Chinese government has diverted the final section of the river's main stream, causing deposits to build up on the delta's northern side.

The Yellow River is the most sediment-laden river in the world. The Chinese idiom 'When the Yellow River flows clear' is akin to the English expressions 'When pigs fly' and 'When hell freezes over', referring to an

Main image: *The Yellow River near Lanzhou, with the deeply dissected landscape of the Loess Plateau in the background.*

The Sanmenxia Dam in Henan province has eight characters painted on it that read, 'When the Yellow River is at peace, China is at peace'.

event that will never happen. On average, the river carries some 34 kg (75 lb) of silt per cubic metre (35 cubic ft) of water, but when it is in flood, this can rise to more than 700 kg (1,543 lb) per cubic metre (in 1977, a record 920 kg/2,028 lb per cubic metre was measured) and the river can resemble a flowing mudslide, its surface becoming 'wrinkled'. Each year, some 1.4 billion tonnes (1.37 billion tons) of sediment is washed into the river, about three-quarters of which reaches the Yellow Sea; in 1933, a record 3.5 billion tonnes (3.4 billion tons) of silt were discharged.

As the river crosses the North China Plain, sediment is continuously deposited along the bottom of its channel, causing the level of the river to rise as much as 15 m (49 ft) above the surrounding farmland, creating the famous 'river above ground'. This silt also causes the river to flow in complex braided streams that weave in and out of each other, blocks off natural drainage channels and forms natural dams that are both unpredictable and essentially undetectable. The huge amount of water that builds up behind these dams eventually breaks free and flows out across the floodplain, inundating farmland and settlements in its path; sometimes whole villages are buried beneath silt.

Over the centuries, Yellow River floods have killed tens of millions of people and brought down dynasties. It's believed that during the 2,540 years between 595 BCE to 1946 CE, the river flooded 1,593 times. The deadliest was the 1332–33 flood, which is estimated to have killed seven million people – the worst natural disaster in recorded history (excluding famines and epidemics). In 1931, China's Sorrow lived up to its name once more, breaking its banks and killing between one and four million people.

The collapse of ice dams in Inner Mongolia has also resulted in devastating floods as large quantities of impounded water is suddenly released. In the past century alone, such disasters have occurred 11 times. Todays, the ice dams are broken up before they become dangerous using artillery or explosives dropped from aircraft.

The build-up of sediment and regular flooding have also caused the river's course to shift regularly and often radically – 26 times noticeably and nine times severely since 602 BCE. Looking back further, over the past 4,000 years, the river's various entry points into the Yellow Sea have been as much as 800 km (497 miles) apart.

On a number of occasions in the past, Chinese leaders have attempted to use the river as a weapon of war. In 1642, the governor of Kaifeng directed his men to break a series of dykes in an attempt to kill peasant rebels who had placed the city under siege. Instead, the city itself was destroyed; the flood and ensuing famine and plague are thought to have killed 300,000 of Kaifeng's 378,000 inhabitants and the once-prosperous city was almost abandoned.

The lesson taught by this disaster wasn't learned. In June 1938, during the Japanese invasion of China, the Chinese Nationalist leader Chiang Kai-shek ordered the breaching of the Yellow River's levees in order to slow the invaders' advance. The resulting flood did slow them down, slightly, but it also killed as many as 900,000 Chinese.

Several dams have been built along the river for water storage, flood control and electricity generation, but they tend to have relatively short lifespans due to the build-up of silt, which also reduces their power production. At present, some 20 major dams punctuate the river, with

The Yellow River Breaches its Course *by Ma Yuan, a celebrated landscape artist of the Song Dynasty.*

Invading Japanese soldiers wade through water from the Yellow River in June 1938 after Chinese Nationalists destroyed dikes at Huayuankou in Henan province to try to slow the Japanese advance.

another 18 scheduled to be built by 2030. The power they produce is vital to northern China's industrial infrastructure.

Early in Chinese history, the Yellow River basin was the country's most prosperous region and, traditionally, it's believed that it was the origin point of Chinese civilization. It was where the Neolithic Peiligang and Yangshao cultures arose some 8,000 years ago, progenitors of some of the world's first writing, alcoholic drinks and musical instruments. Before 4,000 BCE, people were cultivating crops in the fertile yellow soil of the Shaanxi Loess region and 1,000 years later they were using the river's water for irrigation.

For centuries, the Yellow River Basin's water resources have been managed using flood-control works of significant size, including tens of thousands of kilometres of artificial levees. Sometime around the 3rd century BCE, an engineer named Yu instigated a number of flood control works, dredging the river and digging irrigation canals. So effective were his efforts that he became known as 'Great Yu Controls the Waters' and was

Pots from the Yangshao culture which developed along the middle reaches of the Yellow River from around 5,000 BCE.

eventually made emperor of China.

Despite its fearsome tendency to spawn devastating floods, the Yellow River has played a vital role in making northern China habitable. It supplies water to about 12 per cent of China's population – more than 150 million people – and irrigates about 74,000 sq km (28,572 sq miles) of farmland, 15 per cent of China's total area, notably for wheat cultivation. Agricultural irrigation has increased by a factor of five since 1950 and today it swallows 65 per cent of the river's water.

Because much of the Yellow River Basin encompasses arid or semiarid regions, in which significant quantities of water evaporate, the river has a relatively low discharge rate – exceeded by eight other Chinese rivers. Abstraction for irrigation and urban and industrial use, and climate change have reduced the river's outflow even further – it has dropped by 90 per cent compared to the level in the 1940s. In 1972, the river ran dry before it reached the sea for the first time. Since then, this has happened more than 30 times, including all but one year during the 1990s.

The Yenisei River

The world's fifth-longest river system, and the largest to drain into the Arctic Ocean, the Yenisei flows across a vast region of arresting landscapes.

Rising in Mungaragiyn-gol in Mongolia, the Yenisei flows north across the great expanse of central Siberia before draining into the Yenisei Gulf in the icy Kara Sea, an arm of the Arctic Ocean. The river proper begins at the confluence of the Great (Bolshoi) Yenisey and Little (Maly) Yenisei rivers at the city of Kyzyl. The river's upper course is turbulent, with many rapids; for the first 185 km (115 miles) or so, it frequently splits into braided channels that skirt gravelly shoals.

Within Siberia, the river system comprises some 20,000 tributary or sub-tributary streams, with a combined length of almost 900,000 km (559,234 miles); all of the major tributaries flow from the Central Siberian Plateau to the river's east. For part of its length, the river follows the plateau's escarpment. Below the confluence with its major tributary, the Angara, near Yeniseisk, the Yenisei's right bank is often precipitous, while the left bank is a floodplain. Here the riverbed broadens out and

At a glance

Length: 3,487 km* (2,167 miles)

Watershed: 2.6 million sq km (1 million sq miles)

Vertical drop: 630 m (2,067 ft)

Main tributaries: Tuba, Khemchik, Angara, Abakan, Stony Tunguska and Lower Tunguska rivers

Mean annual discharge: 19,800 cubic metres per second (699,230 cubic ft per second)

Countries: Russia

Cities: Krasnoyarsk, Abakan

The headwaters of the Selenga River, which rise in western Mongolia and flow through Lake Baikal into the Angara, may be considered the river's ultimate source, in which case the river would have a length of 5,540 km (3,442 miles).

the flow velocity drops by half as it crosses the Siberian plains. Farther downstream, just before the Stony Tunguska River empties into the Yenisei, the latter cuts through spurs of the Yenisei Ridge, flowing through rapids at Osinovo and then plunging down a rugged gorge that constrains its bed to a width of 730 m (2,395 ft).

The river's 225-km (140-mile) estuary begins at the confluence with the Kureyka River. The estuary is part of a broad wetland complex that consists of a network of rivers, streams, lakes, islands, floodplains and tundra terraces. These wetlands support several regionally rare and threatened birds, and act as an internationally important area for breeding, staging and moulting waterbirds. As is true of many Russian rivers, the estuary also supports valuable sturgeon and salmon fisheries. It is also a busy waterway and is consequently relatively polluted. The river itself was contaminated by radioactive discharges from a factory that produced weapons-grade plutonium in the secret city of Krasnoyarsk-26, now known as Zheleznogorsk.

Melting snow provides about half of the Yenisei's water, leading to violent spring floods that are followed first by a rapid fall in level, then by a slower fall. Smaller floods, induced by summer and autumn rain, punctuate this sequence. In early October, the river's lower reaches begin to freeze and by mid-November the whole river has frozen over. The thaw begins towards the end of April in the upper reaches. The ice in the river's lower reaches begins to melt later, leading to extensive flooding as water backs up behind the river's frozen portion.

The Yenisei has the greatest discharge of Russia's rivers, amounting to about 620 cubic km (149 cubic miles) per year – about a fifth of the total freshwater runoff into the Arctic Ocean. It also carries about 9.5 million tonnes (9.4 million tons) of alluvium into the Kara Sea every year. During spring and summer, sediment makes the waters of the middle Yenisei highly turbid. This is in sharp contrast to the limpid water of the Angara; during summer, the two streams flow in the same bed without mingling for about 14 km (9 miles) from the rivers' confluence.

The Yenisei's upper reaches are mountainous and forested. The dominant vegetation throughout the basin is marshy, coniferous taiga; in the south, Siberian spruce, fir and cedar predominate, giving way to pine- and larch-dominated tundra in the north. Elsewhere, there are also steppe grasslands and even semi-desert. Much of the land is permanently frozen.

The banks of the Yenisei have been inhabited by nomadic tribes such as the Ket and the Yugh for thousands of years. Russians first reached the river's upper reaches in 1605, having travelled along the Ob and Ket rivers and then overland to the Yenisei, which they travelled down as far as the Sym River. Not long after, they began to settle along the river, starting with a winter station established on the Turukhan River, a left-bank tributary, in 1607. Yeniseisk, the first town to be built on the Yenisei, was founded in 1619 as a stockaded town. It went on to serve as the centre of Russian gold mining and as one of the first outposts of colonial expansion into eastern Siberia.

From 1863, Imperial Russia began placing river steamers, brought in across the Kara Sea from Holland and England, on the Yenisei in the hope of using them to open up regular communication with the remote settlements of landlocked Siberia. By 1879, Moscow was using the steamers to bring supplies in and wheat out. One such, the SS *St Nicholas*, carried the future Tsar Nicholas II on his 1891 voyage to Siberia and later conveyed Vladimir Lenin to prison. During the building of the Trans-Siberian Railway at the end of the 19th century, engineers attempted to use river steamers to bring in the rails, engines and supplies, but the route proved to be particularly treacherous and several ships were lost at sea and on the river. The Yenisei's mouth empties into a long, shallow inlet, several hundred kilometres in length, that is often ice bound and prone to high winds, making navigation hazardous. After the railway was

The Yenisei (left) and Ob (right) rivers flow into the Kara Sea.

completed, river traffic was largely reduced to local services.

Today, people living in the basin's north mostly make their living through hunting, fishing, fur farming and reindeer herding; the Taimyr reindeer herd, the world's largest, migrates to winter grazing ranges along the Yenisei. Given the severe climate and lack of resources, the basin is, unsurprisingly, sparsely populated, with an average population density of only two people per square kilometre. However, there is a cluster of cities in the river's upper reaches, where natural resources such as iron ore, and gold and the river's hydroelectric potential have drawn settlers.

The steamer SS St Nicholas, *now a museum, beside the Yenisei River in Krasnoyarsk.*

The Yenisei and the Angara have the greatest hydroelectric potential of Russia's river systems and are among the most heavily exploited. The Sayano-Shushenskaya Dam near Sayanogorsk is Russia's largest power plant and the ninth-largest hydroelectric plant in the world, with a total installed capacity of 6,400 MW. The power stations have been crucial to the development of heavy industry in the region, which produces much of Russia's coal.

Seagoing ships regularly travel as high as Oznachennoye, using a huge rail elevator to pass between the upper and lower waters of the Krasnoyarsk Hydroelectric Station. The main form of cargo on the river is timber sourced from the vast taiga forests, but bread, coal, copper, nickel, petroleum products and machinery also travel downstream.

The Sayano-Shushenskaya Dam, located on the Yenisei River near Sayanogorsk in Khakassia, is the largest power plant in Russia, with total installed capacity of 6,400 MW.

CHAPTER FOUR

Rivers of Europe

Despite the fact that it's a relatively small continent, Europe boasts an impressive diversity of rivers, ranging from powerful Alpine waterways such as the Rhone and Rhine to the more sedate Thames and Seine, and the vast rivers of Siberia. Dotted with imposing castles and grand cities, Europe's great rivers have shaped the continent's history, generating prosperity by powering industry, nurturing agriculture and facilitating trade, and helping both to bring nations together culturally and to geographically separate them. Europe's industrial history, together with its urban growth, has, in turn, shaped the continent's rivers, many of which have suffered from a long legacy of engineering for agriculture, flood prevention, navigation, electricity generation and water supply.

The Danube River.

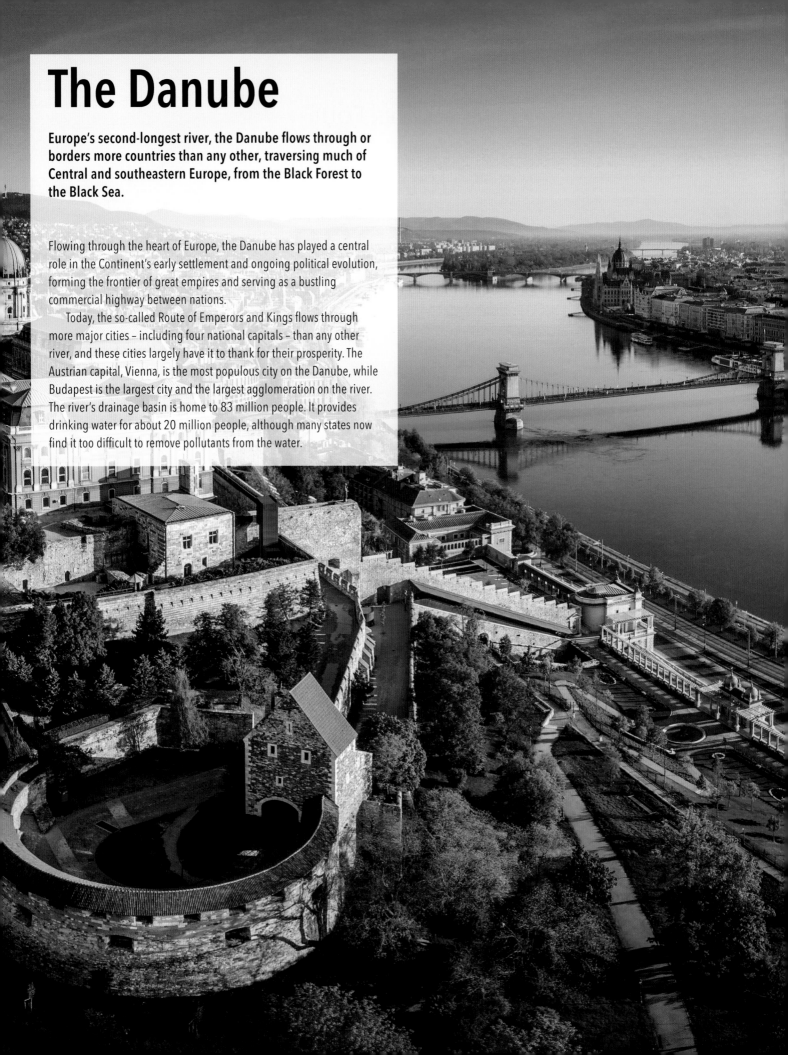

The Danube

Europe's second-longest river, the Danube flows through or borders more countries than any other, traversing much of Central and southeastern Europe, from the Black Forest to the Black Sea.

Flowing through the heart of Europe, the Danube has played a central role in the Continent's early settlement and ongoing political evolution, forming the frontier of great empires and serving as a bustling commercial highway between nations.

Today, the so-called Route of Emperors and Kings flows through more major cities – including four national capitals – than any other river, and these cities largely have it to thank for their prosperity. The Austrian capital, Vienna, is the most populous city on the Danube, while Budapest is the largest city and the largest agglomeration on the river. The river's drainage basin is home to 83 million people. It provides drinking water for about 20 million people, although many states now find it too difficult to remove pollutants from the water.

At a glance

Length: 2,857 km (1,775 miles)

Watershed: 820,000 sq km (316,604 sq miles)

Vertical drop: 686 m (2,251 ft)

Main tributaries: Inn, Drava, Tisza, Sava and Siret rivers

Mean annual discharge: 6,500 cubic metres per second (229 545 cubic ft per second)

Countries: Germany, Austria, Slovakia, Hungary, Croatia, Serbia, Romania, Bulgaria, Moldova and Ukraine

Cities: Vienna, Bratislava, Budapest and Belgrade

The Danube originates in the Black Forest town of Donaueschingen in Germany with the coming together of two small streams from the forest's eastern slopes – the Brigach and the Breg. After passing through or acting as the border of ten different countries, it eventually empties into the Black Sea.

The Danube is a particularly picturesque river, sliding past an ever-evolving landscape of lush vineyards and rolling forested hills; bustling cities brimming with impressive, elegant architecture; storybook villages boasting ancient half-timbered buildings; castles, fortresses and medieval monasteries; the imposing limestone cliffs of the Iron Gate; and the fascinating near-360° sweep of the Great Loop in Austria. This fact is reflected in the popularity of Danube River cruises; during the peak season, more than 70 cruise liners are active on the river.

The Danube Basin is divided into three main sections, separated by constrictions known as gates, where the river cuts through mountainous regions. Among them is the co-called Iron Gate – a gorge that forms part of the border between Serbia and Romania at the point where the river separates the Carpathian Mountains from the foothills of the Balkan Mountains. The gorge itself hosts the Đerdap High Dam and Iron Gate power station, built jointly by Romania and what was then

Yugoslavia, one of the largest hydroelectric projects along the river, with an installed capacity of 2,282 MW. About 60 km (37 miles) downstream, past the exit to the gorge, sits another dam and the Iron Gate II Hydroelectric Power Station. These are the last barriers to the river's flow – downstream, the river is free flowing all the way to the Black Sea, a distance of more than 860 km (534 miles).

Near Tulcea in Romania, about 80 km (50 miles) from the ocean, the river begins to spread out into its delta, splitting into three channels. Between the channels lies a network of smaller reed-bordered creeks and lakes separated by oblong strips of land called *grinduri*, some of which are cultivated; others are covered in dense oak forests.

The delta is the largest in the European Union, with an area of about 4,150 sq km (1,602 sq miles). Lying mostly in Romania (and partly in Ukraine), it's also one of the world's best-preserved and least-urbanized major deltas, home to some 45 freshwater fish species and a stopover for more than 300 species of migratory bird, including the endangered pygmy cormorant.

The delta is comparatively young. About 6,500 years ago, the area in which it now sits was a shallow Black Sea cove. River-borne silt gradually filled in the cove and today the delta continues to expand into the sea at a rate of up to 30 m (98 ft) per year.

Up until the second half of the 20th century, the Danube Delta froze over practically every winter; between 1951 and 2016, it has frozen

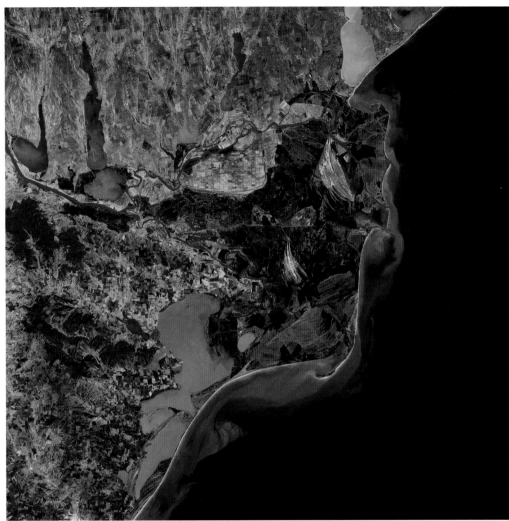

Above: *A satellite image of the Danube Delta.*
Left: *The Iron Gates, a gorge on the Danube that forms part of the boundary between Serbia and Romania.*
Below: *The Aachtopf, Germany's largest karst spring, where water from the Danube returns to the surface after disappearing underground at the Danube Sinkhole.*

A fired-clay Vinča culture figurine, believed to be a household deity, from the late Neolithic period (4,500–4,000 BCE).

over only ten times. While this is partly the result of climate change, the influx of warm wastewater has also had an impact.

Significant quantities of water flow from the Danube to the Rhine along subterranean rivers. During summer, what little water flows in the Danube can completely and noisily seep away into these underground channels at two locations in the Swabian Alb – an upland plateau in southwestern Germany that represents a continuation of the Jura Mountains, which is largely made of porous limestone – referred to as the *Donauversickerung* ('Danube Sink'), before resurfacing 12 km (7.5 miles) to the south at the Aachtopf, Germany's largest karst spring, and flowing into the Rhine at Lake Constance. The large volume of water flowing through these underground channels is gradually eroding the surrounding limestone and it's believed that the Danube's upper course will eventually disappear as it is captured by the Rhine.

The Danube basin hosted some of the earliest human cultures. Around 8,000 years ago, pioneering Neolithic farmers began to move into Central Europe from Greece and Macedonia, bringing with them wheat and barley seeds, and domesticated cattle, goats and sheep. Many settled along the fertile Danube River valley, particularly in the Balkans. Among those living there was what is now known as the

Vinča culture, which was once the largest civilization in Europe, living in permanent settlements of hundreds to a few thousand people – relatively large communities for the time. Lasting for more than 1,000 years, the Vinča culture made significant advances in writing, copper metallurgy and farming – thought to include use of the cattle-driven plough.

Greek sailors reached the lower Danube during the seventh century BCE, naming it the Ister and beginning to trade with settlements along its banks. Some 600 years later, the Danube acted as the northeastern military frontier of the Roman Empire. While military conquests caused the frontier to shift from time to time, in many places the Romans chose to build semi-permanent defensive structures such as watchtowers, camps and forts along the riverbanks (many of which, known as the Danubian Limes, still exist today), connected by the *Via Istrum* ('Danube Way'), a road that ran from Serbia to the Danube Delta. Many of the strongholds developed into larger settlements, some of which eventually grew into the cities of Vienna, Budapest and Belgrade. A Roman fleet, known as the *Classis Moesica*, patrolled the Lower Danube from the Iron Gates to the Black Sea.

The river also acted as the northern border of the Ottoman Empire.

Between the late 14th and late 19th centuries, the empire competed with its neighbours, including the Austrian Habsburgs and the Russian Empire, for control of the Danube, and several wars were fought along it, including the Great Turkish War, the Crimean War and the Russo-Turkish War. The centuries of conflict spawned numerous fortresses and castles along the river.

The Danube has played a central role in European trade since time immemorial and freight transport has long been its most important economic use. The 1815 Treaty of Vienna enshrined the principle of freedom of navigation on the river and, during the 19th century, it was one of the world's most important waterways. Since the end of World War II, river traffic has increased considerably as dredging and canal construction have improved navigability; in 1994, the Danube was declared one of ten Pan-European transport corridors. Today, some 2,415 km (1,500 miles) of the river are navigable; ocean-going ships can travel from the Black Sea to Brăila in Romania; smaller craft can navigate further upstream to Ulm, Württemberg, Germany.

The river forms part of a continent-wide network of connecting waterways thanks to three artificial canals: the Danube-Tisa-Danube Canal in Serbia, the Danube-Black Sea Canal in Romania and the Rhine–Main–Danube Canal, which has integrated the Danube into a trans-European waterway that runs from the Dutch port of Rotterdam on the North Sea to Sulina on the Black Sea, a distance of 3,500 km (2,175 miles).

A view of Ada Kaleh, an island in the Danube that became an Ottoman exclave, c. 1900.

Ottoman exclave

Following the end of the Russo-Turkish War of 1877–78, peace talks at the Congress of Berlin reorganized the states in the Balkan Peninsula, placing the Hungary–Romania and Serbia–Bulgaria borders along the Danube. During the talks, a small island in the river between Romania and Hungary named Ada Kaleh, home to a small community of Turkish Muslims, was forgotten about, allowing it to remain *de jure* Ottoman territory. In 1913, Hungary unilaterally annexed the island and six years later Romania followed suit. The latter's position was strengthened at the end of World War I under the 1920 Treaty of Trianon, but the Ottoman Empire didn't recognize the agreement. It finally ceded control under the 1923 Treaty of Lausanne, which established the Republic of Turkey as the successor to the Ottoman Empire. The island eventually disappeared below rising waters during the construction of the Iron Gates hydroelectric plant in 1970.

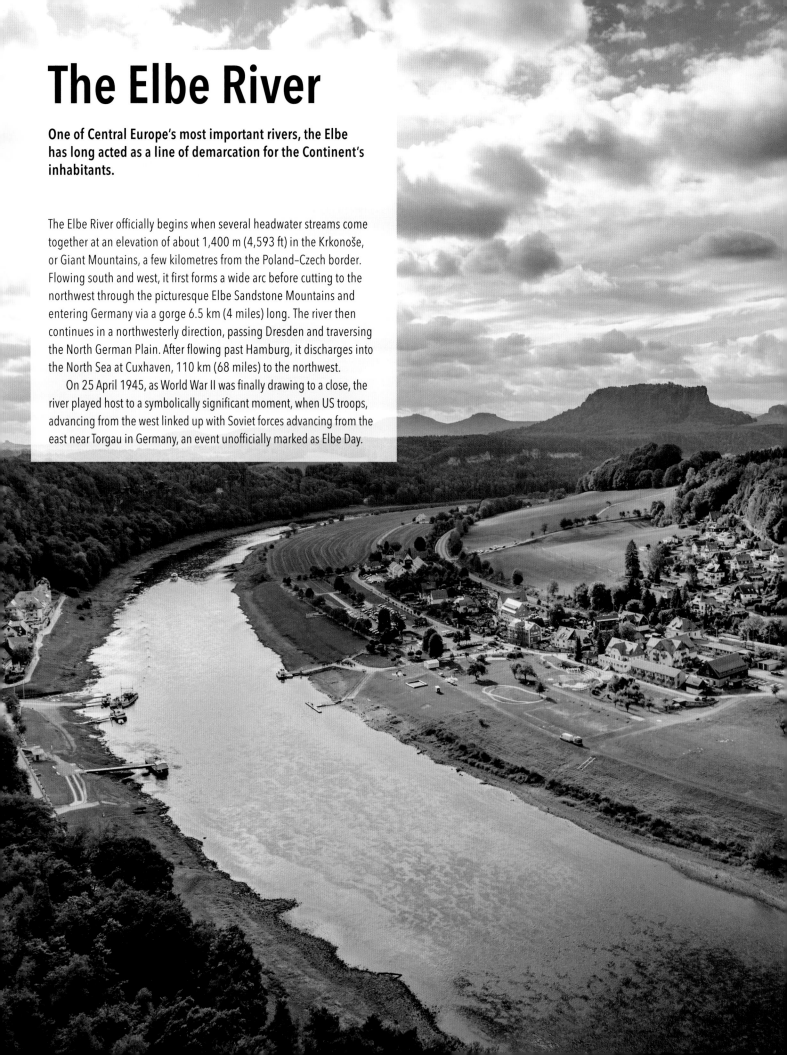

The Elbe River

One of Central Europe's most important rivers, the Elbe has long acted as a line of demarcation for the Continent's inhabitants.

The Elbe River officially begins when several headwater streams come together at an elevation of about 1,400 m (4,593 ft) in the Krkonoše, or Giant Mountains, a few kilometres from the Poland–Czech border. Flowing south and west, it first forms a wide arc before cutting to the northwest through the picturesque Elbe Sandstone Mountains and entering Germany via a gorge 6.5 km (4 miles) long. The river then continues in a northwesterly direction, passing Dresden and traversing the North German Plain. After flowing past Hamburg, it discharges into the North Sea at Cuxhaven, 110 km (68 miles) to the northwest.

On 25 April 1945, as World War II was finally drawing to a close, the river played host to a symbolically significant moment, when US troops, advancing from the west linked up with Soviet forces advancing from the east near Torgau in Germany, an event unofficially marked as Elbe Day.

At a glance

Length: 1,094 km (680 miles)

Watershed: 148,268 sq km (57,247 sq miles)

Vertical drop: 1,400 m (4,593 ft)

Main tributaries: Vltava, Saale, Havel, Mulde, and Schwarze Elster rivers

Mean annual discharge: 861 cubic metres per second (30,406 cubic ft per second)

Countries: Germany, Czech Republic

Cities: Dresden, Hamburg

Sadly, this moment of celebration and optimism was to prove fleeting. Four years later, as the Iron Curtain was drawn across Eastern Europe, the 95-km (59 mile) section of river between Lauenburg and Schnackenburg came to form part of the demarcation between East and West Germany. Because the river now passed through the Communist German Democratic Republic, transport was hindered, a problem solved by the creation of the Elbe Lateral Canal, which connected the West German section of the Mittellandkanal to the Lower Elbe. During the 1970s, the Soviet Union announced that Adolf Hitler's ashes had been disinterred from their original burial-site and scattered in the Elbe.

The cover image from the section on shipping laws in the Hamburg City Charter of 1497.

The Elbe has long played a role in Europe's human geography. The Romans, who knew the river as the Albis, attempted to move the border of their empire forward from the Rhine to the Elbe at the turn of the millennium; however, after they were defeated at the Battle of the Teutoburg Forest in 9 CE they never made another serious attempt to do so. Until the Middle Ages, the river was the western boundary of the area inhabited by the northern Slavs; during the Middle Ages, it formed the eastern limit of the Carolingian Empire of Charlemagne. During the Late Middle Ages, the success of the Hanseatic League rested largely on the trade that it carried out along the river's navigable sections. The Elbe also marked the northern limit of Napoleon's empire in the early 19th century.

Because it has always been navigable by commercial vessels, the Elbe has long acted as an important conduit for trade as far inland as Prague. Several canals and other waterways, some built as long ago as the 14th century, connect Hamburg and the Elbe to Berlin, the industrial cities of Hannover, Wolfsburg and Dresden in the central and southern sections of eastern Germany, the Czech Republic, Poland, the Rhine River and the Baltic Sea. Thousand-tonne barges can use the Elbe itself to reach Prague through the Vltava.

Hamburg, one of the world's busiest seaports, serving some 10,000 ships per year, originally developed on the Alster River during the 9th century, occupying a series of low sandy hills above the marshes; however, the modern port facilities have spread to the low-lying southern bank of the Elbe, about 100 km (62 miles) upstream from the river's mouth. The development of Hamburg has required constant adjustment of the river's morphology to ensure access by large ships and to reduce the risk of flooding. The latter has seen the creation of an extensive protective network of dykes.

The river transverses the city via two arms, the Norder Elbe and the Süder Elbe, before flowing across a floodplain 13 km (8 miles) wide that eventually narrows to about 6 km (3.7 miles) across. The estuary proper of the Elbe, known as the Unterelbe, extends about 90 km (56 miles) from Hamburg to Cuxhaven. The estuary, much of which is flanked by marshes, mud flats and sandbanks, has been occupied for centuries, during which time it has been extensively modified, with large areas of

A heavily loaded container ship in the port of Hamburg near the mouth of the Elbe.

fertile land having been claimed for agriculture.

In its lower reaches – as far up as the dam at Geesthacht, above Hamburg – the Elbe is tidal, the river periodically reversing the direction of its flow and its height changing by as much as 3 m (10 ft) or so. During storms, the water sometimes rises high enough to flood parts of the city.

The flow of water in the river varies considerably, depending on the level of precipitation and snow and ice melt within the drainage basin. At Dresden, for example, the average discharge rate between 1931 and 1975 was 317 cubic metres per second (11,194 cubic ft per second),

but the rate varied from 23 to 3,361 cubic metres per second (812 to 118,693 cubic ft per second). These large variations in flow rate can sometimes hinder navigation. The dams on the upper Elbe in the Czech Republic and at Geesthacht in Germany aren't sufficient to control the river's water level. Heavy summer rainfall sometimes causes the river to break its banks; extreme floods in August 2002 and June 2013 both caused more than €12 billion worth of damage.

Trans-European traffic passes under the river via a six-line railway tunnel and a multilane road tunnel.

Hafencity

Most development in the Elbe estuary has been carried out behind a network of protective dykes, which reduces the risk of flooding. However, Hafencity, a new 157-hectare (388 acre) development in Hamburg's old harbour area, is located on the river side of the dykes. It has been designed to be capable of functioning even during a flood by raising residential and business areas 7.5 m (24.6 ft) above the expected flood level.

Right: *A bridge over a canal in Hafencity.*

The Rhine River

The second-longest river in Central and Western Europe, the Rhine is one of the world's most important arteries for industrial transport and culturally and historically one of the great rivers of the Continent

Germany's longest river, the Rhine connects the Alps to the North Sea and represents Central Europe's most important cultural and economic axis. Passing through six countries and forming six national borders, the Rhine is a powerful symbol, helping to tie those countries together. In parts it is also a breathtakingly beautiful river, attracting tourists in their droves since the 18th century, when the Middle Rhine became one of the symbols of the Romantic movement. No other river has as many old and famous cities on its banks.

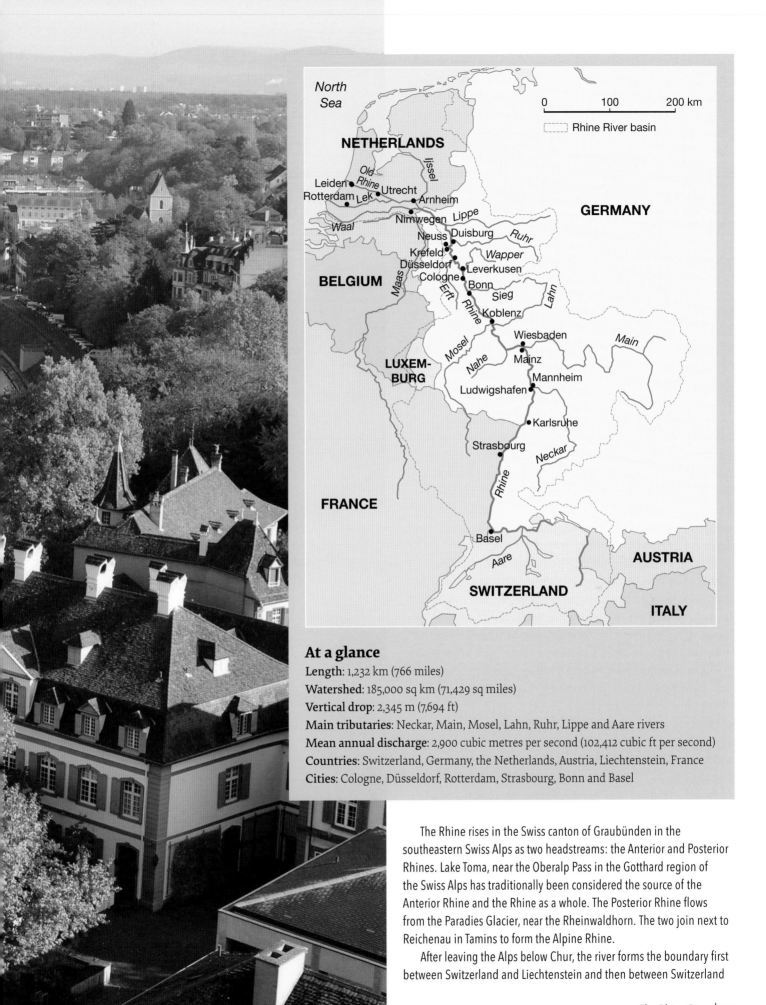

At a glance

Length: 1,232 km (766 miles)

Watershed: 185,000 sq km (71,429 sq miles)

Vertical drop: 2,345 m (7,694 ft)

Main tributaries: Neckar, Main, Mosel, Lahn, Ruhr, Lippe and Aare rivers

Mean annual discharge: 2,900 cubic metres per second (102,412 cubic ft per second)

Countries: Switzerland, Germany, the Netherlands, Austria, Liechtenstein, France

Cities: Cologne, Düsseldorf, Rotterdam, Strasbourg, Bonn and Basel

The Rhine rises in the Swiss canton of Graubünden in the southeastern Swiss Alps as two headstreams: the Anterior and Posterior Rhines. Lake Toma, near the Oberalp Pass in the Gotthard region of the Swiss Alps has traditionally been considered the source of the Anterior Rhine and the Rhine as a whole. The Posterior Rhine flows from the Paradies Glacier, near the Rheinwaldhorn. The two join next to Reichenau in Tamins to form the Alpine Rhine.

After leaving the Alps below Chur, the river forms the boundary first between Switzerland and Liechtenstein and then between Switzerland

and Austria, before entering Lake Constance, which consists of three water bodies: the Obersee ('upper lake'), the Untersee ('lower lake'), and a connecting 4-km (2.5-mile) stretch of the Rhine, called the Seerhein ('Lake Rhine'), which, for most of its length, forms the border between Germany and Switzerland. Where the river flows into the lake, it forms a 2,000-ha (4,942-acre) inland delta, most of which is protected by a nature reserve and bird sanctuary in which more than 340 species have been recorded. At first, the cold, grey mountain water doesn't mix with the warmer, green lake water and, depending on the water level, may be clearly visible along the entire length of the lake.

After the Rhine emerges from Lake Constance, it flows generally westward, roughly forming the German-Swiss border. Not long after flowing over the 150-m-wide (492-ft), 23-m-high (75-ft) Rhine Falls at Schaffhausen, the most powerful waterfall in Europe, the Rhine's flow is bolstered by the input from the Aare River, which typically carries more water than the Rhine. The river then enters the city of Basel, where it abruptly turns north at the so-called Rhine knee, the tripoint of France, Germany and Switzerland, leaving Switzerland and flowing across a broad, flat-floored valley and acting as the border between France and Germany.

The 145 km (90 mile) section of the river between the town of Bingen and the city of Bonn in Germany forms what's known as the Middle Rhine – the most spectacular and romantic reach of the river, in which it has cut the deep and winding Rhine Gorge between the steep slopes of the Hunsrück mountains to the west and the Taunus mountains to the east. Here the river is flanked by dramatic slate hillsides draped in terraced vineyards, and overlooked by more than 40 castles and fortresses from the Middle Ages.

In Bonn, the Sieg flows into the Rhine and the river enters the North German Plain, where it becomes known as the Lower Rhine. The Lower Rhine flows through the largest conurbation in Germany, the densely populated and heavily industrialized Rhine-Ruhr region. After flowing through Germany, the Rhine becomes the border between the Netherlands and Germany. As it crosses the border into the Netherlands at Spijk, near Arnhem, the river splits into three main distributaries – the Waal, Nederrijn and Ijssel – as it forms the extensive Rhine-Meuse-Scheldt delta, which covers an area of 25,347 sq km (9,787 sq miles), making it the largest river delta in Europe. The build-up of sediment in the delta has caused the river channel to shift regularly; during the past 6,000 years, an estimated 80 avulsions (changes in the river's course) have taken place.

Between 1950 and 1997, the Dutch government constructed a series of flood-protection structures to defend land around the delta from the sea, spurred on by a flood in 1953, caused by a storm surge, that killed almost 2,000 people and flooded 9 per cent of the farmland in the Netherlands. Known as the Delta Works, they consist of more than 16,000 km (9,942 miles) of dykes and around 300 other structures, including 13 dams and associated sluices, locks, levees and storm surge barriers that effectively reduce the length of the Dutch coastline by some 700 km (435 miles). The works are the world's largest storm

Right: *The Rhine Falls in Switzerland, Europe's most powerful waterfall.*

barrier and, together with the Zuiderzee Works, were recognized as one of the Seven Wonders of the Modern World by the American Society of Civil Engineers.

The Rhine itself has also undergone significant engineering since as long ago as the Roman occupation. The Upper Rhine is considered to have been 'domesticated' during the 19th century by the engineer Johann Tulla. Heavy floods had recently caused significant loss of life along the river when Tulla began his campaign to shorten and straighten its upper reaches. Tulla argued that a few targeted excavations to cut off meanders and create a new riverbed would ease flooding and make navigation simpler. The work began in 1817. The river was deepened and channelled between embankments, new sections were dug, numerous small islands were removed and stagnant, boggy areas, which fostered waterborne diseases, were drained. The project, which continued until 1879, long after Tulla's death, eventually reduced the river's length between Basel and Worms from 355 to 275 km (221 to 171 miles).

And it broadly worked, taming the floods in the Upper Rhine and improving navigability. However, the work had several unintended consequences. Although Tulla was largely motivated by a desire to do away with floods, to a large extent his engineering work simply moved them downstream. The canalization of the Upper Rhine meant floodwater reached the Lower Rhine more quickly, increasing the incidence of flooding in Koblenz, Bonn and Cologne. When those cities built flood defences, the floods moved even further north. The general reduction in flooding along the river also encouraged farmers to exploit land all the way to its banks, leading to the destruction of the original riparian forests of oak, elm, alder and willow.

The Rhine dates back to the Miocene epoch, some 15 million years ago. At that time, its watershed didn't include the Alps – instead, the Rhone and Danube drained the range's northern flanks. By the early Pleistocene epoch, about two million years ago, the Rhine had captured most of its current Alpine watershed from the Rhône. At that time, the river's course took it through what is now the North Sea. During the so-called Anglian glaciation,

The 9 km (5.6 mi) Oosterscheldekering is the longest dam in the Delta Works, a series of barriers designed to protect the Netherlands from North Sea flooding.

> 'The Rhine is unique; it combines the qualities of every river. Mysterious, like the Nile; spangled with gold, like an American river; and, like a river of Asia, abounding with phantoms and fables.'
> – Victor Hugo

about 450,000 years ago, ice in the northern North Sea blocked the river and led to the formation of a large lake that eventually overflowed, causing the Rhine's course to be diverted through the English Channel. During the glacial periods that followed, the Rhine's mouth was located offshore of Brest in what is now France and several great rivers, including the Thames and the Seine, became tributaries of the Rhine. At the end of the last glacial period, from about 22,000 years ago onward, melting of the great ice sheets caused sea levels to rise, inundating the English Channel and North Sea. By about 8,000 years ago, the sea had reached roughly its current height and the current Rhine-Meuse delta began to form.

A pot from the Linear Pottery Culture, c. 5000 BCE.

Farmers of the so-called Linear Pottery Culture first settled along the Rhine about 7,300 years ago, having travelled west across the fertile plains of what is now Germany from the Danube River.

Together with the Danube, the Rhine formed most of the northern inland frontier of the Roman Empire – the boundary of the civilized world, according to the Romans, who used the river for trade and the transport of goods to its outposts deep inland. They built numerous wooden forts – many of which were later upgraded to castles – and other fortifications on its banks to consolidate the empire's control. The Roman navy also maintained a Rhine fleet that played an important role in the supply and transport of the legions stationed along the river. The large numbers of soldiers manning the Roman defences spent their money in the towns along the river, helping to transform them into important cities, and the Rhineland, which was connected with the Mediterranean by the Moselle, Saône and Rhône rivers, became an important economic zone.

Julius Caesar crossed the river in 55 and 53 BCE, as did a number of Roman generals, but for the most part the Rhine remained the frontier between Roman Gaul (modern France) and Germania (largely modern Germany). The fact that the Rhine formed the boundary of Gaul for a time later resulted in claims by France that to the river was its natural eastern boundary.

On the night of 31 December 406 CE, a mixed group of barbarians that included Vandals, Alans and Suebi began to cross the Rhine near Mainz (it's unclear whether the river was frozen or the invaders used a Roman bridge or boats). Eventually some 100,000 marauding peoples flowed west across the river, hastening the demise of the Western Roman Empire.

For the next 1,000 years or so, the Rhine shifted between acting as a border between empires and kingdoms, and being subsumed within them.

Over this period, the river became increasingly important as a commercial route, as the numerous castles along its banks attest; the Rhine was a major shipping route and a central axis for the Holy Roman Empire.

From as long ago as the 1648 Peace of Westphalia, which marked the end of the Thirty Years' War, the Upper Rhine has, at various times, marked a contentious border between France and Germany, with both countries claiming and annexing territory on either side of the river at various times. In particular, the region around Alsace and Lorraine has shifted between the two nations on a fairly regular basis, often following the cessation of periods of conflict.

From the late 18th century, the Middle Rhine became a focus of the cultural-historical movement known as Romanticism, transforming the river into a popular tourist destination and leading to the rejuvenation of much of its historical infrastructure as princes and other wealthy individuals began to rebuild many of its numerous castles. The Romantic movement nurtured an upsurge in German nationalism ('Memories of what the Germans once were and could be in the future are evoked nowhere so clearly as on the Rhine,' wrote the poet Friedrich Schlegel in 1803), which was bolstered by the Rhine crisis of 1840, when the then French prime minister Adolphe Thiers announced his desire to reinstate the Rhine as a natural border, which would have meant the loss of some 32,000 sq km (12,355 sq miles) of German territory. Later, during the formation of the German Empire in 1871 at the end of the Franco-Prussian War, the Middle Rhine again became an important symbol of German nationalism, acting as a focal point around which the nascent country could unite. The unification of Germany at this time saw internal trade barriers eliminated, boosting commerce on the Rhine.

At the end of World War I, the Treaty of Versailles decreed that the Rhineland would be occupied by the Allies until 1935, at which point it would be a demilitarized zone into which the German army could not enter, resulting in significant resentment in Germany. The decree is often cited as a factor in Adolf Hitler's rise to power.

During World War II, the Rhine presented a formidable obstacle to both German and Allied forces, and numerous pivotal battles took place at various bridges and other crossing points, including the bridge at Arnhem, immortalized in the 1977 film *A Bridge Too Far*.

Under the Treaty of Versailles, France was granted the right to build a canal that diverted water from the Rhine below Basel and then re-joined the river at Strasbourg. The resulting Grand Canal d'Alsace, completed in 1959, greatly improved navigation, while also enabling the production of hydroelectric power. Several more canals have been built to connect the Rhine to other rivers, including the Rhône and the Marne, and for hydroelectric generation; four of the eight dams use Rhine water diverted through canal loops.

Adam Frans van der Meulen's painting of French king Louis XIV crossing the Rhine and entering the Netherlands at Lobith on 12 June 1672.

Crouching low for protection in a DUKW amphibious vehicle, US soldiers of the 89th Division cross the Rhine at Oberwesel in late March 1945.

The Rhine is arguably the world's most important commercial artery, both historically and in terms of modern traffic levels. Since the Rhine Valley was subsumed by the Roman Empire, the river has been one of Europe's busiest transport routes. During the medieval period, traffic increased substantially as trade grew, the poor quality of the roads forcing traders to rely on water transport wherever possible. The river became an international waterway in 1815, when the signing of the Treaty of Vienna enshrined the principle of free navigation on the Rhine. Before they were abolished under the treaty, there were about 200 toll stations along the river.

Historically, the rock barrier at Bingen hindered navigation on the Rhine, dividing the river into mostly upstream traffic by seagoing vessels to Cologne and the mostly downstream movement of commodities from Basel to Mainz and Frankfurt. However, in 1830–32, two navigation channels were blasted out to remove the barrier.

Canalization of the upper Rhine, undertaken between 1817 and 1874, also improved navigation, although seasonal variations of flow and the swift current still hinder movement in the river's upper reaches. Today, the river is navigable as far as Rheinfelden on the Swiss–German border, roughly 870 km (541 miles) from the sea.

Since 1872, the 20-km (12-mile) New Waterway Canal, which was built to improve access to the North Sea from the Dutch city of Rotterdam, located at the river's mouth, has been the primary link between the Rhine and the ocean. Subsequently, Rotterdam has grown to become Europe's largest port; in 2021, it handled almost 469 million tonnes (461 million tons) of cargo.

Since the mid-1960s, however, freight tonnage has been decreasing. Today, more than 300 million tonnes (295 million tons) of goods are transported annually on the navigable Rhine between Rheinfelden on the Swiss border and the North Sea. However, over the past few years, as Europe suffered its worst drought in 500 years, low water levels in the Rhine have caused severe delays to shipping. Vessels have been forced to sail with reduced cargoes, sometimes just a quarter of full capacity, denting Germany's economy and causing fuel shortages in the Netherlands. The problems have been so severe that the German government has contemplated carrying out further engineering works to widen and deepen the river's channel and increase its current. It has even considered installing a series of locks.

Because of the removal of both the political and physical barriers to navigation, as well as the rise of modern industry, which necessitated the bulk movement of coal, ore, building materials, raw materials for the chemical industry and oil, the volume of goods conveyed on the river increased significantly. Cheap water transport helped to keep raw materials relatively inexpensive and, consequently, the Rhine became a major axis of industrial production; the river now hosts a fifth of the world's chemical industries.

Several industrial cities are situated on the river's banks, and the river is heavily polluted; some 6,000 toxic substances have been identified in its waters. In November 1986, a fire at a chemical warehouse in the Schweizerhalle industrial zone in Basel, Switzerland, released 20–30 tonnes (19.7–29.5 tons) of pesticides and other chemicals into the river, turning the river red and killing hundreds of thousands of fish, inspiring the creation of international environmental management plans that have greatly improved the river's water

quality. A combination of stricter environmental controls, a transition from heavy to light industry and an international clean-up project have ensured that the Rhine's waters are the cleanest they've been in decades; many species of fish and invertebrate that were regarded as extinct in the Rhine have returned.

The Romans are believed to have introduced viticulture to the Rhine Valley during the first century CE. Between then and the Thirty Years' War (1618–48), vineyard area grew steadily, but the war saw many vineyards devastated. The industry never fully recovered and the area under vines in the Middle Rhine continues to shrink.

Dotted along the river are large signs bearing a number – these are *Rheinkilometer* markings, a scale that was introduced in 1939 and runs from the Old Rhine Bridge at Constance/Konstanz to Rotterdam and the Hook of Holland, 1,036 km (644 miles) downstream.

Today, the French city of Strasbourg, located on the Rhine near the border with Germany, is the seat of the European Parliament.

A container ship on the Rhine. Each year, more than 300 million tonnes (295 million tons) of goods are transported on the river between the Swiss border and the North Sea.

The Rhône

Born in the Swiss Alps, the Rhône is one of Europe's most significant waterways and the only major river that flows directly to the Mediterranean Sea.

The Rhône is a true Alpine river, scenic and often wild, a milky, surging, tumbling torrent. The river's origins lie in the melting of the Rhône Glacier, which inches its way down the southern flank of the 3,630-m (11,909 ft) Dammastock, about 2,200 m (7,218 ft) up in the Swiss Alps. The glacier forms part of the Saint-Gotthard Massif, which is also the source of the Reuss, Rhine and Ticino rivers.

From its source, the Rhône flows southwest through the valleys and gorges of Switzerland's Valais region, where it receives water from the Massa River, which is fed by the Aletsch Glacier, the longest glacier of the Alps. Here, the youthful river is a powerful torrent, but after the town of Brig, it matures into a great mountain river, flowing to the southwest through a glacial valley. Glacial meltwater flows in from the valleys

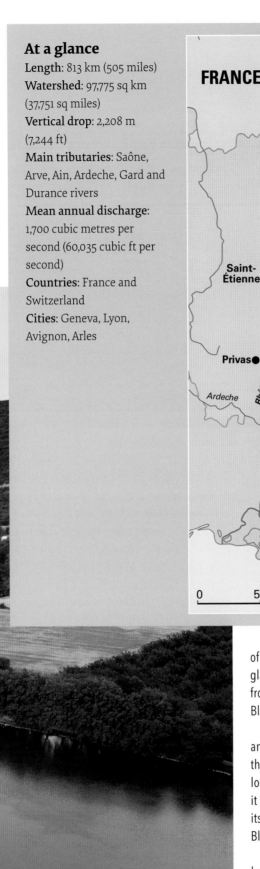

At a glance

Length: 813 km (505 miles)

Watershed: 97,775 sq km (37,751 sq miles)

Vertical drop: 2,208 m (7,244 ft)

Main tributaries: Saône, Arve, Ain, Ardeche, Gard and Durance rivers

Mean annual discharge: 1,700 cubic metres per second (60,035 cubic ft per second)

Countries: France and Switzerland

Cities: Geneva, Lyon, Avignon, Arles

of the Pennine Alps to the south, whose rivers originate in the large glaciers of the massifs of Monte Rosa, Dom and Grand Combin, but also from the steeper slopes of the Bernese Alps to the north, and the Mont Blanc massif to the west.

At Martigny, the river turns sharply to the north and heads towards, and then flows into, Lac Léman (Lake Geneva), which sits in a basin that was hollowed by the Rhône Glacier. As it crosses the lake, the river loses much of the sediment it has been carrying – at its entry point it has formed a large and growing delta – however, it soon regains its milky colour as more tributaries flow in from the glaciers of Mont Blanc.

After passing through the centre of Geneva, the river crosses the border into France, zig-zagging its way through the Jura Mountains before reaching the broad valley of the lower Rhône, where it doubles in size following the confluence of its largest tributary, the Saone, at Lyon. From Lyon, the Rhône flows south along a wide valley that separates the Alps and the Massif Central.

The glacial lake at the terminus of the Rhône Glacier (visible at right) in the Swiss Alps, source of the Rhône River.

At the Roman town of Arles, about 40 km (25 miles) from the Mediterranean Sea, the river reaches its delta, where it splits into the Grand (Great) Rhône and the Petit (Little) Rhône. The delta, the largest in western Europe, forms a 930-sq-km (359-sq-mile) triangle of land between the two arms. Known as the Camargue, this vast plain, dotted with brine lagoons, or étangs (some of which are the remnants of old arms of the river), and reed-covered marshes, is fringed with rice fields and salt ponds. Since the 1920s, some 820 sq km (317 sq miles) of the delta have been set aside as a nature reserve in which more than 400 species of bird, including flamingos, egrets, ibises and many rare types, feed and breed. Its marshes are also said to support some of France's fiercest mosquitos.

The Rhône provides the largest inflow of any river into the Mediterranean, contributing about 12 per cent of the total river influx. Its delta is continuing to expand and extend into the sea, thanks to the significant sediment load carried down from the Alps – roughly 20 million cubic metres (706.3 million cubic ft) of mud are deposited each year.

The Rhône has played an important role as an economic corridor and transport route since ancient times, connecting the North Sea, the Alps and the Mediterranean; it acted as a conduit for the spread of Mediterranean cultures and peoples into northern Europe. During the late Bronze and early Iron Ages, it brought Greek culture to the western Hallstatt and later the La Tène peoples of Western and Central Europe from around 450 BCE. Later, it linked cities such as Arles, Avignon and Lyon to ports on the Mediterranean such as Marseille.

For many years, trade on the upper river was carried out using 30-m-long (98-ft), 75-tonne-capacity sailing barges known as *barques du Rhône*, which were hauled in trains of up to seven craft by as many as 80 horses. At Arles, goods were then trans-shipped into 23-m (75-ft) sailing barges called *allèges d'Arles* for the final run down to the Mediterranean. Today, canals connect the river to several others, including the Seine, Moselle and Rhine.

During World War II, following the collapse of Vichy France in 1942, Italy's forces occupied southeastern France up to the eastern banks of the Rhône. The river then became the route followed by Allied armies moving north from their invasion of southern France in June 1944.

Despite millennia of exploitation by the communities of people who lived along the Rhône, at the beginning of the 20th century it mostly remained a wild, untamed river characterized by untapped resources and devastating floods. However, in the aftermath of the war, the French government began a dam-building phase. There are now 24 hydroelectric schemes along the river – four in Switzerland, one shared on the French–Swiss border and 19 in France – with a total capacity of 2.8 GW, capturing more than half of its total hydroelectric potential. Among them is the Génissiat dam, located on the Upper Rhône not far downstream from the Swiss border, which was designed to provide Paris's electricity needs. In France, a number of nuclear power stations use the river's water as a coolant; this accounts for a fifth of the annual net withdrawals from the river and has a significant effect on its water temperature.

In the Valais, the Rhône has been dyked and narrowed but it is the river's lower course, between Lyon and the Mediterranean, that has been most extensively engineered. Here the Rhône has been significantly canalized to aid navigation, the main channel widened

View of Avignon from the Right Bank of the Rhône near the Tour Philippe-le-Bel *by Claude-Joseph Vernet, 1757.*

and deepened; several diversion channels have also been cut. There are also 14 wide-gauge navigation locks to smooth out the river's impressive gradient, which is maintained almost to its mouth; at Lyon, 330 km (205 miles) from the sea, the river is still 170 m (559 ft) above sea level. About 6 km (4 miles) from the mouth, a large bar blocks the passage of larger vessels, so a short canal, the Canal Maritime Saint-Louis, has been cut to allow movement to and from the Mediterranean. More than 5 million tonnes (4.9 million tons) of goods are transported along the river each year.

The Rhône basin is among the most important economic regions of both Switzerland and France, supporting both industry and agriculture. Downstream from Lyon, the river becomes significantly industrialized, hosting numerous chemical and pharmaceutical companies, which account for more than a third of the annual net withdrawals from the Rhône basin. The river's water is also used extensively for irrigation; 32 pumping stations supply water to some 120,000 ha (296,526 acres) of vineyards, orchards, maize and rapeseed fields, and other crops, as well as for the raising of livestock. The river also provides drinking water for about 800,000 people.

A satellite image of the delta and mouth of the Rhône.

The Seine

One of Europe's great historic rivers, the Seine will be forever entwined with Paris, the City of Light, through which it flows.

After the Loire, the Seine is France's longest river. It rises in the commune of Source-Seine, about 30 km (17 miles) northwest of Dijon on the Langres Plateau in Burgundy. The City of Paris has owned the land around the source of the river since 1864, when Napoleon III placed it under the city's governance.

After crossing the chalk plateau of Champagne in a well-defined trench, the river enters Paris, where it receives its main tributary, the Marne. Flowing through the city in an arc 13 km (8 miles) long, the river divides it into two parts: the Left and Right banks. Within the metropolis, where it has been narrowed and trained, it is spanned by 37 bridges and bordered on both sides by double-decker quays. Planted above with plane trees and below with poplars, the quays are popular for walking and picnicking, and host the iconic *bouquinistes* – roughly 225 booksellers who turn the riverside into an enormous open-air bookshop (the Seine has been described as 'the only river in the world that runs between two bookshelves').

As it leaves Paris, the Seine receives the Oise before flowing in a series of wide, sweeping loops across Normandy. At Tancarville, about 25 km (15.5 miles) from the river's mouth, it forms a broad estuary that eventually empties into the English Channel at the busy port of Le Havre.

At a glance

Length: 777 km (483 miles)

Watershed: 79,000 sq km (30,502 sq miles)

Vertical drop: 471 m (1,545 ft)

Main tributaries: Aube, Yonne, Marne and Oise rivers

Mean annual discharge: 560 cubic metres per second (19,776 cubic ft per second)

Countries: France

Cities: Paris, Rouen, Vernon, Giverny

The river's estuary experiences a tidal bore, known as the *mascaret*, which occurs during spring tides and can reach as far upriver as Rouen. However, since 1867, regular dredging has deepened the river, causing the *mascaret* to gradually diminish. Travelling at a speed of up 10 metres per second (33 ft per second), the bore front sometimes exceeded 7 m (23 ft) in height. It's thought to have been at least partly responsible for the loss of more than 200 ships in the river's lower reaches between 1789 and 1850.

The Seine was once quite shallow as it passed through Paris, consisting of a small channel bordered by sandy or muddy banks. However, during the 1880s, a series of locks was installed to raise the river's level and, today, its average depth in Paris is about 9.5 m (31 ft). In addition, since 1950, a series of large storage reservoirs has been built on the Seine and some of its tributaries, which help to keep its level in Paris relatively constant. The reservoirs also help to reduce the frequency of flooding and ensure a constant water supply during summer. The Marne Reservoir is the largest artificial lake in western Europe, with an area of almost 5,000 ha (12,355 acres).

On the Bank of the Seine, Bennecourt, by Claude Monet, 1868.

Human occupation in the region now occupied by Paris dates back to about 8,000 BCE. Fragments of wooden canoes used by fishermen on the Seine, dating from around 4,800–4,200 BCE, have also been found at Bercy. The city itself was founded in the second half of the 3rd century BCE, when a tribe of Celtic Gauls known as the Parisii established a fishing village beside the Seine, possibly on what is now known as the Île de la Cité, an island in the river that today hosts the cathedral of Notre-Dame. The Parisii built a walled fort, or oppidum, and bridges across the river and began to trade with other nearby river settlements.

The village occupied a strategic position on the main trade route between Britain, the Roman colony of Provence and the Mediterranean Sea, and its inhabitants began to charge a toll for use of the bridges across the Seine, eventually growing so prosperous on the proceeds that they were able to mint their own gold coins. The defeat of the Parisii by the Roman army in 52 BCE saw the establishment of a Gallo-Roman garrison town called Lutetia on the village site, which was later occupied by Clovis I, the King of the Franks, who made it his capital in 508 CE, naming it Paris after its original occupants.

A dugout canoe, dating from the Neolithic period, discovered in 1989 during construction work in Bercey in Paris's 12th arrondissement.

In 845 CE, a Viking chieftain named Reginherus led a fleet of 120 ships bearing more than 5,000 men up the Seine, raiding Rouen and then sailing on to Paris, which at that time was concentrated on the Île de la Cité. They quickly defeated a division of the Frankish army of King Charles the Bald, causing the rest of the army to retreat. Entering Paris on Easter Sunday, 29 March, the Vikings sacked the city, before eventually withdrawing after being paid a hefty ransom.

At Paris, 365 km (227 miles) from its mouth, the Seine sits a mere 25 m (82 ft) above sea level. Consequently, outside flood periods, the river is decidedly sluggish, its flow averaging a few cubic metres per second and thus easily navigable. Especially below Paris, the Seine is a busy traffic highway, linking the city's main port facilities at Gennevilliers with the sea and the huge maritime port of Le Havre. The river and its wider drainage network carry most of France's inland waterborne traffic, mostly transporting heavy petroleum products and building materials.

The final 123 km (76 miles) of the Seine, from Le Havre to Rouen, known as the Seine Maritime, is the only section of the river used by ocean-going craft; dredging keeps the river deep enough to allow their passage. During the 16th century, Rouen was France's main seaport, despite the distance from the sea; however, during the 19th century it was surpassed by Le Havre. Smaller commercial craft such as barges and push-tows can navigate as far upstream as Marcilly-sur-Seine, near the confluence with the Aube, about 516 km (321 miles) from the river's mouth. The lower Seine system is connected to the Rhine by way of the Marne; to the waterways of Belgium via the Oise; and to the Loire and the Saône-Rhône via canals built during the 17th and 18th centuries.

The Seine is the most regular of France's major rivers and its regime is relatively moderate. The limestone rocks that underlie most of the river basin are relatively permeable, and precipitation tends to be modest and evenly distributed over the year, so floods are both infrequent and rarely dangerous or destructive. However, exceptionally heavy rainfall in January 1910 caused the river to rise to about 10 m (33 ft) in Paris, flooding the extensive low-lying quarters along its ancient meander loop (the Marais) – the worst flooding since 1658.

The Seine's waters are an important resource for the sizeable riverine population. The river supplies cooling water for several large power stations, both thermal and nuclear, as well as half of the water used in the region around Paris, both for industry and for human consumption, and three-quarters of the water used in the region between Rouen and Le Havre.

A frequently picturesque river, overlooked by towering white chalk cliffs and flanked by dense forests, apple orchards and charming villages, the Seine has long been a source of inspiration for artists, including Claude Monet, Henri Matisse, Vincent Van Gogh, Camille Pissarro, Auguste Renoir and Georges Seurat. Indeed, the town of Honfleur on the southern bank of the Seine estuary is considered by many to be the birthplace of Impressionism.

The River Thames

The chief river of southern England and the UK's second longest, the Thames has a long and storied history.

Just as the Seine is synonymous with Paris, so the Thames is synonymous with London. Flowing through the centre of one of the world's great cities, the river has played a pivotal role in England's fortunes; the politician John Burns once described the Thames as 'liquid history'.

The Thames is a languid, gently flowing river, pastoral and undramatic. Its traditional source is in the Cotswold Hills at Thames Head. Marked by a stone in a field, this collection of seasonal springs actually dries up for much of the year, meaning that the river begins lower down in its course. However, one of the river's tributaries, the River Churn, is considered by some to be a better candidate for its source. Rising near the village of Seven Springs, 213 m (699 ft) above sea level, just south of Cheltenham, the Churn's source is 23 km (14 miles) further from the mouth than Thames Head (which would make the Thames the UK's longest river).

After passing through some 48 navigation locks, with accompanying weirs, the Thames eventually empties into the North Sea via the Thames Estuary. The transition from freshwater to brackish occurs in the area around Battersea, about 65 km (40 miles) from the river's mouth. The transition from estuary to open sea is marked by the Nore sandbank, which presented a significant hazard for shipping to and from London. Consequently, in 1732, it received the world's first lightship.

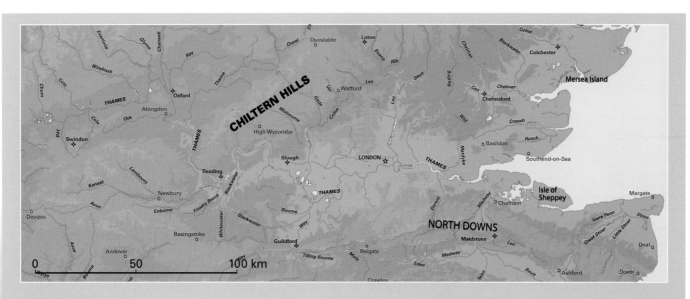

At a glance

Length: 346 km (215 miles)

Watershed: 14,250 sq km (5,502 sq miles)

Vertical drop: 108 m (354 ft)

Main tributaries: Medway

Mean annual discharge: 66 cubic metres per second (2,331 cubic ft per second)

Countries: United Kingdom (England)

Cities: London, Oxford

The stretch of river that passes through Oxford is sometimes called the Isis. In the past, particularly during the Victorian era, gazetteers and cartographers insisted that the name applied to the river from its source to Dorchester. There, it meets the Thame, becoming the 'Thame-isis', which was supposedly subsequently abbreviated to Thames.

The river's lower reaches are known as the Tideway. Teddington Lock, located about 89 km (55 miles) upstream of the Thames Estuary, is the river's usual tidal limit, but high spring tides can reach higher and can briefly reverse the river's flow. At London Bridge, the river rises by as much as 7 m (23 ft) during a spring tide. The Thames Barrier at Silvertown was built during the early 1980s to protect London from tidal surges, when high tides and strong winds from the North Sea combine. It closes several times a year to prevent water from damaging low-lying parts of London.

The Thames contains more than 80 islands, the largest of which, such as Formosa and Andersey, were created when the river divided into separate streams. Many have played starring roles in English history, such as Magna Carta Island at Runnymede and Thorney Island, which used to be an eyot and now hosts both Westminster Abbey and the Palace of Westminster (commonly known today as the Houses of Parliament).

Flowing through some of mainland Britain's driest regions and heavily abstracted – primarily for drinking water; the Thames provides two-thirds of London's drinking water – the river has a relatively small discharge, given its length and breadth. Each day, between Windsor and Hampton on London's western edge, some 1.8 million cubic metres (63.6 million cubic ft) of water are pumped into large storage reservoirs

prior to treatment and distribution; it eventually rejoins the Thames after passing though giant sewage-treatment facilities at Mogden, Beckton and Crossness.

The Thames has existed as a discrete drainage line for at least 58 million years. Until about half a million years ago, the river emptied into the North Sea near present-day Ipswich. About 450,000 years ago, during the Pleistocene Era's most intense ice age, the river was dammed in what is now Hertfordshire by the edge of an ice sheet. Large ice lakes formed and, when they eventually overflowed, the river was diverted onto its present course, in the process carving out the Brent Valley.

People have been living off the River Thames since Neolithic times. For millennia, it presented a formidable barrier, with the territories of the various tribes and kingdoms along its route being defined by it. Among the earliest written references to the Thames appears in Julius Caesar's account of his second expedition to Britain in 54 BCE. The Romans, recognizing the river's strategic and economic importance, built numerous fortifications along the Thames valley. From around 47 CE, they began to establish Londonium (London's precursor) as their British capital on two hills on the Thames's northern bank, now known as Cornhill and Ludgate Hill, which provided a defensible site near a point on the river that was both deep enough for the era's ships and narrow enough to be bridged, as well as a convenient trading centre.

At that time, the lower Thames was a shallow waterway that meandered through fetid marshes. Over the following centuries, however,

Above: *A painting of the frost fair on the Thames during the winter of 1683–84, with Old London Bridge in the distance.*

Left: *An aerial view of the Thames as it passes through London and under Tower Bridge.*

tens of thousands of people. The death of Prince Albert in 1861 from typhoid has been linked to contaminated Thames water from beside Windsor Castle.

The widespread installation of flush toilets during the 1850s brought a sudden new influx of sewage into the river, leading quickly to the 'Great Stink' of 1858, when pollution in the river was so extreme that sittings of the House of Commons were abandoned. This eventually led to the construction of huge sewer systems, along with the building of reservoirs and pumping stations to the west of London to ensure continuity of water supply to the capital, which also slightly improved water quality. By the 1950s, the river was biologically dead, but the decline of heavy industry and tanneries, improved sewage treatment, changing land use and improved pollution control have brought dramatic improvements in water quality and the abundance and diversity of aquatic life.

The Thames has long been an important trade and supply route, both internationally through the Port of London, and domestically along its length and through its connection to Britain's extensive network of canals. Ocean-going ships can travel as far upstream as London Bridge. The river is linked to other river basins by two broad canals – the Kennet and Avon Canal and the Grand Union Canal – as well as several disused or mainly recreational canals. While the Port of London continues to be one of the UK's three main ports, handling 10 per cent of the UK's commercial shipping trade, most trade has moved downstream from the metropolis itself to Tilbury, which was expanded in the late 1960s, and the new London Gateway, which opened on the north bank of the Thames in Thurrock, Essex, 48 km (30 miles) east of central London, in 2013.

it was transformed into a deep tidal canal that flows between about 320 km (199 miles) of solid walls, built to protect the homes and businesses of the 1.5 million people who work and live on the adjacent floodplain.

At the beginning of the 17th century, during a run of bitterly cold winters, the Thames froze over above London Bridge. Visitors to the first Frost Fair, in 1607, could partake in a number of unusual amusements, including ice bowling.

London's growth saw the amount of effluent dumped into the Thames soar. This included human and livestock excrement, and waste from slaughterhouses and manufacturing processes. As early as the 1300s, the river was effectively an open sewer. During the 19th century, it was a source of four serious cholera outbreaks that killed

The Volga River

Considered by many Russians to be the country's national river, the Volga is the principal waterway of western Russia and the historical cradle of the Russian state.

Flowing through central and southern Russia, the Volga is the longest river in Europe; it also has the largest discharge, drainage basin and delta of Europe's rivers. It resides within an endorheic (i.e., closed) basin, the longest river in the world to do so; rather than emptying into the ocean, its mouth opens into the Caspian Sea (the river contributes 80 per cent of the sea's inflow).

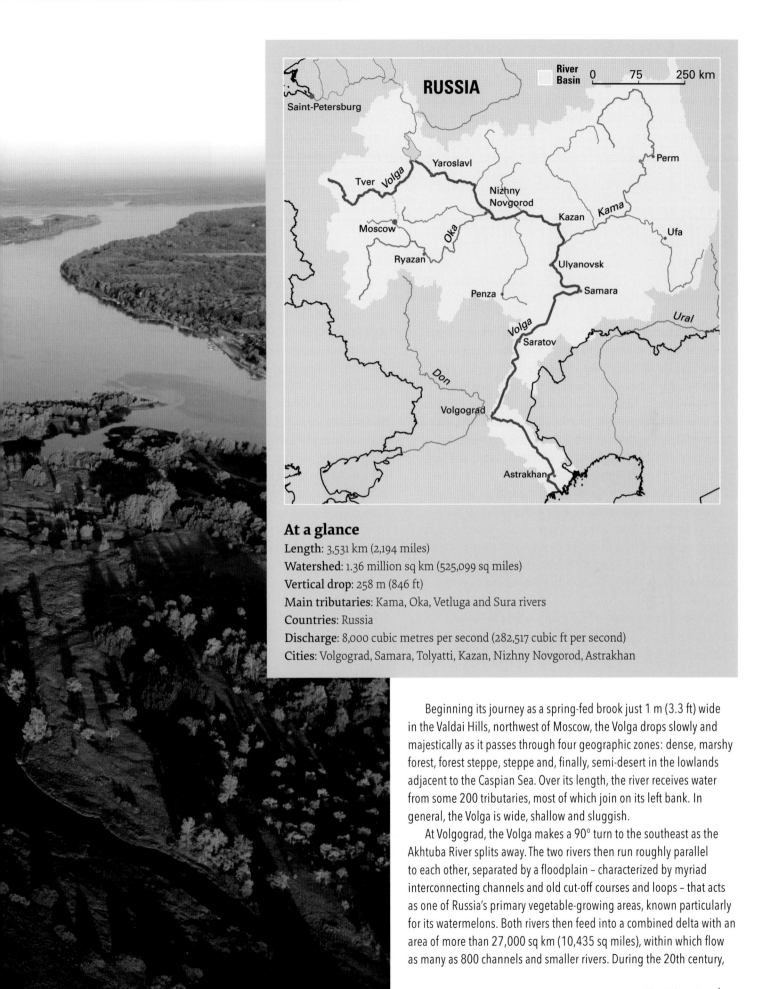

At a glance

Length: 3,531 km (2,194 miles)

Watershed: 1.36 million sq km (525,099 sq miles)

Vertical drop: 258 m (846 ft)

Main tributaries: Kama, Oka, Vetluga and Sura rivers

Countries: Russia

Discharge: 8,000 cubic metres per second (282,517 cubic ft per second)

Cities: Volgograd, Samara, Tolyatti, Kazan, Nizhny Novgorod, Astrakhan

Beginning its journey as a spring-fed brook just 1 m (3.3 ft) wide in the Valdai Hills, northwest of Moscow, the Volga drops slowly and majestically as it passes through four geographic zones: dense, marshy forest, forest steppe, steppe and, finally, semi-desert in the lowlands adjacent to the Caspian Sea. Over its length, the river receives water from some 200 tributaries, most of which join on its left bank. In general, the Volga is wide, shallow and sluggish.

At Volgograd, the Volga makes a 90° turn to the southeast as the Akhtuba River splits away. The two rivers then run roughly parallel to each other, separated by a floodplain – characterized by myriad interconnecting channels and old cut-off courses and loops – that acts as one of Russia's primary vegetable-growing areas, known particularly for its watermelons. Both rivers then feed into a combined delta with an area of more than 27,000 sq km (10,435 sq miles), within which flow as many as 800 channels and smaller rivers. During the 20th century, the delta's area has grown significantly due of changes in the level of the Caspian Sea; in 1880, it covered an area of only 3,222 sq km (1,244 sq miles). The delta is home to more than 200 bird and 30 mammal species, and the waters in and around the delta are productive fishing grounds; the city of Astrakhan, in the upper delta, is the centre of the Russian caviar industry.

> 'The Volga! There is a mystery, a charm in all mighty rivers, which has ever made us gaze upon them with an interest beyond that inspired by other great and glorious sights; but to look on the largest of the European rivers gave a thrill of joy surpassing all former pleasure of the kind.'
>
> – Robert Bremner, 1830

The Volga has a powerful symbolism in Russian culture, not to mention enormous economic and historical importance; it's often referred to as Mother Volga in Russian literature and folklore. People have been living in the region around the river for at least 9,000 years. As civilizations began to develop in Asia and Europe, the Volga acted as an important meeting place for numerous Eurasian cultures, including Slavic, Scandinavian, Baltic, Hunnic and Turkic peoples. During the medieval period, the Volga cities of Atil, Saqsin and Sarai were among the world's largest, and the river acted as an important trade route, connecting Scandinavia and northern Russia with Persia and Constantinople. During the 9th century, the forerunner of the Russian state, the Rus' Khaganate, is thought to have arisen along the Volga's banks, and in the 13th century the Mongol Golden Horde arose in the river's lower reaches; the horde leader Batu founded his imperial capital, Sarai, about 120 km (75 miles) north of the modern city of Astrakhan.

The Volga's basin sprawls across about two-fifths of European Russia, draining most of the country's west. The basin encompasses Russia's most heavily populated region, containing almost half the population of the Russian Republic and four of the country's ten largest cities, including Moscow. Among these cities is Volgograd, formerly Stalingrad, scene of the pivotal Second World War Battle of Stalingrad in 1942–43, possibly the bloodiest battle in human history. The river played a central role in the battle, providing a supply line for the besieged Soviet troops and the eventual Soviet victory reinforced the Volga's standing as a powerful national symbol.

Today, the Volga helps to power Russia. The Volga valley supports a substantial petroleum and natural gas industry, and the river itself hosts eight hydroelectric power stations, with another three on one of its tributaries, the Kama. Together, they have a generating capacity of some 11,000 MW – less than anticipated because the water moves slowly through the turbines.

Most of the dams and power stations date back to the Soviet era, and in particular the years of Stalin's industrialization, and their construction often resulted in the enforced resettlement of whole towns and villages, and the destruction of significant historical heritage. These dams have tamed the Volga's once-wild waters, and turned the river into a string of enormous, placid reservoirs, located at intervals of about 320 km (199 miles) along the river's length. The Kuybyshev Reservoir near Samara/Kazan is the largest in Europe, with an area of some 6,450 sq km (2,490 sq miles) and a capacity of 58 billion cubic metres (2 trillion cubic ft) – not only does it impound the Volga's waters, but it also backs water up the Kama for about 600 km/373 miles). Before the dams were built, the river was much narrower, its banks fringed with lush meadows.

The reservoirs also provide water for irrigation; the fertile river valley is an important centre for wheat growing. As a whole, the Volga Basin accounts for half of the Russian Federation's agricultural production.

Unsurprisingly, given the level of industrial activity in the Volga basin – it accounts for almost half of Russia's industrial production and 40 per cent of its power output – the river and its habitats have been adversely affected by high levels of chemical pollution, which is exacerbated by municipal effluent and agricultural runoff. The pollution, along with the many dams and reservoirs along the river, have had an adverse effect on some of the 70-odd fish species that live within it.

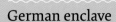

German enclave

In 1763, Catherine the Great issued a manifesto in which she offered incentives to foreigners to move to the Volga region in the hope of spurring its development, while also creating a buffer zone between Russia and the Mongols to the east. At the time, conditions in Germany were tough, and it was Germans who responded in the largest numbers. By 1897, the Volga German minority in Russia numbered almost 1.8 million. Following the October Revolution of 1917, a slice of the region was turned into the Volga German Autonomous Soviet Socialist Republic, with its capital in the Volga port of Engels. However, in 1941, in response to the German invasion of the Soviet Union, the republic was formally abolished and Joseph Stalin had its German inhabitants deported to Siberia and Kazakhstan.

Zhigulyovskaya Hydroelectric Station, located on the Volga near Zhigulyovsk and Tolyatti in Russia, was completed in 1957.

Many, such as the famous beluga sturgeon, producer of the fabled caviar, are anadromous, meaning that they live in the Caspian Sea and swim upriver to spawn in the Volga and other inflowing waterways, but dams restrict their movement upstream.

The Volga has long acted as an important conduit for trade. Before the arrival of steamboats, large gangs of serfs, known as burlaks, pulled barges upstream with ropes. During the Stalin years, the river was widened to enable the passage of larger vessels and today it is navigable along nearly its entire length and acts as Russia's main commercial waterway. The river and its tributaries carry almost two-thirds of Russia's waterborne cargo and almost half of its river passengers. Canals connect the Volga with the Black and Baltic seas, St Petersburg and Moscow, integrating it with virtually the entire waterway system of eastern Europe.

Russian artist Ilya Repin's Barge Haulers on the Volga *was inspired by scenes that he witnessed while holidaying on the river in 1870.*

CHAPTER FIVE

Rivers of Oceania

While Oceania is one of the world's largest geographical regions, as its name suggests, much of that area is ocean and much of the land is made up of relatively flat islands, so 'great' rivers are few and far between. Most of Oceania's largest rivers are situated in Australia, where they play a vital role in the national economy, supporting vast agricultural regions; however, Australia is the world's driest inhabited continent and the river network is sparse compared to those on other continents. Outside of Australia, the islands of New Guinea and New Zealand, which both enjoy higher rainfall, boast a number of major rivers that have great cultural significance to the Indigenous people who live along their banks.

The Murray River.

The Murray River

Australia's longest river, the Murray plays a significant part in the country's economy, supporting Australia's most important irrigated region, but is now over-abstracted and dying.

The Murray River is rich in heritage and history. It has long played a central role in Australia's economic prosperity, particularly through the bounty of agricultural produce nourished by its waters. And despite its ongoing environmental degradation, it retains a beguiling natural beauty.

The Murray is the world's third-longest navigable river, after the Amazon and the Nile. While the river itself is 2,520 km (1,566 miles) long, it forms part of the 3,750-km (2,330-mile) combined Murray–Darling river system. Among its tributaries are five of the next six of Australia's longest rivers (the Murrumbidgee, Darling, Lachlan, Warrego and Paroo rivers).

The Murray–Darling basin is the world's third-largest catchment area, covering more than 1 million sq km (386,102 sq miles) and draining about a seventh of Australia, including most of inland Victoria, New South Wales and southern Queensland. However, compared to similarly sized rivers elsewhere in the world, the Murray carries a relatively small volume of water and the annual variability of its flow is particularly high. The river has dried up completely on three occasions since official records began and sandbars frequently form at its mouth, blocking the river's flow into the ocean.

Rising at Cowombat Flat in the Australian Alps in southeastern New South Wales, the river drains the western side of the Great Dividing

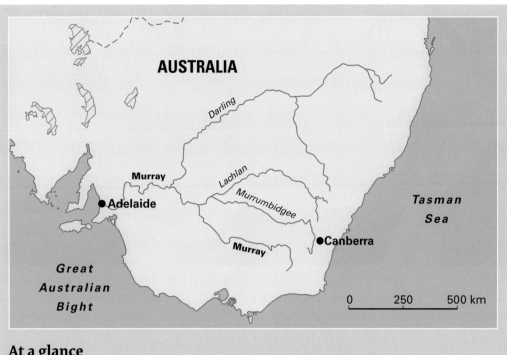

AUSTRALIA

Darling

Murray

Lachlan

Murrumbidgee

●Adelaide

*Tasman
Sea*

●Canberra

Murray

*Great
Australian
Bight*

0   250   500 km

At a glance

Length: 2,520 km (1,566 miles)
Watershed: 1,061,469 sq km (409,835 sq miles)
Vertical drop: 1,430 m (4,692 ft)
Main tributaries: Mitta Mitta, Wakool, Ovens, Goulburn, Murrumbidgee and Darling rivers
Mean annual discharge: 767 cubic metres per second (27,086 cubic ft per second)
Countries: Australia
Cities: Albury, Wodonga, Echuca, Swan Hill, Mildura, Renmark, Murray Bridge

Range, Australia's highest mountains. It then enters a flatter central section as it meanders across a broad, mature floodplain, where it forms the border between New South Wales and Victoria. For most of its lower course through South Australia, the river flows across a narrower floodplain, hemmed in by 30-m-high (98 ft) limestone cliffs.

After flowing through Lake Alexandrina, the river empties into the Great Australian Bight through Murray Mouth, also known as Cadell Passage. Only a small percentage of the river's flow reaches Murray Mouth and its waters there are almost invariably sluggish and shallow.

During periods of particularly low flow, dredging machines, operating continuously, are used to move sand from the channel in order to keep seawater flowing into the Coorong, a series of long, narrow estuarine lagoons separated from the Southern Ocean by the coastal sand dunes of the Younghusband Peninsula.

The Murray is known for its fringing corridors and forests of majestic river red gums, which often support huge, raucous flocks of parrots such as corellas and galahs (the river also hosts the world's largest ibis rookery). However, extreme droughts are placing significant stress on the forests and there are concerns over their long-term survival. Today, the most common tree along the Murray's banks is the introduced willow, whose extensive root mats help to prevent erosion but also choke out other plants and even the river itself.

In 1824, Hamilton Hume and William Hovell crossed the Murray where the city of Albury now stands, becoming the first Europeans to see it. Hume named it the Hume River after his father. Six years later, Charles Sturt reached the river after floating down the Murrumbidgee and then continued down its remaining length before finally reaching Lake Alexandrina, near the river's mouth. Having already explored the Darling River, Sturt established that it, the Murrumbidgee and the Murray were all part of the same river system. He named the river after Sir George Murray, the then British secretary of state for war and the colonies, unaware that Hume and Hovell had already named it.

For many years, the Murray represented a significant barrier to land-based travel and trade.

A paddlesteamer and barges tied up at Murray Bridge in South Australia, site of the first road bridge across the lower Murray, in 1920.

This led to the development of numerous ports along the river, which acted as both conduits for the transport of goods and sites for bridges or ferry crossings. In its heyday, during the latter half of the 19th century, the Murray was a virtual liquid highway as shallow-draft paddle steamers carried out a substantial commercial trade, carrying wool, wheat and other commodities up and down the river system. By the 1870s, 30 steamers and a similar number of barges were working the Murray in season. (Barges used steam-driven winches to clear the river of so-called snags – fallen trees hidden beneath the surface of the brown water.)

Such was the volume and value of river trade that Echuca, 1,720 km (1,069 miles) upriver from Murray Mouth, became Victoria's second-largest port, the bulk of the wool-clip travelling there by river and then transferring to the railway for transport south to Melbourne. However, the unpredictability of the river's level meant that boats were unable to compete with rail and, later, road transport. Today, most traffic on the river is recreational – mostly water skiing, fishing and houseboats.

In 1887, the Canadian engineer George Chaffey introduced an irrigation system in Mildura, sparking a period of rapid settlement and accelerating the exploitation of the river's water supply. The establishment of the River Murray Commission in 1915 led to the building of four large reservoirs along the Murray to even out the effects of drought and flood. These dams inverted the river's natural flow pattern, shifting the annual flood from winter–spring to the summer. During the 1950s, small-scale pumping plants began to draw water from the Murray, helping to fuel the expansion of farming and the development of irrigation areas, eventually turning the so-called Riverland in the Murray Valley into Australia's most productive agricultural region. Today, it supports Australia's greatest area of irrigated crops and pastures (about 1.5 million ha/3.7 million acres – more than 70 per cent of the national total), and the country's second-largest wine-producing region.

During the 19th century, Echuca grew to become Victoria's second-largest port.

Drip irrigation in a vineyard in the Riverland region in South Australia.

However, the river's salt content has increased due to decades of irrigation and land clearing, which have increased the amount of salt flowing into the river, and drought and abstraction, which has reduced flows, so the salt isn't flushed out, and there is now widespread concern that its water will eventually become too salty to use. High salinity is also damaging the soil, threatening the agricultural industries. Run-off from agriculture, which contains salt, fertilizers and pesticides, along with the disruption of the river's natural flow, have also had a devastating effect on its health. The river provides the major domestic water supply for more than 1.5 million households – Adelaide is almost completely dependent on the Murray for its water supply – but the water quality is often so poor that it's unfit for drinking without treatment.

Much of the river's aquatic life is declining, rare or endangered, including the mighty Murray cod, which can grow to almost 2 m (6.6 ft) in length. Introduced carp have been particularly devastating, consuming aquatic plants and stirring up sediment, making the water turbid. In some sections of the river, carp are the only fish present.

Although legislative arrangements were drawn up in 1987 and 1992 to introduce comprehensive basin-wide responses to the various environmental crises facing the Murray, little progress has been made and the states and the farming industry continue to bicker over water allocations.

Murray cod can grow to a length of almost two metres.

Murray River dreaming

As part of the most significant river system on one of the world's driest continents, it's hardly surprising that the Murray has significant cultural relevance to Aboriginal Australians, who have been living in the vicinity of the river for at least 40,000 years. According to the Ngarrindjeri people of Lake Alexandrina, the Murray was created by Pondi, the Murray cod, as he was chased by the Great Ancestor, Ngurunderi.

The Sepik River

The longest river on the island of New Guinea and the second largest in Oceania by discharge volume after the Fly River, the Sepik is one of the world's least developed rivers.

Meandering sinuously through one of the world's last remaining wildernesses, a steamy world of dense jungle, sago and nipa palm swamps, lagoons dotted with floating islands of vegetation, massive man-eating crocodiles, electric-blue butterflies the size of your hand and (once, but no longer) savage head hunters, the Sepik is often hailed as the world's largest 'pristine' river, untainted by dams, pollution, bridges or industry.

Tumbling out of the lofty, cloud-forested mountains near Telefomin in the Victor Emanuel Range in Papua New Guinea's central highlands, the river begins life as a torrential stream flowing through deep, rocky gorges, its channel constricted to a width of less than 10 m (33 ft) in places. It leaves the mountains abruptly near Yapsei, before crossing briefly into Papua, the Indonesian side of the island. It then turns eastwards and meanders in serpentine fashion along the extensive,

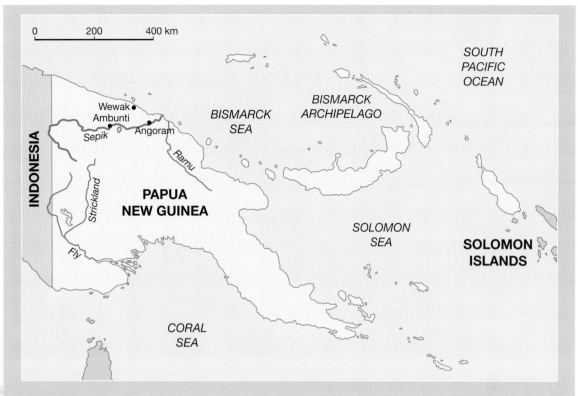

At a glance

Length: 1,126 km (700 miles)
Watershed: 80,321 sq km (31,012 sq miles)
Vertical drop: 2,170 m (7,119 ft)
Main tributaries: Yellow, April, Karawari, Yuat and Keram rivers
Annual mean discharge: 7,000 cubic metres per second (247,203 cubic ft per second)
Countries: Papua New Guinea, Indonesia
Cities: N/A

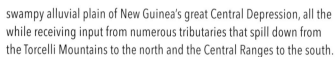

swampy alluvial plain of New Guinea's great Central Depression, all the while receiving input from numerous tributaries that spill down from the Torcelli Mountains to the north and the Central Ranges to the south.

Because the elevation doesn't change dramatically along the river's lower course, it flows more slowly than many long rivers and also exhibits back-flowing, which creates lagoons and backwater swamps along its route. Along most of its course, the river is flanked by a belt of active meanders 5–10 km (3–6 miles) wide. The river's densely forested floodplain is up to 70 km (43.5 miles) wide and features some 1,500 oxbow and other lakes, the largest of which are the Chambri Lakes.

Unusually, the Sepik lacks a delta, flowing straight into the Bismarck Sea about 100 km (62 miles) east of the town of Wewak. This is due to the fact that the adjacent continental shelf is less than 2 km (1.2 miles) wide near the river's mouth and about 90 per cent of the 85 million tonnes (83.6 million tons) of sediment that flows from the river each year falls into a deep submarine canyon that extends for a kilometre from the shore, eventually forming a plume that discolours the seawater for more than 30 km (19 miles) beyond the river mouth.

People have been living along the Sepik River for millennia and, for many, life has changed little for centuries. Headhunting and

Left: *Traditional painted clay figures wearing masks from the village of Karau Village in the Sepik River region.*

Below: *The* haus tambaran *or spirit house, in which important decisions regarding the community are made, where boys are initiated and ceremonies to please the spirits are performed, in the village of Kanganaman, located a short walk from the Sepik.*

cannibalism were once common in the region, but they haven't been practised since the early 20th century.

Despite being one of the least developed areas in one of the world's least developed countries, today the Sepik basin – a region the size of France – is home to some 430,000 people (a population density of about 10 people per sq km/26 people per sq mile), the majority of whom are subsistence farmers, primarily growing sago. At least 100 distinct villages and hamlets are spread along the river's length. The river represents the beating heart of every village, providing inhabitants with fish and other food resources, transport, recreation and water for domestic use. Traditionally, the 'river people' have exchanged fish for processed sago starch with the 'bush people' living farther inland.

During the Southeast Asian monsoon (November–April), when the southeast trade winds bring heavy rain, floods are frequent and the river may swell to a width of 70 km (43.5 miles) for as long as five months. Village huts, which are raised on stilts, become isolated and, in extreme cases, whole villages can be washed away. The ubiquitous wooden dugout canoe comes into its own at these times, enabling people to travel and fish while the land is submerged.

The Sepik River region is among the world's most culturally and linguistically diverse, with estimates suggesting that more than 300 different languages are spoken among those who live in the Sepik basin. Unsurprisingly, given this incredible linguistic diversity, the river has numerous local names, which typically apply only to the short stretch of water adjacent to a particular village. While none apply to the whole stream itself, one – Sipik or Sepik – which was used by an indigenous group that lived at the river's mouth, was eventually chosen for the river after Germany lost colonial control over the territory in the aftermath of World War I.

The pattern of isolation that has driven the Sepik River basin's linguistic diversity has also spawned one of the most original, profuse, diverse and extensive artistic traditions in Oceania. Distinct art styles are found along the river; each community has its own artistic canon and cosmology. Sepik art is bewilderingly inventive, utilizing a staggering array of materials, including pig tusks, feathers, worked and polished shells, clay, human and animal bones, hair and teeth, wood, mammal skins, and a vibrant palette of ochres. It encompasses sculptures of supernatural beings, wooden masks and shields, clay pottery, ornate shell jewellery, the ornamentation of household and cult objects, and other arts and crafts. At the spiritual centre of each village is an intricately decorated high-gabled spirit house, or *haus tambaran*, where village matters are debated.

While there are no large cities or industry along the Sepik, threats do exist, including mining, invasive species and industrial logging. Of particular concern is a proposed open-pit copper and gold mine, and a hydropower plant on one of the Sepik's major tributaries, the Frieda River, which could have a devastating effect on the Sepik itself. The proposed mine will feature a tailings dam, in which mining waste and toxic by-products will be stored, that will be two and a half times the size of Sydney Harbour and there are fears that the tailings could make their way into the river system.

Crocodile hunters

The Sepik is home to two species of crocodile – one saltwater, one fresh. In the river's middle reaches, its human inhabitants are economically reliant on these reptiles, harvesting their eggs, eating their meat and selling their skins. They are also culturally and spiritually tied to the crocodiles, which feature prominently in the legends and rites of passage of Sepik tribes. Initiated men undergo ritual scarring that makes their skin resemble that of a crocodile. The origin myths told by the Iatmul people, who live along the banks of the river's middle reaches, state that the world was created by a primordial crocodile. In some stories, the crocodile's back forms the land – floods are caused by it settling down into the waters, earthquakes by its movement – while in others, the reptile's upper jaw represents the sky and all within it, and the lower jaw is the land and the river.

A local holds a baby crocodile at the annual Sepik River Crocodile and Arts Festival.

The Waikato River

New Zealand's longest river, flowing for 425 km (264 miles) through the North Island, the Waikato is revered by the indigenous people who live along its course.

Shaped by volcanic eruptions and considered sacred by several Māori tribes, the Waikato is New Zealand's longest and most economically important river. The eight dams and nine hydro-electric power stations along its length generate about 10 per cent of the country's electricity and it supplies drinking water to hundreds of thousands of people in the cities of Auckland and Hamilton.

The river begins life as a collection of small, glacier-fed streams that flow down the eastern slopes of Mount Ruapehu, high in the central North Island volcanic zone. After flowing northward, parallel to State Highway 1, it enters Lake Taupō, Oceania's largest freshwater body. (Up to this point, it's known as the Tongariro River.) After leaving the lake, it drops over Huka Falls and then passes through six more lakes, all of which are artificial. At Karāpiro, the river leaves the volcanic plateau, passing through Maungatautari Gorge and flowing through the city of Hamilton and the town of Ngāruawāhia, seat of the Māori kings, where it's joined by its largest tributary, the Waipa River.

Leaving the Hamilton Basin, the river passes through Taupiri Gorge near Huntly. Here the river is overlooked by Mount Taupiri, where the sacred burial ground for the Waikato tribes is located. The river flows gently across its floodplain, which hosts the 7,290-ha (18,014-acre) Whangamarino Wetland, whose swamps and channels host tens of thousands of birds. West of Tuakau, the river enters its long, thin delta, a network of channels that snake among islands of deposited sediment. And then, finally, at Port Waikato, the river passes through a narrow channel and empties into the Tasman Sea in Maioro Bay.

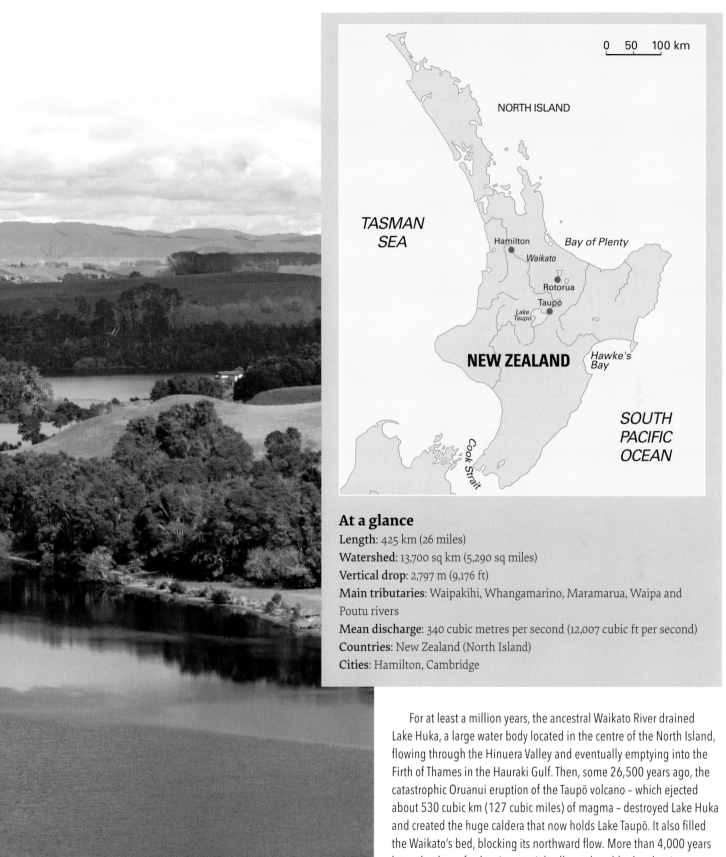

At a glance

Length: 425 km (26 miles)
Watershed: 13,700 sq km (5,290 sq miles)
Vertical drop: 2,797 m (9,176 ft)
Main tributaries: Waipakihi, Whangamarino, Maramarua, Waipa and Poutu rivers
Mean discharge: 340 cubic metres per second (12,007 cubic ft per second)
Countries: New Zealand (North Island)
Cities: Hamilton, Cambridge

For at least a million years, the ancestral Waikato River drained Lake Huka, a large water body located in the centre of the North Island, flowing through the Hinuera Valley and eventually emptying into the Firth of Thames in the Hauraki Gulf. Then, some 26,500 years ago, the catastrophic Oruanui eruption of the Taupō volcano – which ejected about 530 cubic km (127 cubic miles) of magma – destroyed Lake Huka and created the huge caldera that now holds Lake Taupō. It also filled the Waikato's bed, blocking its northward flow. More than 4,000 years later, the dam of volcanic material collapsed, suddenly releasing some 80 cubic km (19 cubic miles) of water over a few weeks, rolling boulders 10 m (33 ft) in diameter through the river gorges like marbles and causing the Waikato to turn westward and flow into the Hamilton Basin. There it left alluvium deposits more than 25 m (82 ft) deep, damming several tributary streams, which in turn led to the formation of small lakes, some of which still exist. As the remaining volcanic debris was eventually washed away, the river changed from a braided form to a single shallow course, deepened its bed and became locked into what is essentially its present course, discharging into the Tasman Sea rather than the Pacific Ocean.

The Taupō volcano erupted again around 232 CE. Copious volcanic debris from the so-called Hatepe eruption blocked the Waikato's outlet from Lake Taupō, creating a dam 30–40 m (98–131 ft) high and causing the lake's level to rise by some 35 m (115 ft). About 20 years after the eruption, the catastrophic failure of the dam led to the re-establishment of the Waikato and the release of about 20 cubic km (5 cubic miles) of impounded water in just a few weeks – the peak discharge rate of 15,000–30,000 cubic metres per second (529,720–1 million cubic ft per second) is equivalent to that of the modern Mississippi River in flood and about 200 times the Waikato's current natural flow rate.

Māori people have been living along the river for at least the past 700–800 years; the river's name means 'flowing water' in Māori. It acted as a conduit for trade, travel and communication, while also providing an abundance of food in the form of fish, crayfish, waterfowl and wild vegetables. The river was also used for healing, the cleansing of the dead, the baptism of newborns and spiritual cleansing.

When European settlers arrived during the 1840s and 1850s, the river acted as the primary access route for traders and missionaries travelling into the interior of the North Island. It also came to play a

> 'The impression made by the sight of the majestic stream is truly grand. It is only with the Danube or the Rhine that I can compare the mighty river which we had just entered.'
>
> – Austrian geologist Ferdinand von Hochstetter, who travelled up the Waikato River in 1859

central role in the so-called Invasion of the Waikato, the largest and most important campaign of the 19th-century New Zealand Wars.

During the late 1850s, the refusal of a number of Māori chiefs in the Waikato region to sell their tribal lands to the colonial government eventually led to open warfare. The Māori set up entrenched positions along the river and, in 1863, some 14,000 British and Colonial troops invaded the Waikato basin. In preparation for the conflict, the New Zealand government had created the so-called Waikato Flotilla – the colony's de facto navy – which consisted of several shallow-draught boats, including eight purpose-built armoured gunboats and barges for transporting troops and supplies. Among them was the armoured 41-tonne (40-ton), 20-m (66-ft) paddle-steamer *Avon*, which was armed with a 12-pounder Armstrong gun in its bows. The boats enabled the movement of soldiers and supplies past the Māori fortifications, and the bombardment of Māori positions, and eventually helped to turn the tide in the colonists' favour. By the following year, the Māori had been defeated and their land confiscated.

The river is considered to be a *tupuna* (ancestor), a *taonga*

Every second, almost a quarter of a million litres of water flow over Huka Falls on the Waikato River.

A contemporary carving of Ngatoroirangi, a visionary Māori navigator, on Lake Taupo.

A chart from the journal of an assistant surgeon in the Waikato Flotilla.

(treasure) and the *mauri* (life force) of the Waikato-Tainui and Ngāti Tūwharetoa people. For many years, the Tainui sought to re-establish their links to the river but were advised not to bring a case before the Waitangi Tribunal – the permanent commission of inquiry that makes recommendations on claims brought by Māori – because it was thought it would be unsuccessful. However, in August 2008, a settlement was reached. Today, Waikato-Tainui and the Waikato Regional Council are jointly in charge of the river's management. During troubled times, Māori people still gather at the river in the early morning, patting its surface to invoke their ancestors then turning to face the sun and sprinkling themselves with its water to rejuvenate their spirit.

The river's flow typically peaks in July and August. However, flow regulation and groundwater storage in pumice mean that the variation in flow isn't excessive. The winter flood surges once kept the river flowing freely, but clearing for agriculture – mostly dairy farming – and dam construction have led to it silting up (as it flows through the volcanic highlands, the river picks up a significant sediment load, much of it ancient ash). The fertile farmland through which the river flows has also been a source of agricultural run-off, and arsenic levels, which are elevated due to the release of waste fluid from the Wairakei Geothermal Power Station, are high enough to render it unsuitable for drinking without treatment.

Glossary

Abrasion: a form of erosion caused by the rubbing of fine particles against an object

Abstraction: the removal of water from a river, typically for irrigation or drinking water

Aggradation: the progressive build-up or raising of the channel bed and floodplain due to sediment deposition

Affluent: a stream or river that flows into a larger one; a tributary

Alluvial: deposited by running water

Alluvium: loose inorganic material such as sand, silt, gravel and boulders eroded, transported and deposited by a river

Alluvial river: a river that deposits large amounts of debris

Anabranch: a diverging branch of a river that later re-enters the main stream

Anadromous: fish that spend most of their life cycle in salt water and migrate to freshwater to reproduce

Attrition: the wearing away of the edges of rock as it's transported along the riverbed, causing it to become smaller and more rounded.

Avulsion: a change in the course of a river's channel that occurs when the river suddenly breaks its banks

Backwater: a small, usually shallow water body attached to the main channel but with little or no current.

Bank: the land at the edge of a river

Bar: a linear landform within a river, usually formed of sand

Barrage: a type of diversion dam that consists of large gates that can be opened or closed to control the amount of water passing through

Basin: the total area of land that is drained by a river and its tributaries

Bed: the ground at the bottom of a river channel

Bedload: material carried by a river along its bed (compare to suspended load)

Benthos: the community of organisms that inhabits the solid floor or benthic zone of a river

Bifurcation: where a river divides into two or more separate water courses

Biome: a large biogeographical region characterised by a particular ecological community type, broadly defined by climatic variables

Biota: all of the organisms in a river

Braided river: river characterised by multiple channels that successively divide and rejoin

Canal: an artificial channel constructed for transporting water

Canalisation: converting a river into a canal-like waterway, usually by installing artificial banks and straightening the channel

Catchment: the total land area from which water drains to a single stream or river; also known as a river basin or watershed (North American usage)

Channel: the groove in the land along which a river flows

Confluence: where two rivers converge

Course: the path taken by a river from its source to its mouth

Current: the flow of a river

Dam: a barrier built across a river to hold back or divert the flow of water

Delta: an area of new land formed at the mouth of a river when material is deposited, typically where a river flows into the sea but also sometimes when it flows into a lake or reservoir

Deposition: when suspended material drops out of a river and settles

Dredging: removing material from a river's bed to deepen the channel

Discharge: the volume of water passing a particular location on a river per unit time

Distributary: a river or stream that branches off and flows away from a main channel

Downstream: the direction a river's flow from its source to its mouth

Drainage basin: see basin

Dyke: an embankment built to confine a river; a levee.

Effluent: discharged wastewater

Endorheic basin: a 'closed' river basin in which the river doesn't enter the sea

Ephemeral river: river that flow only in direct response to precipitation

Erosion: the wearing away of the bed and banks of a river channel

Estuary: the tidal mouth of a river where it meets the sea where freshwater from the land mixes with sea water

Eutrophication: the enrichment of a water body by nutrients and the subsequent depletion of dissolved oxygen caused by excessive plant growth

Flood: when a river has too much water in its channel and breaks its banks

Floodplain: the wide, flat area onto which a river floods, consisting of sediments (alluvium) deposited by the river

Flow: the amount of water passing a particular point in river; discharge

Fluvial: of or pertaining to rivers or streams

Fork: where a river divides into two or more separate water courses

Gorge: a narrow, deep, steep-sided valley

Gradient: the slope of a river's profile

Headwater: another name for a river's source

Hydropower: electricity created using the flow of water

Hyporheic zone: the area of saturated substrate beneath and spreading laterally from a river bed

Inflow: water that flows into a river during a specified period

Irrigation: the supply of water to farmland

Lag time: the time delay between the heaviest rainfall and the maximum discharge of a river

Lentic: Referring to standing-water habitats (contrast with lotic)

Levee: an embankment constructed to prevent a river from overflowing (flooding)

Lotic: referring to flowing-water habitats (contrast with lentic)

Mean annual discharge: the mean discharge averaged over a year or multi-year period

Meander: a natural bend in the river

Meltwater: water formed by the thawing of ice or snow

Mouth: the end of a river, where it empties into another water body, usually the sea but sometimes a lake or another river

Nick point: the place where a river is actively eroding the streambed to a new base level

Oxbow lake: an arc-shaped lake formed when a meander is cut off from a river's main channel

Periphyton: community of microorganisms attached to submerged surfaces; serves as the food source for grazers

Perennial river: a river that flows year round

Pollution: contaminants that detrimentally affect a river's water quality

Pool: A reach of a river or stream characterised by deep, slow-flowing water and a smooth surface.

Plunge pool: A pool at the base of a waterfall.

Precipitation: general term for water that falls from the sky

Rapid: A reach of a river or stream characterised by small falls and turbulent, fast-flowing water, typically where rocks are near to the surface.

Reach: a section of a river between two defined points

Reservoir: artificial lake formed when a dam is placed across a river

Return flow: the portion of withdrawn water that returns to its source or to another body of water

Riffle: a stretch of relatively shallow, fast-flowing water, usually over stones, pebbles or gravel creating a ripple effect on the water's surface.

Riparian zone: the area of terrestrial habitat adjacent to and most directly influenced by a river or stream.

Run-off: water that flows across the ground and into a river

Scour: the erosive action of running water in a river

Sediment: small mineral particles transported by the flowing water of a river

Sedimentation: a build-up of sediment in a river due to the settling out of suspended particles

Sewage: liquid waste from domestic, commercial and industrial sources

Silt: fine substrate particles smaller than sand and larger than clay (3 to 60 um).

Source: where a river begins

Spillway: channel for reservoir overflow

Spit: linear land form produced when a river deposits large amounts of pebbles or small rocks

Spring: a natural phenomenon in which where subterranean water rises to the surface

Step pools: a series of pools separated by areas of high-gradient water flow

Suspended load: fine material transported in suspension within the body of a river with little contact with the streambed

Terrace: abandoned floodplain located at a higher elevation than the current, active floodplain

Thalweg: the middle, main or deepest part of a navigable river

Tidal bore: a phenomenon in which the leading edge of the incoming tide forms a wave (or waves) of water in an estuary

Tributary: a smaller river or stream that flows into a larger river

Turbidity: a measure of the amount of suspended matter that interferes with the passage of light through water

Upstream: the opposite direction to a river's flow, towards its source

Waterfall: a place where a river's course is interrupted by a tall step

Watershed (European usage): the boundary between two catchments or drainage basins

Watershed (North American usage): a synonym for catchment

Weir: an impervious barrier constructed across a river to raise its water level on the upstream side

Recommended Reading

Fiction

Heart of Darkness by Joseph Conrad

The African Queen by C.S. Forester

The Wind in the Willows by Kenneth Grahame

A River Runs Through It by Norman Maclean

Huckleberry Finn by Mark Twain

Non-fiction

Thames: Sacred River by Peter Ackroyd

Empires of the Indus: The Story of a River by Alice Albinia

The Infinite River by William Hopkins Amos

The Last River: The Tragic Race for Shangri-la by Todd Balf

Meltdown in Tibet: China's Reckless Destruction of Ecosystems from the Highlands of Tibet to the Deltas of Asia by Michael Buckley

Blood River: A Journey to Africa's Broken Heart by Tim Butcher

The Rhine: Following Europe's Greatest River by Ben Coates

Down the Great Unknown: John Wesley Powell's 1869 Journey of Discovery and Tragedy Through the Grand Canyon by Edward Dolnick

Blue River, Black Sea by Andrew Eames

The Emerald Mile: The Epic Story of the Fastest Ride in History Through the Heart of the Grand Canyon by Kevin Fedarko

The River's Tale: A Year on the Mekong by Edward Gargan

Head Hunters of the Amazon by F.W. Up de Graff

Great River: The Rio Grande in North American History by Paul Hogan

Holding Back the River: The Struggle Against Nature on America's Waterways by Tyler J. Kelley

The Journals of Lewis and Clark by Meriwether Lewis and William Clark

Original Highways: Travelling the Great Rivers of Canada by Roy MacGregor

Encounters with the Archdruid by John McPhee

Raven's Exile: A Season on the Green River by Ellen Meloy

River of the Gods: Genius, Courage, and Betrayal in the Search for the Source of the Nile by Candice Millard

The River of Doubt: Theodore Roosevelt's Darkest Journey by Candice Millard

Riverwalking: Reflections on Moving Water by Kathleen Dean Moore

The White Nile by Alan Moorehead

The Blue Nile by Alan Moorehead

Slowly Down the Ganges by Eric Newby

Rivers of America by Tim Palmer

Travels in the Interior Districts of Africa by Mungo Park

Exploration of the Colorado River by John Wesley Powell

Old Glory: An American Voyage by Jonathan Raban

Rivers of Power: How a Natural Force Raised Kingdoms, Destroyed Civilizations, and Shapes Our World by Laurence C. Smith

Journal of the Discovery of the Source of the Nile by John Hanning Speke

Through the Dark Continent by Henry Morton Stanley

Rivers Run Through Us: A Natural and Human History of Great Rivers of North America by Eric B. Taylor

The Amur River: Between Russia and China by Colin Thubron

Life on the Mississippi by Mark Twain

Majestic River: Mungo Park and the Exploration of the Niger by Charles W.J. Withers

A World of Rivers: Environmental Change on Ten of the World's Great Rivers by Ellen Wohl

Black Dragon River: A Journey Down the Amur by Dom Ziegler

Run, River, Run: A Naturalist's Journey Down One of the Great Rivers of the West by Ann Zwinger

Index

Picture Credits

t = top, b = bottom, l = left, r = right

Adam Symington: 44-5

Alamy: 20, 30, 31, 32b, 34, 37, 43, 48, 51, 55, 58b, 99t, 108t, 117, 152, 177t, 185t

David Woodroffe: 49, 57, 73, 83, 89, 107, 111, 115, 119, 129t, 133, 137, 143, 149, 155, 161, 165, 171, 175, 187, 193, 209, 223, 241

ESA: 8, 19, 201t

Flickr: 151

Getty Images: 41, 191t

Library of Congress: 99b, 130

Metropolitan Museum of Art, New York: 36, 53, 68t, 98b, 131t, 138t, 150, 182t, 185b

National Archives and Records Administration, USA: 215

NASA: 14

Science Photo Library: 10

Shutterstock: 1, 2, 4t, 4b, 6, 11, 12, 17, 21, 22, 23 (x2), 24, 25, 27 (x2), 28, 39, 40, 42, 44l, 45, 46, 52, 56, 58t, 60, 61b, 62b, 64, 66, 67, 69tr, 69br, 70, 71, 72, 74, 75, 76, 78, 79, 80, 82, 86 (x2), 87b, 88, 90, 93t, 94, 95b, 96, 97, 98t, 102, 103, 106, 108b, 109, 110, 112 (x2), 113, 114, 116, 118, 120 (x2), 121, 122, 123, 125, 126, 128, 129b, 131b, 132, 134, 135, 136, 139, 140, 141, 142, 144 (x2), 146, 148, 153, 154, 156, 158 (x2), 159, 160, 162, 163t, 164, 166, 167b, 169, 172, 174, 178, 179, 180, 182b, 184, 186, 188, 189 (x2), 192, 195 (x2), 196, 198, 199, 200, 204, 205, 207t, 208, 211, 212, 216, 218, 219, 222, 226, 228, 230, 233t, 234, 236, 237 236, 237, 238b, 239t, 240, 242 (x2), 243, 244, 245, 246, 247t

USGS: 93b

Wikimedia Commons: 9, 13, 18, 26, 32t, 33, 38, 44r, 50, 54, 61t, 62t, 65, 68b, 77, 84, 85, 87t, 92, 95t, 100, 101, 104, 105 (x2), 124, 138b, 147, 149, 157, 163b, 167t, 170, 173, 176, 177b, 190, 191b, 194, 201b, 202, 203, 206, 207b, 213, 214, 220, 221 (x2), 224, 225, 227, 229, 231, 233b, 238t, 239b, 247b